To Rend<del>er Safe</del>

To Render Safe

Colin Churcher, MBE

The Pentland Press Limited
Edinburgh • Cambridge • Durham • USA

© Colin Churcher 1999

First published in 1999 by
The Pentland Press Ltd.
1 Hutton Close
South Church
Bishop Auckland
Durham

British Library Cataloguing in Publication Data.
A Catalogue record for this book is available
from the British Library.

ISBN 1 85821 695 8

Typeset by CBS, Martlesham Heath, Ipswich, Suffolk
Printed and bound by Antony Rowe Ltd., Chippenham

Contents

Foreword by Commander David Hilton, Royal Navy
Superintendent of Diving Royal Navy

I have known the author for some thirty years. I first met him when I joined the Portsmouth Bomb and Mine Disposal Team as a Leading-Seaman Diver 2nd Class. Lieutenant Colin Churcher was the 'boss' of the Team at that time, and he taught me a lot about the disposal of Explosive Ordnance. I was surprised by the number of incidents that we had to deal with: on average, about one every day.

Over the years we became firm friends, and when I got promoted from the 'lower-deck', he promised me that I would have his Naval Sword when he retired, and I was proud to wear it.

More than half of the present generation cannot remember World War Two, and I feel that stories like this need to be written, so that we shall not forget the arduous and dangerous conditions that our servicemen had to endure.

Foolhardy chaps as live in towns,
What dangers they are all in
And now lie quaking in their beds,
In case the roof should fall in.
Poor fellows, how they envies us,
And wishes, I've a notion,
For our good luck, in such a storm,
To be upon the ocean.

Anon.

CHAPTER 1

The Rookie

Seven thirty on a winter's morning in 1943. Dave shivered as another icy trickle of rainwater went down his neck and made its way down his back. He was standing on the platform at Birtley railway station; it was still quite dark, no light visible anywhere, with the blackout regulations enforced.

He was about to embark on the biggest adventure of his life. Still only seventeen, he was leaving his home for the first time, to join the Royal Navy until the cessation of hostilities against Germany.

He thought about the arguments he had had with his father over this step, finally succeeding when he had said to his father, 'I am volunteering so that I can go into the Royal Navy; when I am eighteen I will be conscripted and if they put me into the Army, I will never forgive you as long as I live.'

He remembered his mother saying, 'Oh, let him go; the war will be over before he gets to sea.' His father had succumbed and signed the papers – blackmail, I suppose, he thought.

His tearful mother and sister had said their farewells half an hour earlier and had been too emotional to accompany him to the station, being satisfied to fill him up with a hearty breakfast.

There was a cough from a darkened corner and he saw another huddled traveller crouched against a coal-dust grimed wall with rivulets of rain water coursing down. The darkened train hissed and rumbled to a stop in the station and an unseen voice called, 'Birtley, Birtley!' There was no other way for passengers to know where they were, with no lights in the station and blackout boards covering the windows in the train. Dave opened a door and pushed his way into a crowded corridor, stepping over a sailor asleep on the floor. Almost everyone was in uniform, all looking exhausted. He found a corner and sat down on his suitcase. The train started again with a jerk. He knew this part of the railway well, between here and Chester-le-Street, and he could imagine where they were passing, places he had played as a boy, and it wasn't long before it slowed and stopped again.

1

'Durham, Durham.' Dawn was beginning to spread some light and he could make out the familiar outline of the castle and cathedral. From now on nothing else would be familiar; he would be further south than he had ever been and soon he would be out of Durham County for the first time.

In no time he was fast asleep. He hadn't slept much last night, with the excitement of leaving, and at 11 p.m. the sirens had sounded and he had spent the next two hours watching Sunderland and Newcastle being bombed by German aircraft. The constant bangs of anti-aircraft guns, the deeper rumble and flashes of the bombs dropping, the falling flares, the probing searchlights, the occasional hum-hum of an aircraft passing high overhead; not many people could sleep whilst all this was going on. The mining village where he lived had never had a bomb on it, the nearest having been two landmines which had fallen quite close to the LNER railway line down which he had just travelled, but every morning after a raid, lots of shrapnel, mainly from the AA guns, could be found in the street. Lots of boys had quite big shrapnel collections.

Dave woke with a start. He must have been asleep for a few hours. He pulled his joining instructions from his pocket: change at Grantham and Boston for Skegness; he must be close to Grantham now.

Late afternoon he arrived at Skegness. There were a lot of sailors around and a big sign across a desk proclaimed, 'New entries report here.' The desk was manned by sailors wearing green gaiters and armbands with 'Naval Patrol' marked on them, and a very important looking officer in charge (later Dave found that he was a petty officer).

He reported to the officer. 'Name?' he was asked. Dave gave his name and the officer checked his clip board.

'Right,' he said. 'In front of the station there is an RN lorry; climb into it.'

Dave went out of the station: there it was, half a dozen lads already sitting in it. They waited fifteen minutes, chatting about their journey, and Dave was amazed at the number of different dialects, from all parts of Britain.

A few more recruits climbed in, the lorry started up and soon they were driving along the sea front of Skegness. Dave gazed at the sea; he hadn't seen it very many times and now he was to serve on it. 'Here we are,' said one of the lads and he saw that they were passing a high wire fence with barbed wire along the top. They entered a wide gate, with a naval sentry on guard, and he looked at the big sign at the side. It said 'Butlin's Holiday

Camp', partly covered by 'HMS *Royal Arthur*'. He climbed down with the others to the front of a low Nissan hut, and an officer with one gold ring on his sleeve addressed them.

'OK, lads, we are going to give you supper now, then show you your accommodation, and tomorrow you will be called early to start your joining routine.'

They were led into a huge building marked 'Dining Hall' which had obviously been the holiday camp ballroom, going by all the peace time fittings, chandeliers, bandstand and the cartoon characters on the walls. The floor was now covered by rows and rows of trestle tables and forms, capable of holding a few hundred men. They queued at a serving counter and were given a big plate of sausages and mash. Dave suddenly realised how hungry he was and wolfed down the food, his eyes taking in all the new and strange sights, and he listened to the excited babble of his companions. As they ate they were approached by a big sun-tanned sailor; he had a stripe and an anchor on one sleeve and crossed guns on the other.

'Hello, gentlemen,' he said, 'my name is Leading Seaman White; you are in my class. I am your instructor until you complete your seamanship training. You can call me Hooky.'

When they had finished he led them to a part of the camp where there were row upon row of chalets. As a holiday camp they had been double chalets; now they each had four sets of double bunks, one on top of the other, and he divided them up eight to a chalet. He left, telling them that he would see them in the morning.

Once again Dave was surprised at the numerous dialects and he was also surprised to find that some of the others had difficulty in understanding him. Later on he realised that he had also picked up a nickname as one or two started calling him 'Geordie'. He turned in early and, left to his own thoughts, he began thinking of home. This was the first time he hadn't slept in his own bed and he was startled to find tears running down his cheeks. So this is what home sickness is like, he thought.

The next few days passed with whirlwind speed. They were issued with kit bags and all the uniform kit they would require: underwear, two pairs of bell bottom trousers, two sailor's jumpers, two white front shirts, two blue jerseys, two blue jean collars, two black silks, two caps, two cap ribbons, one overcoat, one oilskin jacket, one hammock with mattress, blanket, and rope lashings and clews, a seamanship manual and a seaman's knife. The patient Hooky hardly ever left them during these days. He showed them how to sling a hammock, how to swing up into a hammock and how to lash up a hammock, and then the hammocks were stowed away until their training was over. He showed them how to mark all their kit with their names, how to dress in their uniform, how to tie the silk, how to put on a blue jean collar, how to put the cap ribbon on the cap, with HMS over the nose and the bow over the left ear. He taught them how to press the bell bottoms with seven creases in each leg, one for each of the seven seas and how to wash the blue jean collars so that the blue dye didn't run into the three white tapes bordering the collar. And while all this was going on, Dave suddenly realised they were learning a new language, the floor became the deck, walls became bulkheads, ceilings became deckheads, upstairs became up top, stairs became ladders, left became port, right became starboard. As they marched past the main gate and wistfully looked through it, they realised they were looking ashore. Even the food changed names: sauté kidneys on toast was 'shit on a raft', tinned tomatoes was 'train smash', and one of the Navy's favourites, tinned steak and kidney pies, were called 'baby's heads'. After a week, they looked at each other and realised that they were sailors, matelots, jacks. Their last contact with civilian life was finally cut when they were instructed to parcel up their civilian clothes and send them home.

Now they started training in earnest: squad drill, knots and rope work, semaphore and morse, physical training, poring over their manuals learning the Rule of the Road for ships at sea.

After three weeks in the Navy the war came home to Dave. After a particular strenuous and hot period of squad drill, they were marched to the dining hall for tea, and inside they found the class ahead of them sitting white faced and in a state of shock. Whilst they had been pulling a cutter under oars from the jetty that ran out to sea from the camp, a Messerschmidt, flying low, had opened fire on the recruits with its machine guns. Fortunately, the bullets, though running along both sides of the cutter, had hit no one and there were no casualties.

The next day it was announced on the Tannoy system that all seamanship trainees would be moved to another establishment.

HMS *Glendower* in North Wales at Pwllheli came as a complete surprise to Dave and the class. It was another Butlin's Holiday Camp, taken over by the War Department. The layout was much the same as Skegness, and soon the training went on as though it hadn't been interrupted, the only big difference being that it was much colder and in the distance they could see the snow covered mountains. Hooky had come with them and soon they were hard at work again.

In Skegness most of the trainees had been earmarked for the Signals Branch (Bunting Tossers) or as Radio Operators (Sparkers). Here in North Wales, most were going to the Gunnery Branch, although quite a few would go as DEMS Gunners, that is, on Defensively Equipped Merchant Ships. Nearly all merchant ships were now armed with anti-aircraft guns and surface guns and these were manned by Royal Navy ratings.

Another milestone was reached in their training when after six weeks they were allowed their first 'run ashore' until 10 p.m. Dave and a couple of mates went ashore to a pub, feeling a bit self conscious wearing the RN uniform for the first time in public. They went into the bar and all conversation seemed to stop. When it started up again they found that everyone was talking in a foreign language, Welsh; they didn't seem very friendly either.

Their seamanship training was coming to an end. They all paraded in front of the commander who rated them acting Ordinary Seaman. Dave had opted to qualify as Radar Control Gunner and was given orders to report to HMS *Valkyrie*, on the Isle of Man. They all took Hooky on a farewell run ashore and he offered them all this final piece of advice before they managed to get him drunk: 'Act green, keep clean, and always catch the first liberty-boat.' They all returned on board singing their favourite camp song,

> We had to join,
> We had to join,
> We had to join old Butlin's Navy.

Dave left the next morning for his first leave in the Navy, for Christmas at home where he was paraded around by his proud parents in front of all his relatives and friends, the only sailor in his mining village.

On 2nd January he went to Fleetwood to catch the Isle of Man steam packet boat to Douglas. The weather was terrible. He looked at the ship and looked at the sea, whipped up into white horses. This would be his first time at sea and he wondered about sea-sickness. Hooky had told them many times, 'With seasickness there are three types of people: those who never get seasick; those who are seasick and gradually get used to it until they are seasick no more; and those who are always seasick and will always be seasick. If you belong to the first group, it is a gift and you are very lucky. If you are in the second group you are one of the majority. For the unfortunate ones who are in the third group you have my sympathy; I can only say you are in the best of company as our national hero, Admiral Lord Nelson, was in your group.'

Half an hour later the ship was in the teeth of an Irish Sea gale, bucking like a horse gone mad. The ship was packed with uniformed men and women, mostly khaki and Air Force blue with fewer navy men. Well over half of them had already succumbed to seasickness. The decks were slimy with vomit; you couldn't move around unless you held onto something; a horrible smell of seasick was everywhere you went; you didn't dare go near the guardrails at the ship's side, as people were being sick over the side and the wind was whipping it back inboard over anyone who got near the side. Dave checked his stomach. It seemed to be OK, he didn't feel queasy, his head was clear; maybe he would be one of the lucky ones. He went below to the heads, more naval jargon for 'toilets'. The sight in there was terrible. The deck was covered with three or four inches of water and vomit, which ran from one side to the other as the ship rolled. In this mess lay two soldiers, who also slid from side to side with the mess they were lying in. The smell was unbearable. Dave got out of there as quickly as he could.

Three hours later they were in Douglas and a lot of pale faced service personnel filed ashore to go to their various units. Dave felt triumphant at his own performance on board during the very bad weather.

HMS *Valkyrie* turned out to be dozens of hotels and boarding houses on the promenade, again with a high wire fence around the front. The rest of the hotels were wired off in the same way, and these turned out to be a POW camp for captured Italian soldiers. Dave was shown into a dormitory and where the mess room was, and for the next four weeks his class was bussed up to Douglas Head where they were taught the mystery of operating Radar sets, locking onto targets and directing the guns onto the target.

One weekend Dave and two of his mates went up to Ramsey by tram. The sea looked atrocious as ever. They sat in a seaside shelter, with the rain streaming down, ate their sandwiches and were bemused by a big poster in the shelter which announced that '£20,000 will be awarded to any person giving information which leads to the destruction of a German Pocket Battleship.' They scanned the horizon, there was no sign of any Pocket Battleship, so they returned to Douglas.

After completing the course at Valkyrie, they were drafted to HMS

Excellent at Portsmouth. It was with a feeling of apprehension that they arrived at Portsmouth station, because the 'buzz' had gone round that Whale Island, where *Excellent* was situated, was a place to fear, being the home of the Navy's legendary Gunner's Mates with their infamous reputation for stern discipline. However, they were taken to the northern part of Portsmouth, to a big school called Northern Parade School which had been commandeered by the Navy as accommodation. As they drove through the city, they were overawed by the bomb destruction and the fact that sailors seemed to be everywhere. At Northern Parade they were issued with gaiters, did their joining routine, passing the doctor and the dentist and so on. They were given Station Cards which divided them into four watches: First and Second of Starboard Watch and First and Second part of the Port Watch. One of these watches was duty every day, the other part of the Duty watch was the Stand-by watch. The other watch could go ashore during liberty hours.

Next morning all the training classes fell in and marched about a mile into Portsmouth, turning right at Tipner, then onto the footbridge that led to Whale Island. As each squad left the footbridge, the order was given 'Double March'; all movement around the Island would now be carried out at the double until all the classes marched back again in the evening. Everyone paraded at Divisions on the parade ground and was inspected by the Gunner's Mate; anyone picked up for dirty boots, long hair or any other fault was usually sent on a double around the parade ground. For more serious offences, it was a double around the Island.

The Gunner's Mates and Chief Gunner's Mates marched around the Island with a silver whistle on a silver chain around their neck and a pace stick under their arm. Whilst doubling from class to class, the worst fear that everyone had was that a whistle would shrill out, and a strident voice roar out, 'Halt that class, class leader report to me!' Whereupon the unfortunate class leader would get a loud dressing down, because someone had been out of step or talked in the ranks. This usually ended with, 'Double your class around the Island.' It didn't even end there, because at strategic intervals as they doubled round, a Gunner's Mate would appear from somewhere and order 'About Turn', and would continue to double them backwards and forwards maybe half a dozen times before allowing them to continue. This could happen sometimes three times on their way round the Island.

It wasn't all hard work. The classes included theory of gunnery, types of shells and explosives, fire control methods and actual gun drill itself. The gun drill took place at West Battery, with 3-inch and 4.5-inch guns, and even a mock-up of a battleship's 15-inch turret. The guns crews 'changed round' so that everybody knew every position on the gun. West Battery itself must have been years old; its walls were about five feet thick and there were open embrasures looking over the mud flats at the northern end of Portsmouth harbour. Huge ring bolts were at either side of these embrasures, where run-out tackles for naval cannon, from the days of sail, had once been hooked. The wooden decks themselves had been worn into two grooves, where the cannon's wooden wheels had run in and out over the years.

Everyone was fit, but they all longed for five o'clock as they all doubled up to the foot-bridge and the order came, 'Quick March.' They made their way back to Northern Parade School for supper, and maybe a run ashore in Portsmouth, if they weren't duty watch.

During his stay there, Dave was chosen by the PTI (Physical Training Instructor) to represent his Division as a boxer in a forthcoming boxing competition. The method of choosing was the usual 'you, you and you', which they had now become used to. This method was used quite a lot, and they had all learned very quickly that you never volunteer for anything. Eventually his turn came round to go into the ring. He was only seventeen and he found himself matched with a bald-headed man of about forty-five years, with a broken nose and a cauliflower ear. The fights were only three rounds each, and old 'Baldy' could have finished it off in fifteen seconds, but he proceeded to practise his skills against Dave, cutting him up ruthlessly. By the end of the third round, Dave was covered in blood and had lost his first tooth. He was sure that his opponent was a professional. It was Dave's first venture into the ring, and he was determined that it would be his last.

On the last week of their course they went to Eastney firing range, to practise live firings. They banged away, with Oerlikon and Bofors guns, at drogue targets towed by aircraft approaching from the sea. One of the favourite stories at Eastney was that a training class had once shot down a German aircraft that had been unfortunate enough to stray into the practice area.

At the end of the week, they paraded in front of the Training Commander, who awarded them their qualifications. Dave was made a RC3, Radar Control rating 3rd class, and he was given a red badge with two crossed guns and RC underneath, to sew onto the left arm of his jumper. He was also given a draft to HMS *Victory*, the Royal Naval Barracks Portsmouth, to await draft to a ship. Dave's initial training was over.

CHAPTER 2

First Ship

In *Victory* Dave had his first taste of the real Navy, and the seamy side of the Navy.

There were literally thousands of sailors, some just off ships, others, like him, waiting drafts to a new ship, some survivors from torpedoed ships. The petty officers tried to keep them employed, and it became an art to avoid getting caught for work. One ploy was to walk around with an industrious look in your eye, carrying a sheet of paper in your hand. This gave the impression that you were carrying out your joining or drafting routine. As there were dozens who were genuinely involved in doing just that, it was relatively easy to mingle with them and escape the clutches of the hovering petty officers.

The messes were a continuing changing complement of men, and stealing kit was rife. It was a full time job keeping your eye on your kit, and a lot of men adopted the habit of sleeping with their boots on to ensure that they would still be there in the morning. He also had his first contact with the 'rum bosuns', whom he had heard about from time to time. Although, at seventeen, he himself was too young to draw his 'tot', Dave was quite interested in the ceremony and was looking forward to the day when he would qualify. Neat rum was issued at 1100 to the chiefs and petty officers and at 11 o'clock, when 'Up Spirits' was piped over the Tannoy, the overpowering smell of rum spread through the ship or shore establishment. This was happening on RN ships throughout the world. The ratings got their issue at noon as one part rum and two parts water; this was called grog, after Admiral 'Grogram' who introduced the practice to stop sailors storing up their tot.

At noon the leading hands of messes went with a rum fanny and were issued with the number of tots of grog for the number of men entitled in their mess. The 'rum bosuns' were usually 3-badge leading seamen; that is, they had three chevrons under their anchor badge, each one denoting four

9

years service. They never seemed to get a draft; some had been there months, and even years. On arrival back at the mess with the rum, the rum bosun would be joined by his crony, and they would start the ceremony of rum issue. From the Rum List he would call out someone's name, dip the rum measure into the fanny and pour it into a glass and hand it to the recipient, who would down it in one gulp. This went on until all the names on the list had been ticked off. Dave watched all of this with rapt curiosity, and he noticed that every time the measure went in, the rum bosun had his thumb well into the measure, consequently everybody was getting short measure. He also noted that when the issue was over there were still three or four inches of grog in the rum fanny, which the rum bosun and his crony carried off and they wouldn't be seen again until the evening. He also heard one of the tot receivers talking in a Geordie accent, and was amazed to find that he came from Birtley, only about two miles from his own village. He and Jim became very good friends, reminiscing of all the places, and even people, that they both knew. Jim was a Stoker 3rd Class but unfortunately he had a draft and was leaving the next day to join his ship, a new destroyer nearing completion on the River Tyne. They had a last drink together and Jim left to join his ship.

A few days later, while Dave was carrying out his evasive duties, he heard his name broadcast on the Tannoy and 'Report to the Drafting Office.' On arrival, a CPO checked his name and said, 'Right, here's your draft order and rail voucher, get on and do your drafting routine, you leave the day after tomorrow. Report to the Coxswain on the destroyer HMS *Myngs*, lying in the River Tyne at Walker, in the Vickers-Armstrong Shipyard.' He was amazed and delighted; this was the ship that Jim had just gone to.

The next morning Dave started his drafting routine, this time for real. He thought, with a wry smile, he ought to be good at it after all the practice he had gone through. It was a routine that he would go through hundreds of times in the Navy. There was a sheet of paper, with a box for every department you could think of. He had to visit them all, get a stamp in every box and return it to the Drafting Office. It was a sensible idea. He went to his Divisional Office, who made sure his Service Certificates were written up and forwarded to his new ship, and the same went for the Pay Office, Sick Bay, Dental Department, Supply Office, Bedding Store (return your bedding!), and even the Padre's Office.

Two days later Dave saw his first warship. It was everything and more that he had imagined, lean and sleek, a greyhound of the sea as they were affectionately called. She looked fast even tied up alongside. He was savouring the sight of his first ship, something that he would never forget, when a loud voice shouted out, 'Come on, you lot, get your bags and hammocks on board and I'll detail you off into your messes.' This was the Cox'n, the most senior CPO on board and responsible for discipline. Dave was sent to No. 1 Mess, a seaman's mess, right for'd in the fo'c'sle on the starboard side, 'Odds to starb'd, evens to port' the cox'n muttered to him as he stowed his hammock in the hammock netting. This was another rule to remember about ships, he told himself.

The for'd messdecks, he found as he stepped through a bulkhead door, narrowed to the 'pointy end' of the ship, the stem. Rows of portholes ran down both sides, closed now, but not big enough to get your head out when open. Two Mess ran down the other side, and both messes had trestle tables secured to the deck, which was bare steel. The ship's side this far for'd was quite a slope, and along the base were steel benches covered in leather cushions. These were the seats and also the lockers where the sailors stowed their kit. Right for'd was a bulkhead door behind which was the paint store, and below that was the cable locker, where the ship's anchor chains were stowed.

Between the two messes, there was a hatch in the deck, and a ladder leading to 3 and 4 Messes below. Either side of the paint store were two areas for stowing hammocks, known as the 'hammock netting'.

That night for the first time, Dave slung his hammock from special hooks on the deckhead. The leading seaman in charge of his mess showed him a place to sling it, and how to do it, and how to swing himself up into the hammock. He was pleasantly surprised to find how comfortable it was to sleep in a hammock.

The next morning he found his way to the stokers' mess, and Jim was delighted to find that they were both serving on the same ship. They didn't see a great deal of each other during the next three weeks as they were kept hard at it, preparing the ship for sea, painting ship, storing ship, taking aboard provisions; and at the end of each day, after the evening meal, Dave was ready to climb into his hammock and fall asleep. One morning four large barges were secured alongside and a pipe was made over the loud speaker system, 'Clear lower deck, all hands to ammunition ship.' No one was excused; cooks, stewards, stokers, everyone had to turn to and start carrying the explosive stores inboard. There was everything from small arms ammunition and hand grenades to 4.5-inch shells, depth charges and torpedoes. They all had to be manhandled through compartments and messdecks to the magazines in the bottom of the ship. By this time Dave knew the ship thoroughly; he had worked in every compartment, store rooms, engine room, boiler room, magazines, and he was learning more about his trade: he felt like a sailor.

Another milestone came in his life. He became eighteen and was allowed to draw his rum ration. It was a bit of a ceremony in the mess. Everyone gathered round to see him drink his first tot and sure enough the strength of the rum completely took his breath away; he had to fight it to stop having a coughing fit. His voice went, and he could only whisper 'Cheers' in a hoarse voice, much to everyone's amusement. He was also able to invite Jim around for 'sippers'. Although strictly illegal, it was a naval tradition to pay for services rendered or repay a favour, by inviting someone to your mess at rum issue. Rum became a currency and it was quite common to hear someone say, 'Come round at tot time.'

Dave's mining village was only about twelve miles from where his ship was berthed, so he was able to get home to visit his parents at weekends. His ex-school mates used to look at him in awe in his uniform. Most of them had never seen a ship, some hadn't even seen the sea, and it was obvious that a lot didn't really believe him when he said he was on a destroyer. One Sunday morning he made them get their bikes out and they cycled the twelve miles through the Durham countryside to the banks of the Tyne and there, on the opposite bank, lay his ship.

It was the first time he had seen the ship from a distance, and HMS *Myngs* looked lethal, with her four 4.5-inch single gun turrets, two for'd and two aft, twin Bofors guns amidships and two single Bofors either side of the bridge. With the two sets of quadruple torpedo tubes, several depth charge launchers and Oerlikon anti-aircraft guns scattered around, she really looked ready for business. On the way back he noticed that the sight of the ship had a sobering effect on his chums; they were quieter and he saw that they treated him with a new respect.

Two days before she was due to put to sea, the remainder of the Ship's Company arrived, over two hundred officers and men. The ship buzzed with activity, machinery hummed, cooking smells spread out from the galley and at 0800 on a Tuesday morning she slid away from her berth and headed down river. There were a few cheers from the shore, from the dockyard workers who had built her, and a big Red Ensign was flying from the ensign staff on the stern.

The Red Ensign denoted that *Myngs* was not yet one of His Majesty's ships and during that day the ship was put through every trial imaginable: full power trials, firing practices, every part of the ship's equipment was tested by the Ship's Company. A large number of dockyard officials were on board to oversee the trials, and late in the day, as the ship approached the mouth of the Tyne, a ceremony took place in the Captain's cabin, as he signed the documents, accepting the ship on behalf of the Admiralty, as a new addition to the fleet.

This was followed by another ceremony, in front of the whole Ship's Company, where the Captain read out the Commissioning Orders, after which the Red Ensign was hauled down to be replaced by the White Ensign. At the same time the commissioning pennant was broken at the mast head.

After dropping off the dockyard officials onto a waiting tug, the ship turned north and an announcement on the Tannoy informed the crew that they would be joining the Home Fleet at Scapa Flow, in the Orkney Islands.

The sea was quite calm, but a big oily swell made the ship roll quite heavily. Dave was very confident after his Irish Sea experience, but within an hour his stomach began to feel queasy and an hour later he was being violently sea-sick. His only consolation was that he wasn't alone. On one of his frequent visits to the heads, he could hear retching in all of the other cubicles, the majority of the crew having never been to sea before. So he wasn't going to join the ranks of 'those who never get seasick'; he could now only hope that he was one of those who would gradually get used to it.

Two days later the ship passed between two low islands in the Orkney Islands and entered Scapa Flow, the northernmost base of the Home Fleet. As they passed a beacon in the middle of the bay, bosun's pipes sounded 'the Still', and on the Tannoy 'Attention on the Upper Deck; Face to Starboard.' Dave found out later that this was the Royal Oak Beacon, the upper part of the mainmast of the battleship HMS *Royal Oak*, sitting on the sea bed at this spot. Shortly after the beginning of the war, a German U-boat had managed to penetrate the Scapa Flow defences by squeezing between two block ships that had been sunk to seal off an entrance to the Flow. The U-boat captain had lined up his sights and fired a torpedo at the *Royal Oak* which was sitting at anchor. He missed, and the torpedo was sighted by an alert lookout. The ship closed up at 'Action Stations' and boats carried out patrols while the submarine sat on the bottom. An hour later it was decided that it had been a false alarm and the alert was relaxed. The U-boat had a second chance and this time he didn't miss. The *Royal*

Oak sank with a huge loss of life, resting on the bottom with just the top of her mast showing. The U-boat managed to escape and get back to Germany, where the captain was awarded the country's highest honour, presented to him by Adolf Hitler. Since then all British warships sound the 'still' as they pass the spot where she sank, paying their respects to the sailors who died that night.

The *Myngs* sailed into the Small Ships anchorage, and Dave gazed in wonder at the large number of ships at anchor. There must have been well over forty ships: destroyers, frigates, sloops and corvettes with all the activity of all types of boats plying between them and the shore. Aldis lamps flashed away between them and the signal tower on the shore; the bay seemed almost landlocked with the low islands surrounding it. The shore itself looked bleak and forbidding, with no houses and no trees, only a long pier with a few large Nissan huts at the shore end of it. Through a gap in the islands, Dave could see the shapes of battleships, aircraft-carriers and cruisers: that was the Big Ship anchorage. As his ship swept in, with hands fallen in for entering harbour, signals were flashing from all directions, welcoming the new arrival to the fleet. With her pennant numbers fluttering from the starboard yardarm, the ship closed on a line of destroyers, all looking remarkably similar to herself. This was her flotilla, of which *Myngs* was now to be the leader, her Captain being the senior officer in the flotilla. In fact he was a four ring captain, now known as Captain (D).The *Myngs* had a broad black band painted around her funnel to show that she was the leader. The flotilla were all Zambesi Class destroyers, and had names starting with Z except the *Myngs*; their names were *Zambesi, Zest, Zephyr, Zealous, Zodiac, Zulu* and *Zenith. Myngs* herself, although Zambesi Class, was named after Admiral Sir Christopher Myngs, a former Admiral in the old Navy.

Two days later the flotilla steamed out of Scapa Flow, in line ahead. Two other flotillas were also on the move and later in the morning they were joined by an aircraft carrier and three cruisers. The destroyers formed a screen around the big ships and they turned towards the north. The sea was very rough and soon Dave was being sick again. It appeared that half of the ship's company were making regular visits to the heads. It wasn't really surprising. In a quick census they had taken in the mess the night before they had sailed, they had decided that the average age on board was nineteen and that only about six of the crew were regular Navy; the rest were 'Hostilities Only' ratings, HOs as they were called, in for the duration of the war.

The ship had gone to Defence Stations as soon as they had cleared the boom: that is, Port Watch closed up, Starboard Watch off, changing round every four hours. They would keep this up for the next month, except when the ship went to Action Stations, when everyone would be closed up. Down in the messdecks, even so early in the voyage, things looked pretty grim. The deadlights had been screwed down tight over the port holes, to keep any light from showing and to make the ship even more watertight. This was an optimistic hope. Each time the bow dipped deep into successive waves, a trickle of water ran down the bulkhead from various port holes and already a pool of water ran backwards and forwards across the deck each time the ship rolled. Already a rim of ice had formed around each port, and as the fleet pushed further north, it would spread out across the bulkhead until it was like living in a freezer. Men were trying to sleep wherever they could find a space: on the benches, on the lockers, on the tables, some in their hammocks. The problem was that with a war-time complement there just weren't enough points for everyone to sling a hammock, so people just had to sleep wherever they could. Fortunately half of the ship's company were on watch at any given time which eased the situation somewhat.

Dave felt his duffel coat, already wet from the spray on the upper deck. The clothes he was wearing, he would be in until they got back into harbour in about fourteen days time. It just wasn't possible to undress; if the 'Alarm Bells' sounded, you had to be at your Action Station in seconds; you couldn't waste precious seconds to get dressed. So everyone lived and slept with what they had on, including sea-boots; you just had to make sure that you had enough on to keep you warm. The 'buzz' had gone round that they were on their way to Russia and at that moment, as if to confirm his thoughts, the messdeck loudspeaker crackled, then, 'This is the Captain speaking. We are heading north to rendezvous with a large convoy of merchant ships *en route* from USA to Murmansk in north Russia. We expect to meet them in about twenty-four hours, and we will be escorting them for the rest of the way to Russia. Intelligence has told us that there are several U-boat packs operating in the area, so everyone must be alert in case we run into any of them. We should be back in Scapa in about a month's time. That is all.'

That's something exciting to look forward to, thought Dave, remembering the grim and dark shoreline he had seen in Scapa Flow. He had started to make a strop out of a piece of 1-inch hemp, under the guidance of an able seaman, who taught him how to splice two hand holds into the strop. He would wear the strop permanently around his waist, like most of the crew. Experience had taught these older hands that if your ship was sunk and you were in the water, you were very quickly covered with fuel oil, and it was almost impossible to get a grip on a survivor and haul him out of the sea unless he was wearing one of these strops. This, and his inflatable life preserver, he would wear all the time he was at sea.

At tea time, 8 bells, they piped, 'Starboard Watch to Defence Stations.' This was the First Dog Watch, only two hours, as was the Last Dog Watch; all other watches were four hours. The Dog Watches were designed so that you didn't end up with the same watches day after day and night after night.

Everyone had a Defence Station. Some manned a gun, some stood by the depth charge racks, some by the torpedo tubes, some were helmsmen in the wheelhouse, others were detailed as seaboats' crew. Dave was the port lookout on the port wing of the bridge. There were four of them around the bridge, sitting in swivel seats, with binoculars that they could raise or lower to different angles. They each had a segment of sea and sky to cover and had to report everything that they saw in their zone to the Officer of the Watch on the bridge, and you were in real trouble if he saw something before you had reported it. Because of the concentration needed, and the cold and the wet, the lookouts were changed every thirty minutes. Dave sat in his seat, eyes glued to his binoculars. First he quartered the sky, searching for any aircraft, then he turned his attention to the sea. He watched for the tell-tale feather of a periscope, a mast or smoke on the horizon, or any sort of flotsam that they passed; everything had to be reported. He was almost flung out of his seat as the bows crashed down under the water after a big wave; the anchors shook, rattling the cable in the cable locker, and the sound reverberated throughout the entire ship.

As the ship recovered, she shook herself and the bows came up again, throwing tons of water into the air which was quickly blown aft by the strong wind and came down on the open bridge, soaking everyone, including the lookouts. Dave had been told that when they got further north, this sea water could freeze before it reached the bridge and the ice pieces could cut your face quite badly. Under these conditions the lookouts had to wear masks similar to ice-hockey masks, and you could also get your nose badly frost-bitten during your thirty minutes of exposure. At the end of his watch, Dave made his way down to the mess for his supper.

Messing on small ships was a bit strange. It was called canteen messing. Weekly, each mess received basic victuals, according to the number of men in the mess. This was sugar, tea, coffee and flour; nearly all other food was tinned, except frozen meat which was drawn daily. The victuals were rationed, the same as everybody else in Britain, but the servicemen's rations were a bit better than those of civilians. Bread and fresh vegetables were usually all used up after three days at sea; after that it was dried peas and beans and ship's biscuits. The leading hand of each mess was responsible for making out a menu for each day, and he chose anything he wished within the food available. Two mess members were detailed each day as 'cooks of the mess' and they were responsible for preparing the meals on the menu and taking it up to the galley to be cooked by the Chief Cook and his staff. They had to collect the cooked food from the galley at meal times, when 'cooks to the galley' was piped, wash the dirty dishes after each meal, clean the mess and make tea, coffee or cocoa at the proper times during their twenty-four hour stint as 'cook'.

This meant that all the sailors on board had quickly to learn how to make pastry, Yorkshire pudding, gravy, toad in the hole, jam tart and other gourmet delicacies. They had to learn quickly because a spoiled meal usually meant a punch in the nose from someone.

On this particular day Dave found that, because it was so rough, the usual bad weather meal had been prepared. That was 'pot mess', which meant that lots of things like tinned beans, tinned tomatoes, tinned steak and kidney and corned beef were all emptied into a big cooking pot and taken up to the galley, and after it was cooked, it was brought back to the mess and secured to a hammock hook on the deck head, where it swung wildly with the motion of the ship. When the weather was really bad, almost every mess on board would be on pot mess. Everyone coming off watch for supper just used to dip a mug in and have a mug of steaming hot pot mess.

Dave only had a couple of hours off, the last Dog, then he was back to his Defence Station at 8 o'clock for the First Watch, 8 till midnight. He would then be off during the Middle Watch and back on again at 4 o'clock for the Morning Watch, 4 till 8.

Thank goodness the sea had moderated, but the thermometer had plummeted, and he could hear the ice crunching beneath his sea boots as he took up his post on the lookout position. 'Nothing in sight,' muttered the lookout that he was relieving, and disappeared as quickly as he could. 'Bridge, Port Lookout,' Dave called out, and the faint voice of the Officer of the Watch answered, 'Bridge.' Dave made his report. 'First Watch Port lookout closed up. Nothing to report, sir.' 'Very well,' came the acknowledgement, and Dave settled down to start his watch. As he scanned the dark sea, looking for the tell-tale white plume, it was a scary feeling that a periscope could be looking at you at any time. He was sure that all of his mates felt the same way and were a lot more conscientious whilst on watch. The incessant pinging of the ASDIC was a constant reminder of the danger lurking beneath the surface.

By now he was becoming used to the constant movement of the ship, having always to hang on to something as you moved around, 'One hand for the ship and the other for yourself,' as the older seamen used to say. He had learned that when you had a cup of tea you never put it down or it would be on the deck. He still suffered from spasms of nausea and had accepted the fact that it was going to take some time to overcome the sea sickness. A hot mug of chocolate was pushed into his hand by one of the 'watch on deck', making his rounds of the exposed positions, and he resisted the temptation to take a swig of it. He had found out the hard way that a scalding hot layer of chocolate sticking to your lower lip was a very painful experience and would take the skin off. On the other hand, in these temperatures it quickly cooled down, so you had to judge the exact moment to drink your 'kye' and enjoy the warm feeling in your belly. This was one of the few pleasures of being on watch, the hot chocolate or 'pusser's kye' as it was called, which was dark chocolate bars, cut up and melted and boiled in a mess fanny on the galley stove. It had to be so thick that you could stand a spoon up in it, and so much sugar was put in it that it was sweet and syrupy. The lookouts, sitting freezing in their exposed positions, used to long for the kye to come round.

During the morning watch, Dave made his first report as a lookout. 'Bridge, Port lookout, Smoke bearing Red 40.' 'Very good, Port lookout,' the officer of the watch replied. Lots of activity started, Aldis lamps started flashing between the ships and the whole formation turned together towards the smoke. By this time a lot of masts had appeared on the dawn horizon as the convoy came slowly into view. As they came closer it could be seen that there were about sixty merchant ships of all shapes and sizes: tankers, cargo ships, bulk carriers, old ships and modern ships, with the US escorts, mostly destroyers and one cruiser, fussing around them.

Greetings were exchanged by signal lamp between the American and British ships, then the US ships formed up and turned west towards the United States.

The senior officer of the British escort vessels allocated stations for each ship around the convoy, and he also ordered a zig-zag plan to commence at 0800; these plans were contained in Confidential Books that each ship in the convoy carried. It was quite amazing to see the whole force alter course 15 degrees to starboard at the same time. The zig-zag plans were quite complicated and might have up to six course alterations every fifteen minutes, but were designed so that the convoy was advancing along a base course. Any U-boat commander could only have a few seconds to look through his periscope, and in that time he had to decide what course the convoy was on and the best course he should take to get into an attacking position. By the time he reached that position, the convoy could have altered course three or four times and quite often, by the time he raised his periscope again, he could find the convoy steaming away from him. The zig-zag had hazards for the convoy too. Each ship had to work with a stop watch on the bridge. If one ship altered course too early or too late, it would cause havoc in the columns. The escorting ships had to keep a close eye on all of the ships to make sure that they all came round at the same time, and also that they all kept up in station. Any ship that lagged behind became a sitting target for any watching U-boat; consequently, the speed of the convoy was the speed of the slowest ship. The speed of this convoy was 7 knots and it would take two weeks to reach north Russia.

As the convoy slowly moved further north, the temperature dropped lower and lower, and was now well below freezing point. Every forenoon the watch on deck had to go around the upper deck with hammers, chipping away at the ice. This was always worst right for'd on the fo'c'sle, where anchor cables were sometimes four times their normal size with the ice. It was vital to get rid of the ice as the weight made the ship top-heavy, she rolled more heavily, and could even turn over if the condition became worse. It was also necessary to clear the ice so that the gun turrets could rotate. One night it snowed so heavily that the ships looked like ghosts; some of the off-watch sailors made a snowman on the fo'c'sle.

On the third day *Zealous* reported a sonar contact on the port side of the screen. *Myngs* raced across to join her and also picked up the contact and, whilst she held the target, *Zealous* crossed it and dropped a pattern of depth charges. Then *Zealous* regained contact whilst *Myngs* made her attack, after which the sonar echo became faint and vague and they re-classified it as a non-submarine contact and re-joined the convoy. It could have been a shoal of fish or a thermal layer of water, but as they steamed away from the scene, Dave saw the petty officer cook looking longingly at a number of

19

stunned cod floating on the surface.

The days passed. Three times in the next few days escorts detected possible submarine contacts and ran over them, dropping charges, but there were no satisfying oil bubbles gushing to the surface, no German sailor's hats, or even dead German sailors, and in each case they were classified as 'non-submarine echoes'.

The force started to go to Dawn Action Stations at first light every morning. The alarm bells would ring and everyone in the Ship's Company went to his designated Action Station as quickly as possible and the ship was on full alert. Below decks was deserted except for ammunition supply teams and damage control parties. Dawn was the traditional time for an attack to take place, when the senses were at their lowest ebb and visibility played tricks with everyone's eyes. Normally they would stay at Action Stations for about an hour, and were then stood down and reverted back to Defence Stations again. It played havoc with people's sleep; for the men who had the Middle Watch it meant they had been on watch from midnight to 0400 then Action Stations from about 0600 till 0700, then they were back for the Forenoon Watch at 0800. Down in the messdeck Dave surveyed all of the bodies stretched out wherever they could find a space. With half of the Ship's Company on watch, he had often wondered what it would be like if they all tried to get into the mess at the same time; it was too crowded with only half of them.

The one bright moment of every day, that everyone looked forward to, was at 11 a.m. when the bosun's pipe shrilled out over the Tannoy and the voice announced 'Up Spirits'. Then, slowly, through every passageway in the ship, pervaded the sweet smell of rum. Tot time was the time of discussions and heated arguments as the rum loosened everyone's tongue; it was pretty powerful stuff.

On the eighth day *Myngs* and *Zephyr* were detached to go into Reykjavik in Iceland to re-fuel; all the small escorts would take their turn to do this. As they approached Iceland they could see a bright glow on the horizon. At first they thought it must be a ship on fire, then, as they got closer, they saw that it was a city all lit up. They gazed in wonder at the bright lights, as it was something that none of them had seen for over four years. All over Britain cities were 'blacked out', but Iceland, being a neutral country, had never had the need to extinguish her lights and the sight was truly remarkable. They went alongside a tanker in a remote area of the harbour and started to take on fuel. Two hours later they were on their way back to the war. The tanker had also given them six sacks of potatoes and two large bags of bread, which was very welcome, as after about three days at sea any bread you had left turned green with mildew and potatoes went rotten. After that it was ship's biscuits and tinned or powdered potatoes.

As they approached the convoy they were told by signal lamp to assume the 1st degree of readiness, Action Stations, as hostile aircraft had been detected on the radar. Later in the day the aircraft was sighted visually, circling the convoy, and always keeping outside gunfire range. It was a Fokker-Wolf long range aircraft, shadowing the convoy. By tonight every U-boat commander in the vicinity would know the convoy's position.

The following day they had their first casualty. A merchant ship on the port side of the convoy suddenly exploded, having been hit by a torpedo on the port bow. The force went to Action Stations and five escorts were quickly in the area, searching for the submarine with sonar and picking up survivors. They dropped several depth charges, but didn't manage to make contact with the submarine, which must have managed to slip away. The merchant ship lasted for four minutes before she sank, but during this time a corvette managed to put her bows alongside the burning wreck and several crew members were able to scramble and jump across. This dramatic incident made everyone even more alert and aware of the danger that lurked below, lookouts paid more attention to every little wave and shadow as they scanned their sector, and even the off-watch ship's company found themselves searching the sea around them as they passed along the upper deck.

They were having a period of calmer weather and meals became a little more civilised, all tinned or frozen stuff of course, but a nice change from the usual pot mess that sometimes lasted for three days.

That day was the birthday of the leading hand of Dave's mess and, as was the tradition and custom, he had been invited around to most of the messes for 'sippers' of rum by his mates. This was strictly illegal of course, both to offer your rum ration or to partake of someone else's, but this had been going on for over two hundred years and was difficult to prevent. Rum on board was used in a bartering system as a kind of currency, and someone who was desperate to go ashore when he was Duty Watch in harbour, might offer 'a week's sippers' to anyone who would do his duty for him. If anyone did a favour for someone else he would usually be told to 'come round at tot time'. So it was with birthdays; anyone who had a birthday was normally well under the weather by two o'clock, and his mates would conceal him and cover for him for the rest of the day. It was also a dangerous practice, and there were a few cases of sailors drowning in their own vomit or dying from falling down a hatch. Whilst, on most occasions, the birthday boys just slept it off, on this occasion, to Dave's astonishment, his 'Hooky' became quite belligerent, pulled out his pusser's dirk, opened it, and stood in the bulkhead door, daring anyone to try and get past him. A very big able seaman walked up to him and said, 'Come on, Hooky, no need for that, I'll help you to get into your hammock,' and he took the knife off him. Hooky, now in tears, allowed himself to be led to his hammock and was soon in a deep sleep.

So the days passed. The coxswain started a beard growing competition and most of the ship's company entered it, as it meant a few more minutes sleep instead of shaving, and a beard did keep your face a bit warmer. You had to put in a request to see the First Lieutenant or 'Jimmy' as all first lieutenants were called in the Navy, to 'discontinue shaving'. You couldn't just start growing a beard unless you had your request granted as the Navy was quite strict about beards, and you couldn't shave it off again without another request being granted. You could only grow a full beard, no moustaches or fancy beards like 'Van Dykes' were allowed. Anyone who couldn't display anything that looked like a beard after a week was quickly told to take it off. Other diversions like tombola and quiz competitions were attempted but most men were too tired or too cold to take part.

The convoy was well over the Arctic Circle by now, and everyone who hadn't crossed it before was given a 'Blue Nose Certificate', giving the time, date and latitude and longitude that they had crossed the line which was signed by King Neptune.

Early one morning, while Dave was on watch, the sound of thunder or gunfire could be heard to the north. He scanned the horizon with his binoculars but nothing was in sight. Then a group of ships appeared over the horizon, which Dave duly reported. It was obvious by the huge plumes of water going up, completely dwarfing the ships, that they were engaged in depth-charging a submarine below them. The 'buzz' went around the ship that this was Captain Walker's hunter-killer group, a force of five or six frigates which had been specially trained to search out and destroy U-boats. It was their main purpose in life and it had proved to be very successful; very few submarines that they detected lived to see another day. They had several U-boats to their credit. The group came straight towards the convoy, constantly dropping depth charges, the merchant ships and the escorts scattered, and the hunter-killer group went through the middle of the convoy, still dropping their lethal charges. They gradually moved to the south and finally disappeared over the horizon, still engaged in their task.

On the fourteenth day the convoy approached the shore near the northernmost point of Russia, for the crews of most of the escorts, the first sight of land since leaving Scapa, and even longer for the merchantmen as they had come from America. Intelligence reports that they had received had informed them that U-boat packs were operating in this area, but no contacts had been detected up till then.

Kola inlet was a large bay with a narrow entrance, which had been sealed by a boom stretched across the mouth. The boom was a line of buoys below which hung steel nets to prevent submarines from entering the bay. It was capable of being opened in the centre by a tug anchored there for that purpose. At the moment that the tug was opening the boom gate in the bay, a line of five Russian destroyers came out to assist the merchant ships to enter. These destroyers were really old, not much bigger than a minesweeper, and each had five funnels not much higher than a man. They were, in fact, pre-war American destroyers which in the early years of the war had been given to Britain, until the Royal Navy had built up its strength. Once this had happened, we in turn had given the destroyers to the Russian Navy.

The merchant ships, by now, were starting to line up in single file, ready to pass through the boom as soon as the Russian destroyers were clear. The convoy escorts were taking station either side of the merchantmen, when suddenly, the third ship in line just exploded in a huge flame and black smoke. When it cleared there was no sign of the ship, just a lot of debris on the water. Then further down the column another ship was hit in the bows, a huge plume of water rising up alongside it. By this time the escorts were racing along the flanks of the convoy dropping depth charges as they went though no one, as yet, made sonar contact. While all this was going on, the five Russian destroyers had done a 180 degree turn and gone back through the boom gate.

Right across near the boom buoys, HMS *Lapwing*, a sloop, started flashing by Aldis lamp to *Myngs* but, before the yeoman of signals could start to reply, she just broke in the middle, leaving the bows and the stern, separately, pointing to the sky; she had been hit amidships. *Myngs* raced across to her assistance but, by the time she got there, the stern had sunk, there were a lot of men in the water and the crew on deck had dropped scrambling nets over both sides of the ship for the survivors to climb up.

The ship weaved at a snail's pace among them, dragging men from the sea, stopping occasionally, while crew members jumped into the water to help dazed and wounded survivors. These were dangerous moments for the ship as a stationary ship was a sitting target for a submarine, and they wouldn't be the first ship to be hit whilst picking up survivors. However all the seamen knew that no one could last more than a few minutes in the icy cold water, and speed was essential. The survivors were rushed to the wardroom, which had been turned into a sick bay and operating room; sea boots had to be cut off some men's legs as they had swollen so much with the cold.

Dave glanced across to the bow section of *Lapwing* that had been sinking lower and lower in the water, and behind it he saw that several men had climbed onto the boom buoys and were waiting to be picked up.

The merchant ships were by now steaming through the boom gate, but back in the line yet another one was hit. The U-boat pack had obviously been waiting for the moment when the convoy started to disperse before starting their attack.

At that moment the yeoman called out, 'Signal from Senior Officer, sir, Join *Zest* and *Zealous* with submarine contact.' The engines thundered into life, the ship heeled over as she turned, and a huge wake rose higher than the quarter deck as she headed towards the other two destroyers, already dropping patterns of depth charges about a mile away. Dave looked back. At least there were no men left in the water and another sloop was closing with the boom buoys to pick up the men still waiting there.

As they drew closer to *Zest* and *Zealous*, they reduced speed and started to operate their ASDIC sonar and they were rewarded by hearing a firm, clear return echo. 'Definitely submarine echo, sir,' the sonar operator reported on the bridge loudspeaker. 'Stand by Depth Charges, Set depth 100 feet,' the Captain ordered, and there was a flurry of activity around the racks and the depth charge throwers as their crews set the depth ordered. If indeed they did have a submarine, it was in a precarious position, as the sea was little more than 100 feet deep in this area, and the U-boat couldn't dive into deeper water.

Myngs went in for her first attack, whilst the other two stood off, holding the target by sonar. As the ship approached the position of the submarine the sonar repeat echoes became closer and closer together until they merged as she went over the top of it. At that point they dropped a pattern of twelve depth charges, some from the throwers, the others from the racks on the quarter deck, so that the pattern would straddle the sub. Astern, the sea erupted as the charges exploded one after another, hurling huge plumes of water into the air. They were plotting the submarine's course in the operations room and there was no doubt that it was moving along the line of boom nets. They continued the attack all afternoon. By now all the other escorts and the merchant ships were safely inside the boom, including the last two that had been hit but had not sunk. At three o'clock the contact was stationary and lying on the sea bed. They continued depth charging in turns, until all of their depth charges were expended. Between them they had dropped over five hundred depth charges, but there had been no oil on the surface, no air bubbles or debris. The target was however still a good, clear submarine echo, stationary and lying on the bottom.

They left the area and headed into Kola inlet. No submarine could have survived the punishment they had given it, so possibly it had just flooded up and sunk to the bottom. Later they were to be credited with sinking a U-boat between them.

As they got well into Kola Bay, across on the starboard side they could see Murmansk, and all of the merchant ships that they had escorted here. The big warships were also berthed at Murmansk, but they altered course to port further into the bay towards a small port called Polyano, where the small escorts would refuel, store ship and rest up for about three days before escorting another convoy back. Everywhere looked very bleak. Thick snow covered the shore and high mountains to the south, and there was no sign of habitation anywhere. The sea in the bay was partly frozen, like slushy ice; it would be really frozen by the arrival of the next convoy and the ships would have to break the ice to get to Polyano. One of the older sailors had told Dave a story about when he had come here in a convoy in the winter. As they had been making their way up to Polyano, breaking ice as they went, the starboard lookout reported, 'Horse and cart bearing Green 45, sir.' The astonished officer of the watch looked through his binoculars, and sure enough, on the starboard bow, a horse and cart was crossing the ice, on a course that would intercept them. He racked his brain, going through the rules of the road for the prevention of collision at sea, and he couldn't remember anything about horses and carts. Then he remembered the rhyme that said, 'If on your starboard red appear, it is your duty to keep clear.' He decided to apply that and give way to the horse and cart, so he ordered the helmsman 'Starboard Fifteen', gave one blast on the siren, which meant, 'I am altering my course to starboard,' and passed under the stern of the horse and cart, which continued on its way. The old man, hunched under a blanket on the cart, didn't even seem to notice them.

As they entered the harbour at Polyano, all the other escorts were snugged down and it looked as though everyone was asleep. They were ordered to go alongside a tanker to refuel and Dave saw the big, brawny crew on the tanker waiting to take their lines. They were dressed in fur hats and fur coats and he thought, I wouldn't like to tangle with that lot. Then he heard their voices and realised they were all women, built like Japanese wrestlers. He saw a flicker of interest pass over his mates' faces as they discovered that the crew were all women; even some of the stokers came from below to have a look. It was a rare occurrence to see a stoker on the upper deck, but when they had seen the women, he also saw the 'I wouldn't like to tangle with that lot' look come over their faces, and they were gone. Some bartering went on, coffee and Navy cigarettes for fur hats, Joe Stalin badges and knives made out of crashed German aircraft. Some claimed to have got more than that, but everyone put it down to bravado and didn't really believe them.

Then they too were snugged down, alongside a sister ship. They were told 'no work tonight', and everyone found somewhere to stretch out, and the whole ship slept.

Next day was very busy. An ammunition lighter came alongside and they had to take on board a full outfit of depth charges. Fresh bread also came on board which had been baked on a Russian battleship called *Archangel*, another former Royal Navy ship, HMS *Royal Sovereign*. We had given it to the Russians and possibly it had never been to sea since; it made nice bread though.

In the evening all the sailors were invited to a concert in the Red Navy Club, so Dave went to the stokers' mess and persuaded Jim to go. They had had very few opportunities for a 'run ashore' since joining the ship, in fact, this seemed to be the only one, so they put their suits on and went.

The town consisted of one long street of wooden houses, no shops or bars. The snow was knee deep, but to stretch their legs, they walked to the end of the street. The road came to an abrupt end and all that they could see was mile after mile of snow covered plain. There were lots of Russian sentries around, and it was most disconcerting the way they pointed their sub-machine guns at their stomachs as they approached, and followed them around with the gun pointing at them as they passed. They felt like shouting, 'Hey, you are supposed to be our allies, we've just brought you a load of war supplies.'

The Red Navy Club was a very imposing building, with large pillars outside, and marble floors inside. Just inside the main door was a huge statue of Joseph Stalin and all round the walls were hung pictures of 'Heroes of the Soviet Union', and busts of Russian leaders and generals. There were lots of Russian sailors and soldiers, but they didn't seem interested in mixing and, of course, nobody knew each other's language. The biggest disappointment to everyone was that there was nothing to eat, and even worse, nothing to drink. The band was quite good, but it was all opera and ballet music. The singer was a girl who looked terrified of the looks she was getting from the Russian officers; maybe she was letting the side down by singing for foreigners. Dave thought everyone seemed glad when it was all over and they could all get back to their ships.

The next day was a quiet day. It snowed like hell, but they put on their own entertainment, a 'Sod's Opera' as the Navy calls it. The turns were always very good but most of it certainly 'unfit for public consumption'.

In the evening thirty ratings joined the crew. They were survivors from the destroyer *Caprice*, which had been torpedoed three days out from Murmansk on the convoy before theirs. She had been hit for'd, and the bows had been blown off for'd of B gun. The ship was unable to steam ahead as the remaining bulkheads were not strong enough to take the buffeting they would receive from the waves if the ship was pushing into the sea, so the Captain had turned the ship around and, for the next three days, they had steamed stern first to get into Murmansk.

She was there now, in a dry dock, where the Russians were building a wooden jury bow section onto it which would be strong enough for her to get back to the UK.

The survivors had been split up around the escorts for passage back to England, where they would be drafted to new ships. That evening the Captain also informed them on the Tannoy that they would be sailing at noon the next day, to escort a convoy back to Britain.

At 1 p.m. the following afternoon, *Myngs* led her flotilla, in line ahead, out through the boom gate, their pennants flying in the brisk north wind. It was icy cold, well below freezing point. The other small escorts were coming up astern and the big ships were already outside waiting. They immediately went into an Asdic search and covered a large area before the merchant ships started coming out, but there were no submarine contacts. During the search *Myngs* managed to cross to the area where they had attacked the U-boat. It was still in the same position, still giving a firm, clear echo; had she been able to, she would have quickly left the area once the Captain realised that the destroyers had gone.

Soon, the convoy, with the escorts in station around the flanks, turned west on the homeward leg, and everyone settled down to Defence Stations, four hours on, four hours off. The big ships were in the centre of the convoy, with the Flag Officer controlling everything. Their main task was defence of the convoy if they came under surface attack or from enemy aircraft.

Dave had become friendly with one of the *Caprice* survivors who had been billeted in his mess, and that night at supper, he told Dave about the torpedoing of his ship. All these Emergency class destroyers were similar in their construction, so Dave could relate to the story just by looking around him. The man was called Mike, an able-seaman gunner, and he had just come off the last Dog watch, and was passing through the Canteen flat, where, in fact, they were now sitting in *Myngs*. He was about to go through the bulkhead door, into the for'd mess deck, when the torpedo hit; there was a sheet of flame, all of the lights went out, and he was thrown to the deck by the blast coming through the bulkhead door.

He climbed to his feet. Sea water was already pouring aft through the door, and men were sitting or lying on the deck, some covered in blood, others very still. Mike went into the mess deck and started to help the walking wounded to get out of the mess. Several men from the Damage Control Party had now appeared, and were also trying to get the shocked men out. The emergency battery lanterns had come on, but it was still difficult to see as smoke was belching up through the hatch that led to the mess below. Mike's blood ran cold as he heard the noises coming from that mess deck below, screams, moans and the deafening sound of water rushing in. He rushed across to the hatch, but the smoke pouring out was so hot that he was forced back. He dragged another man, lying on the deck, back to the bulkhead door, and he noticed that there was a huge gash in the ship's side, on the port side, where the water gushed in each time the bows hit a wave. Looking for'd, he also noticed that the bows and the rest of the ship were acting independently of each other; as they crossed a wave, the bows went down but the rest of the ship was still climbing the wave. The gap in the ship's side widened, and there was an awful sound of grinding steel. 'My God,' thought Mike, 'the bows must be hanging on by a few rivets.' As if on cue, the Tannoy came to life. 'For'd Damage Control Party, close all watertight doors on Bulkhead 3.' Some of the Damage Control Party stumbled out of the for'd messdeck. They looked at each other; they all knew that there were still men inside. Once again the Tannoy boomed, 'For'd Damage Control, report when Bulkhead 3 W/T doors are clipped shut. As quickly as possible. If the bows go we may lose the ship.' They closed the door and started to hammer the clips on. 'Stop, wait a minute,' shouted the petty officer in charge of the Damage Control Party, and held his hand up for silence. In that minute Mike was sure he could hear someone banging on the other side of the bulkhead door, then with a rendering scream of tortured metal, the bow section tore loose and sank. Water immediately started spurting in around the edges of the door, and they started hammering the clip on again until it was reduced to a tiny trickle.

They spent the next hour and a half shoring up the bulkhead with huge battens of timber, using hammocks and wedges to stop small flows of water. Then they attempted to get under way again, but it was soon obvious that the bulkhead, open to the sea, would not take the strain of the pressure of water as they pushed into the sea. You could actually feel the bulkhead bending with the force, and new leaks started up.

It was then that they had the idea of steaming stern first, and it worked, although they had to keep the speed down, as the sea flooded across the quarter deck.

The next morning they found that they had lost 32 men. They had seven bodies, but the rest had gone with the bow section. Mike was very distressed as he came to the end of his story and he confessed to Dave that he woke up every night with a nightmare of the sights and sounds of that for'd messdeck, just before the bow section went.

The next few days the sea became very calm, with an oily swell, but it was bitterly cold and far off to the north, they occasionally caught a glimpse of an iceberg. It was perfect U-boat weather, so the Asdic operators had to be on their toes constantly. On the other hand, any U-boat that put up its periscope was also taking a risk because in that flat, calm sea a plume of white water would stick out like a sore thumb. To make matters worse, the Fokker-Wolf long range reconnaissance aircraft found them again, and started its constant circling of the convoy, just outside of gun range; now every U-boat within range would know their position.

The routine of 'watch on' and 'sleep' settled down. In the messdeck Dave had become used to the permanent haze of tobacco smoke. Rum and tobacco were part of Navy life, and the tobacco was really very, very strong Navy tobacco. You could buy it as pipe tobacco, loose shag, called 'tickler', for rolling your own cigarettes or 'tailor made' cigarettes, which cost about sixpence for a packet of twenty. These were called 'blue liners', as they had a blue line running the length of them to stop people selling them ashore. All this tobacco was duty free, and almost everyone in the Navy smoked. You could also buy leaf tobacco. A lot of the older hands used to buy this and soak the leaves in their rum ration for about two weeks, then roll it up into a cone shaped lump, called a prick. Then they would take a ball of small diameter tarred hemp rope and, starting at the point, they would wind the rope around the prick, as tightly as they could. It was quite an art. You would see 'old stripey' sitting on his ball of rope, which then went over a couple of hammock bars on the deckhead, and back to the tobacco, which he held in his hands. He would take a turn around the tobacco prick, then haul it tight, so that you could see the rum oozing out of it. He would continue like this until all of the tobacco was bound tightly inside the rope, and he would put this in his locker to dry out and harden, then he would use it, cutting pieces off to put in his pipe.

Dave didn't smoke. After being in the Navy a week, at HMS *Royal Arthur*, he had decided that he was going to be a real sailor, a real Jack Tar, so he had bought himself a pipe and a tin of pipe tobacco. That evening he lit up. After five minutes he turned green; after ten minutes he was being violently sick. He sold his smoking gear the next morning and had never smoked since. In later life he would realise that it was the best investment that he had ever made.

The barometer started to fall and they all knew that they were in for a hard blow. The off-watch men started to lash down anything that might move on the upper deck; they double frapped the sea boat and the motor boat, and put extra lashings on the Carley floats. You couldn't get from the for'd part of the ship to the after part below decks, because the two boiler rooms and the engine room took up the entire middle section of the ship. They were connected to each other by watertight doors, but not to the rest of the ship.

So they rigged lifelines on the upper deck, leading from the fo'c'sle door, which was the entrance to the fore part of the ship, to the after deck house, called the sick-bay flat. Lifelines were rigged both sides of the ship. They were steel wire ropes that had pennants attached to them by a thimble; you grabbed a pennant and walked along the upper deck, with the pennant sliding the length of the lifeline. It meant you had something to hang onto all the time that you were on the upper deck. It could be quite a perilous journey in rough weather, as the seas crashed inboard, and you could find yourself up to the waist in water, or knocked off your feet. As long as you hung onto the pennant, you were just carried aft along the wire until you crashed into the bulkhead, quite close to the door into the after deckhouse.

The sea started getting up by the evening, back onto pot mess again. When Dave went on watch for the Middle, they had stopped any unnecessary traffic between for'd and aft. There were certain trips that were necessary, of course; for instance, a stoker had to go right aft to the tiller flat every hour, to check that the propeller shaft bearings were not overheating. The routine for these trips was that the person concerned had to report to the wheelhouse, where the Bosun's Mate would call the sick bay flat by phone and report, 'Able seaman Jones coming aft.' On his arrival the report would come back, 'Able Seaman Jones arrived aft.'

The ship was rolling wildly. It was impossible to move without holding onto something. From the lookout position, Dave could see the waves crashing inboard and rushing along the upper deck. He had come to an arrangement with a messmate in the opposite watch to share a hammock. It was a common practice, called 'the hot pit routine'; one rolled out and went on watch, the other came off watch and climbed into a warm hammock. They had slung the hammock in the canteen flat, and when Dave had finished his watch he was looking forward to turning in. He walked along the passageway towards the flat, listening to the cacophony of sound, the groaning of the ship under stress, the crash as waves hit the side, the banging of the anchor cables, a louder bang as something broke loose. One moment he seemed to be weightless, walking on air; the next he had legs of lead as the ship came up again, and the rolling threw him from one side of the passageway to the other.

When he reached his hammock, he had quite a job to swing up into it. He had to choose the moment when he was weightless to get in. The motion of the hammock didn't bother him so much now; the only problem was that it was slung next to a bulkhead so that when the ship made a heavy roll to port, he was pressed hard against the bulkhead. It was almost like sleeping on the floor. Nevertheless, he was asleep in about five minutes.

It must have been about an hour later that he was woken with an almighty crash, like an explosion. He sat up, startled. The ship was rolling to port; already he was pressed hard against the ship's side and the ship was still going over. There was a clatter of feet pounding along the passage below him, heading for the upper deck, someone shouted something that sounded like 'torpedo', then he was struggling to get out of his hammock. A feeling of panic swept across him, probably caused by the story of the *Caprice*, still fresh in his mind. Whatever it was, one of his feet had got tangled in the hammock nettles, the small lines attached to the base of the hammock. The ship was still rolling to port, she must have been almost on her beam ends by now; the next moment he was out and on the deck. He looked into the for'd messdeck, it was a scene of utter chaos. All of the lockers from the starboard mess had broken loose and had crashed over onto the port side; men were trying to extricate themselves; there was another crash as the locker containing all of the mess traps broke loose and the cups and plates and cutlery flew across the mess. Then Dave was racing down the passage after the others, heading for the upper deck. Before he reached the bulkhead door leading outside, the ship gave a shudder and started rolling upright again. He stopped by the door; there was quite a crowd there, looking out, watching the sea crashing along the deck, listening to the scream of the wind. He felt sure that some of them that had raced under his hammock before he had got out must have jumped straight over the side, to get away from a sinking ship.

In the light of dawn, the damage that had been caused was terrific. Both boats had gone, and their davits were bent out of recognition. All of the Carley floats had gone and every guard rail stanchion had been bent flat to the deck. There were no longer any guard rails around the ship; they were all trailing over the ship's side. One of the torpedo tube mountings had been lifted out of its roller path and was jammed at a peculiar angle. All of the depth charge throwers on the port side had gone, and there was a huge dent in the funnel.

No one had gone over the side, but two ratings had had very narrow escapes. They had both been swept off their feet and washed to the ship's side, where there were no longer any guard rails. Both had got their legs tangled in the mess of guard rail wires, which had saved them. One managed to crawl to the after deck house and get inside; the other was washed back inboard, under the torpedo tubes, and he had hung on there until he was found. He had a broken arm. The upper deck shone like burnished steel, the water had scoured it so much, but later on, when it dried, it turned a rusty colour.

The First Lieutenant informed the crew that the ship had been hit by a freak double wave at about 0500 which had caused all of the damage. It took days to get things cleared up again.

They also decided that it was far too dangerous for the convoy to continue sailing and carrying out zig-zags in close proximity to each other, as any small mistake could lead to a collision. So all ships were told to operate and proceed independently, and to rendezvous in three days at a prearranged position. It was argued that no submarine could operate in that kind of a sea.

Three days later it was a different world. The sea had moderated, all of the ships appeared at the designated rendezvous, they hadn't lost a single one, and they were now heading in a south-westerly direction into warmer latitudes. They had never had a smell of a U-boat during the homeward voyage but while Dave was on watch the next night, the Radar Operator reported an aircraft echo approaching fast from the south. The Action Stations bells sounded, everyone scrambled to his action station and the 4.5-inch guns were brought to the ready. The aircraft was now being plotted in the Operations Room, and they were waiting for it to come into gun range. As it came into range the whole convoy opened up, one sector of the sky becoming covered with shell bursts. At the same time, over the intercom, the Radar Operator reported, 'Bridge Radar, Target showing IFF, repeat, aircraft is a Friendly.' The Captain's voice came over the Tannoy: '4.5s Cease firing,' and *Myngs'* guns fell silent, but some ships were still firing, and it was too late. A bright light appeared in the sky, slowly descending until it was reflected in the water, then, with a splash, it hit the sea. One of the destroyers was sent at full speed to see if there was anyone to rescue and, to their surprise, they found an inflatable dinghy with five US airmen on board. The plane, which was a Flying Fortress, had already sunk.

The IFF was a transponder, which was carried by all Allied aircraft. It stands for 'Identification, Friend or Foe,' and when triggered off, it transmitted a coded signal which identified it as a Friendly. It was never discovered what a Flying Fortress was doing so far north in Arctic waters.

Dave, being a Gunnery Radar Operator, quite often went into the Radar Room when he was off watch. It was always warm in there, the lights kept dim so the radar screen could be seen better, and it was restful on the eyes. He quite often dozed off sitting in the chair chatting to the radar operators. The equipment was different to that which he had been trained on, but the theory and principle were the same. This radar was used for navigation, and for observing everything for up to a hundred miles around them, a sort of electronic lookout that saw far beyond the range of the lookouts on the bridge. The operators were called Radio Direction Finder ratings, and they wore the same badge as Radio Telegraphists on their sleeve. While he was in there on this afternoon, they picked up a very strong 'peak' on the radar set, dead ahead of them and, when they measured the range, three hundred miles away. They reported this to the bridge, and the OOW replied that it would be the mountains of northern Scotland. Dave marvelled at the wonders of modem science. He could see the land, he could lean forward and touch the land on the radar screen, but it would take them three days to reach there.

They escorted the convoy past the Orkney Islands, where the big ships peeled off and entered Scapa Flow, but they continued into the Pentland Firth, and guided the merchant ships into Loch Eribol. They left them there at anchor to await dispersal to British ports or the formation of another convoy to continue on their way to America.

The escorts turned back towards Scapa and 'home', if you could call such a forbidding place home. Nevertheless, there was a feeling of light-heartedness; the weather was fine, the sea was calm, and the sailors were laughing and skylarking among themselves.

They passed the *Royal Oak* beacon, and as they approached their designated buoys, the signal tower ashore started flashing: '*Myngs* proceed alongside Tyne to effect minor repairs.' They swung around and headed for HMS *Tyne*, a large depot repair ship, with cranes, workshops and trained artificers who could deal with most small ship defects.

As they came alongside to tie up, a sailor on board the *Tyne*, seeing all of the damage, shouted, 'Blimey, did you blokes meet the *Tirpitz* out there?' Some of the perks of coming alongside the *Tyne* were her spacious bathrooms, and the smell of newly baked bread, which they were soon enjoying, and a meal of fresh meat and green vegetables.

Dave, Jim and Mike decided that they would have 'a run ashore' in Scapa that evening, especially as Mike had heard that he would be leaving for Portsmouth the next morning. Leave was only from 4 p.m. till 8 p.m., as there was nothing to do ashore except the cinema and the canteen; there were no women or civilians ashore, and although it was rumoured that there were a few Wrens, nobody had ever seen them.

Their drifter was lying alongside them, with a name plate *Myngs* over the wheelhouse, and when the Bosun's Mate piped, 'Liberty men fall in amidships,' they were there among the others. There was quite a crowd as this would be their first run ashore in Scapa and everyone was curious to see what it was like. After the Officer of the Day had inspected them, they climbed down the ladder into the drifter, minus two or three of them who had been sent back to their mess for not having shaved well enough or for having dirty shoes; they would have to catch the next liberty boat.

The drifter headed out into the Flow then turned and steered towards a long jetty sticking out from the shore. The other ships were all swinging round their buoys, and dozens of drifters were all converging on the jetty, all racing to get a berth as close to the jetty as possible. When *Myngs'* drifter arrived at the jetty, they had to go alongside two other drifters, which they all had to climb over to get onto the jetty, then they started the long walk to reach the shore.

At the end were several large Nissan huts and everyone seemed to be heading for one about two hundred yards long. When they entered, they found that it had a bar counter running the entire length of the hut. On one side there were hundreds of shouting sailors, already about eight deep at the bar, trying to attract the attention of dozens of harassed NAAFI canteen assistants, who were dispensing beer in pint glasses, mess fannies and even buckets. The entire wall on their side was stacked with beer barrels; you could have anything you wanted as long as it was beer.

A lot of sailors were already well under the weather; the noise was ear-shattering. In one corner someone was playing a piano, but you couldn't hear a single note and everyone seemed to be singing his own song. They managed to get themselves a pint each and positioned themselves against the wall, shouting at each other to make themselves heard. Dave had to laugh. As the buckets of beer were passed back over people's heads to the owner, an empty glass kept dipping into it as it passed and they reckoned he would have only half a bucket by the time it reached him. They decided that they would have a few pints, then go and watch a movie in one of the other Nissan huts, which is what they did.

It was a recent movie, about the war in North Africa, but it was difficult to hear the dialogue, with all the ribald comments being shouted, and when a woman appeared, the wolf whistles were deafening. From time to time a recall message would be flashed onto the screen, such as, 'Ship's Company from HMS – are to return to their ship immediately', and a few men would get to their feet and move out, followed by boos or cheers depending on your inclination. These were ships that had to put to sea on some sudden emergency or operation. At least they won't recall us, thought Dave; it would be unusual, in the middle of a three day repair programme.

After the movie they still had about half an hour before the last liberty boat left for the ship, so they went back to the beer canteen which, by now, was in even greater pandemonium than before. Several sailors had already succumbed to intoxication, and were piled up against a wall, and everyone was roaring out the usual Navy songs:

> Side, side, loverly ship's side,
> Jimmy looks on it with pride,
> He'd have a blue fit,
> If he saw all the shit,
> On the side of the *Myngs'* ship's side.

everyone roaring out their own ship's name, and:

> This is my story,
> This is my song,
> We've been in commission,
> Too fucking long,
> Roll on the *Nelson*, the *Rodney*, *Renown*,
> This one funneled bastard is getting me down.

everyone shouting out how many funnels they had.

Already, along one end wall, about forty sailors dressed in white gaiters, white belts, with cap chin stays down and wearing a white armlet bearing the letters RNP were standing, nervously fingering their batons which they held in one hand. This was the RN Shore Patrol, men detailed from the duty watch of all ships present. It was an unpopular duty as you had to put up with all sorts of abuse, such as someone screaming in your face, 'All coppers are bastards,' and occasionally having to whack somebody with your baton. But in general, it was mostly light-hearted, because everyone knew that it could be them standing there in a white belt tomorrow night.

At 2000 an electric bell rang out and the shore patrol moved in, herding everyone out of the beer hall and along the jetty. Most were sober, a lot were staggering and a few were being carried, towards the end of the jetty where about forty drifters were waiting. There was keen rivalry between the ships and a lot of banter went on; a few fights broke out. Some ABs who had been in the service about two years and considered themselves to be hardened veterans, would goad the younger ordinary seamen, calling them ODs and 'green', and telling them that they hadn't been in 'half a dog watch'. Everyone hoped that their drifter would be close to the jetty, as they tied up about eight deep; it was no fun to have to climb over about six boats to get to your own. Your ribs were sore by the time you got there, because someone on every boat would take a swing at you. A few caps were lost over the side and it always amazed Dave that nobody fell over the side between the drifters and got crushed.

Finally they were all under way, spreading out to their ships. As the drifter came alongside *Myngs*, Dave noticed that the Duty part of the watch had been called out and were waiting to deal with any unruly libertymen. 'Right, fall in two deep,' shouted the Duty Petty Officer, and the Officer of the Day started his inspection of the swaying men. The inspection was simple. If you could stand up without assistance you could carry on to your mess, if you fell down or couldn't stand up on your own, the duty watch escorted you to the Tiller Flat, where you were lowered down through the hatch and left to sleep it off overnight, with a sentry to keep an eye on you.

These unfortunates were paraded in front of the First Lieutenant, at his Defaulters the next morning. The Cox'n would call out, 'Able Seaman Brown,' who would reply 'Sir,' and march up to the desk in front of the First Lieutenant. 'Off caps,' the Cox'n would rap out, and when this had been carried out, he would read out the charge.

'AB Brown, Sir, was guilty of an act prejudicial to good order and naval discipline, in that he did return to His Majesty's Ship *Myngs* drunk at 2030 on Tuesday 15th October.'

'How do you plead?' asks the First Lieutenant.

'Guilty, Sir,' is the usual reply; it's not much good pleading otherwise when the OOD, the Duty PO, and God knows how many other witnesses had seen you fall down on the upper deck.

'I award you four days stoppage of leave,' says the First Lieutenant, giving the normal punishment for this offence.

'Four days stoppage of leave,' repeats the Cox'n. 'On caps, about turn, quick march,' and the defaulter marches off.

No one is bothered about stoppage of leave in a place like Scapa Flow, but going with that is a couple of hours extra work during the Dog Watches, when they pipe, 'Men under punishment to muster.'

For repeated or more serious offences, you could get longer leave stoppages, or stoppage of pay, or, even worse, stoppage of rum. If it was a really serious offence the First Lieutenant would say 'Captain's Report,' they were then going to throw the book at you.

CHAPTER 3

Norway

Three days later they slipped from the Tyne and headed towards the big ship anchorage. *Zest* slipped from her buoy and took station astern, and two destroyers from another flotilla fell in astern of *Zest*. *Myngs* was looking very smart, with her new davits, new boats and new Carley floats, and her guard rail stanchions gleaming with a new coat of pusser's grey paint covering the welding where they had all been repaired.

In the big ship anchorage two cruisers and three aircraft carriers were already under way and the four destroyers took station as a screen around them as they nosed out into the open sea. The aircraft carriers were the small type which, in fact, had been converted from merchant ships, and which were known throughout the Navy as Woolworth carriers.

The previous night they had been told that they would be sailing this morning, although they hadn't been told where to. A notice had also been posted on the Ship's Company notice board telling them that they could write home and inform their next of kin that they had been on a convoy to Russia, although they were warned that they mustn't mention dates or names of ships or refer to any incident that occurred during the trip. Consequently everyone had been busy writing letters, which had to be put into the mail box unsealed. The officers on board were responsible for the censorship of letters. They had to read every letter and had to score out, with a black pen, any word or sentence that should not be divulged and could give information to the enemy. There were, of course, things of a private or intimate nature that a man and his wife might want to discuss, and for this purpose they could get a Privilege envelope from the ship's office. Printed on the outside of this envelope was a declaration that it contained nothing of service or operational nature, and the writer had to sign it and then he could post it sealed.

As they drew away from the land, the Captain came on the Tannoy and informed them that they were on their way to carry out an operation against the German pocket battleship *Tirpitz*. She was holed up in a Norwegian fjord, a constant threat to the northern convoys if she ever decided to come out. Some said that she was afraid to come out, because the Germans were aware of the large fleet always present at Scapa, not too far away, always waiting for an opportunity to have a go at the *Tirpitz*. The operation that they were sailing on was a regular occurrence. Almost every week a task force, mostly carriers, would arrive at the fjord and fly air strikes against the *Tirpitz*. The RAF also regularly bombed it, with much bigger bombs but, up to now, without much success.

The two biggest reasons for this were firstly, that the fjord she was holed up in was very narrow with high cliffs either side, making low level attack impossible and bombs had to be dropped very high. It was also easy to defend, with anti-aircraft guns along the cliff tops. The second reason was that she had developed a highly successful smoke screen system. At the first warning of an air raid, the smoke screen, spread around the banks of the fjord, was activated, and the airmen often found that they were just dropping their bombs into a cloud of smoke.

The group arrived off the Norwegian coast the next morning, and flying operations started immediately. The carriers turned into the wind, and the first strike started to take off. An escort was detailed to be stationed just off the quarter of each carrier; these were the 'crash boats', and were there to rescue the pilot of any aircraft that went into the sea on landing or take-off. *Myngs*, being the senior escort, had a roving station, keeping a sonar watch for submarines. Dave had had a change of Action Stations, and was now the Radar Controller on the twin Bofors gun, positioned abaft the funnel. His job was to lock the radar onto a target; the gun would then automatically follow it, whatever manoeuvre the target made. A computer worked out its 'future' position and allowed for 'aim off'.

Most of the strike force had now taken off, and quite a few formations were circling the ships. Most of them were the single engined, bi-plane Swordfish, which had proved itself to be a very good torpedo bomber; the others were Seafires. At a given signal they turned eastward, and flew towards the Norwegian coastline.

Two hours later they started to return, in ones and twos. The sea had got up quite a bit and Dave watched in fascination as the planes approached the sterns of the carriers, which were rising and falling about twenty feet. The planes were only travelling a few knots faster than the ship and their approach looked painfully slow, watching from the beam. The pilot had to judge just the right moment to put his wheels on the deck, and he saw several get 'waved off' at the last moment, as the deck fell away from them. These had to go around and try again. Even when their wheels did touch down, their ordeal wasn't over. Each plane had a hook near the rear, and there were three sets of arrester wires stretched across the deck. The hook had to snag one of these wires which brought it to a sudden stop. If they missed all of the arrester wires, the plane was stopped by a rope net stretched across the deck, which was to prevent the plane from running on and toppling over the bow into the sea, or to stop it running into parked aircraft on the bow. If they were lucky they got away with nothing worse than a broken propeller. Dave saw two aircraft run into this net.

During the rest of that day they flew off three more sorties against the *Tirpitz*. There was no good news announced, such as that she had been sunk, so all that they could hope for was that they had scored some hits and maybe caused her some damage. On the evening of the following day they were back swinging around their buoy at Scapa.

This week was another milestone in Dave's life. He was told to put in a request form to see the Captain 'To be rated Able Seaman'. Captain's Requestmen and Defaulters were held once a week. You had to wear your No. 1 suit, your best suit, and usually all the officers attended.

According to custom, Requestmen saw the Captain before Defaulters, and when Dave's name was called he marched up to the Captain's table and saluted. The Cox'n read out his request: 'Request to be rated Able Seaman, Sir.'

The Captain looked through his Service Records and said, 'I have noticed your work around the ship. You seem to be very good and enthusiastic about seamanship, your Divisional Officer has given you a very good report and it gives me great pleasure to rate you Able Seaman as from today.'

'Thank you sir,' Dave said, saluted, turned about and marched away. At last he felt like a real seaman, and there was more pay, of course. The petty officer of his Division congratulated him. His 'part of ship' was 'the Iron Deck', or mid part of the ship (the other parts were 'the Fo'c'sle' for'd and 'the Quarterdeck' aft).

The petty officer said, 'Now that you are an AB I want you to take over as bowman in the 35-foot motor cutter.' This boat was the workhorse of the ship which had a crew of three: AB bowman, stoker engine driver and a Leading Seaman as cox'n of the boat. They had to be ready at any time during day or night, to man the boat, whenever they heard the pipe, 'Away motor-boat's crew.'

Another incident, the same week, shook the whole crew. In one of the after messes was an AB named Knocker White. A lot of the crew called him 'Dad' as he was a lot older than most of them, about twenty-seven, with a wife and two kids. He was a steady sort of a bloke, very rarely went ashore, never got into trouble, and he was treated with a great deal of respect by everyone. On this particular day, the Cox'n went to his mess, and told him to get dressed in his best suit, and to muster in the Wardroom Flat at Captain's Defaulters. Knocker went white with shock and asked what the charge was. The Cox'n replied, 'Breaking censorship regulations.'

In a few hours the whole story had spread throughout the ship. Knocker had written home and told his family that he had been to Russia with a convoy. Then he made a big mistake: he had run out of envelopes and had used one of the Privilege envelopes, never thinking that, when he signed it on the front, he was signing to say that the letter bore no reference to Service matters. They also found out that 'Privilege envelope' did not mean that your letter would not be opened. Somewhere ashore, a random one in a hundred were looked at to make sure that no one abused the regulations, and Knocker's letter had been one of these. The charge he was on was very serious, akin to helping the enemy, and although, in his defence, his Divisional Officer pleaded that they had been informed that they could write home and tell their families that they had been to Russia, the damning piece of evidence was his signature on the envelope, declaring that it contained no references to service matters. He was found Guilty. The Captain, though sympathetic, told him that he had to make an example of him, to prevent other people from doing the same thing. He said that the charge was a Court Martial offence, but he would offer him the choice of a Court Martial or Captain's Punishment. Knocker opted for Captain's Punishment and he was remanded for twenty-four hours, while the Captain considered it and sought legal advice.

The next day he was again up in front of the Captain, who read out the punishment: 'to be confined in Naval Detention Quarters for 30 days.' He was taken straight to his mess, his kit was packed, two seamen were detailed as escort with white belts and gaiters, and they carried his kit-bag and hammock to the accommodation ladder where the 35-foot motor cutter was already waiting.

So one of Dave's first duties, as bowman of the motor boat, was the unpleasant task of taking Knocker White to Detention Quarters. In Scapa

Flow, the RNDQ was an old First War battleship called Iron Duke. She was so old that they had deliberately sunk her in shallow water in a remote corner of the Flow, and she was sitting there as if she was at anchor. She was now used as a store ship and, of course, as Detention Quarters. Painted a dark grey, she looked very menacing as they approached her Quarterdeck and, once alongside, the prisoner and the escort climbed the long ladder to the deck, where two very big Royal Marine sergeants were waiting, and the last they heard of Knocker was 'Left, right, left, right . . .' as he was quickly marched for'd.

Everyone on board talked about little else for the rest of the day. All decided that Knocker had had a 'green rub'. One stoker had actually done detention on board *Iron Duke* and he happened to mention that the cells were right for'd in the bows. The motor boat's crew got together and decided that they would try to do something. They would attempt to contact him and the opportunity came two days later on a legitimate run to the big ship anchorage with official correspondence. They had to pass close to the *Iron Duke* and they slid in under her bows, where they couldn't be seen from the upper deck because of the flare of the ship's side. 'Knocker!' they called, keeping their voices low so that they wouldn't be heard by anyone on the upper deck. After about half a dozen attempts they heard a faint reply. After confirming that it was him, they called: 'Lower a line down,' and after a few minutes a piece of string came snaking down from a small porthole. They tied a small package onto the line that they had ready, containing cigarettes, matches and chocolate, gave a tug on the line and it disappeared upwards and through the porthole. They were jubilant. From that day on, whenever they had a bona fide trip in that area, they would deliver a small package to the *Iron Duke*.

That weekend, it happened to them. On the Saturday night as Dave and his mates were watching a cowboy movie ashore, it flashed on the screen, 'All personnel from the ships *Myngs* and *Zephyr* return to your ship immediately.' They got to their feet self-consciously amid the usual banter of jeers, boos and cheers, and shouts of, 'Go to sea, you bastards,' and left the cinema.

They made their way along the jetty. It seemed so strange and quiet without the shouts and drunken songs and fights of other libertymen. At the end of the jetty was the single drifter with *Myngs* on her wheelhouse. It made a change just to climb on board without having to dodge punches and pushes as they crossed other drifters.

There were about a dozen libertymen returning, and as they drew near to their ship they could see that the slip rope had already been rove to the buoy and everything was bustling with activity. The Chief Bosun's Mate, known to everyone as the Buffer, was waiting for them at the gangway. 'Come on, chop chop, get below and change into your working rig, prepare the ship for sea, we sail at 2000.' Of course nobody said where they were going, as usual; they worked on the principle that if you didn't know anything before you sailed, no secrets could leak out.

At exactly 2000 they slipped from their buoy and got under way. It was a beautiful starlit night and the sea was flat calm. Dave reflected on his day. He had gone ashore at 1600 to watch the movie, and before doing that they had gone to the canteen and had egg and chips, followed by a couple of pints, then he had just started to enjoy the movie when the recall came up on the screen. Now they were off to God knows where, and to top it all he now found he had the First Watch, so he was up until midnight, and back on watch again at 0400. With the sea so calm and the light from the stars, he was able to make out that there were six ships in the group, two cruisers and four destroyers. They passed out into the open sea and turned their bows towards the east.

Next morning again was a beautiful sunny day. The course was still east, and no sign of land anywhere. At 0900 the Captain came on the Tannoy. 'This is the Captain speaking. This operation is a very important one. For some time the Germans have been moving war supplies and personnel around the Norwegian coast in perfect safety between a minefield that they have laid and the coast and our torpedo boats and coastal craft have been unable to reach them. The minefield is about two miles from the coast, but last night, as we were leaving Scapa, a flotilla of RN minesweepers cleared a channel through the minefield near to Stavanger. Tonight we will be passing through this channel, and following the coast inside the minefield, and we hope that we can intercept one of these coastal convoys. That is all.'

An excited buzz of conversation started up as everyone began to discuss this. To the best of anyone's knowledge it was the first time that this had been tried. The general feeling was that it would make a nice change to be the predator instead of the hunted, especially among the men with several Russian convoys under their belt.

At 1800 that evening they arrived at the opening in the minefield, marked by the minesweepers with two buoys, a green one and a white one. The

43

ships went to Action Stations and turned cautiously into the entrance, fervently hoping that the minesweepers hadn't overlooked a mine. Thirty minutes later, now quite dark, they knew that they were through, and they turned towards Stavanger, running parallel to the coast, the four destroyers stationed around the cruisers, *Kent* and *Euralyus*. Dave looked over the side of the gun sponson. Everything was so quiet and still, he could hear the sea gurgling its way along the waterline. They were moving very slowly, less than 10 knots. He looked across to the mountains of Norway which stood out distinctly in the moonlight, particularly the snow covered summits.

Suddenly the Tannoy crackled to life and he raced back to his seat at the radar console on the Bofors gun. 'Bridge, Radar, group of echoes dead ahead, 25 miles. Closing at 10 knots.' It could only be a convoy. 'Director Radar,' came the report over the speaker; this meant that the Director, a large turret above the bridge which controlled the 4.5 inch guns, was now locked onto the target by radar. A few minutes later came the report, '4.5's Radar' which meant that the 4.5 inch guns had followed the Director and were also locked onto the target, loaded and ready to fire. At the moment only the for'd guns were pointing at the target, the two 4.5 guns aft, X and Y guns, were 'wooded', meaning that they couldn't point at the target because of the ship's superstructure.

'Range 20 miles,' came over the speakers. Down below in the Transmitting Station the computers would be assessing the target's course and speed, own course and speed, wind speed and direction, and other ballistic settings and would automatically aim the guns so that a shell fired would fall in the same position as the target, even allowing for the target's movement during the 'time of flight' of the shell.

'Range 15 miles,' came over the speaker, followed shortly by '10 miles'. Dave was unable to see directly ahead of the ship because the funnel was immediately in front of the Bofors gun, and the bridge superstructure was in front of that but, unable to contain his curiosity, he jumped from his seat and ran to the side of the sponson. Peering ahead he could make out the vague shapes of the ships that they were approaching, illuminated by the bright moon. He was wearing a headset and microphone on a long lead, so that he could hear orders directed to his gun. The speaker crackled into life again, 'Range now 8 miles,' and he jumped in alarm as, with a deafening roar and a brilliant flash of flame, the cruiser on their starboard side opened fire with her for'd 6-inch guns. Dave, still standing at the side of the gun deck, saw one of the ships in the centre of the convoy literally lift out of the water in the centre of a huge explosion, then settle back burning furiously. The other cruiser had now also opened fire, and over the Tannoy came the order, '4.5s Engage' and *Myngs* shook as the for'd guns opened fire. Glancing around, Dave saw that every ship in the strike force was firing as quick as they could reload.

By now nearly all the vessels in the convoy had opened fire with different calibres of guns, and it took a few seconds for Dave to realise that they were all firing into the air. The sky above the convoy was full of shell bursts, and it was obvious that they were under the impression that they were under air attack.

He looked for'd again. The convoy had got much closer, steaming in all directions, and in the short passage of time since the first shell was fired, at least five ships in the convoy were blazing. He went back to his position on the Bofors, telling the rest of the gun crew what he had seen. They were still unable to bear on any target, but he knew it would be only a few seconds before they were up to the convoy. A burning merchant ship appeared around the port side of the funnel only about three hundred yards away. The order came, 'Bofors gun, Engage burning ship, Bearing Red 45.' The gun swung round on to the target, Dave quickly locked the range into the control box, and they opened fire. He could see the Bofors shells exploding along the superstructure, he saw two men jump over the side into the sea, he looked around and realised that the strike force were going through the middle of the convoy. There were ships all around them, the majority on fire. Two sank as he watched. Their after 4.5s had also opened fire, the noise was deafening. They started to come out of the other side of the convoy.

He heard the bridge radio on the Tannoy say, 'Stand-by to execute, alter 180 degree turn to starboard together, Stand-by, Execute.' *Myngs* heeled over to port as she started her turn and Dave watched in admiration as all the ships came round in perfect synchronisation and they headed back towards the convoy. The guns had not stopped firing, and more ships were burning, although there seemed to be a lot fewer than before. They got the order, 'Engage targets independently as they appear,' and they opened fire again, the captain of the gun directing them onto different targets as they passed. The convoy had been totally wiped out. Two ships were steaming as fast as they could go towards the Norwegian coast, one of them belching thick black smoke.

As what was left of the convoy fell astern, the command came, 'Cease Firing,' and the guns fell silent. The Gunnery Officer ordered, 'All positions report state of guns,' and reports came in from all of the armament, 'All guns empty,' except for A Gun which reported, 'A Gun loaded, half cock.' Then the order, 'A Gun train on Green 90, Angle of sight 50 degrees, Clear Gun.' In a few seconds there was a bang as A Gun discharged the gun and the Gunnery Officer said, 'A Gun, your shell will have landed somewhere in Norway.' Dave had visions of some poor Norwegian farmer waking up with a start as a 4.5 shell exploded in his farmyard.

The senior officer had asked for reports of casualties and structural damage in the force and, amazingly, there were no casualties and very little damage. In *Myngs*, the next morning, they found a line of machine gun bullet holes along the side of the bridge superstructure, but no one had been hit and there was a steady stream of off-watch personnel up to the bridge to view the bullet holes.

By this time they were back through the minefield and the Captain came on the Tannoy and gave them more details. The convoy had consisted of fourteen ships, four of which were minesweeper type escorts. The entire convoy had been destroyed, though two ships had run themselves aground on the Norwegian shore to prevent themselves from sinking, where they would receive the attention of RAF Beaufighter patrols which attacked this area almost on a daily basis. He congratulated everyone on what had been a most successful strike.

So it was a jubilant crew as they headed back towards Scapa. Everybody went over every part of the action, filling in parts that other people hadn't seen. Jim came up from the stokers' mess and Dave had to relate the whole story again. He really felt sorry for the stokers, down below in the boiler room and the engine room, where they could hear and feel the guns and the explosions, and the ship altering course and speed, but they didn't have a clue about what was happening.

As they approached Scapa Flow *Myngs* received a signal that made everyone even happier. It said, '*Myngs* detach from main body and proceed to Greenock on the Clyde for five day boiler clean.' This was the dream of all escorts in Scapa. After several thousand miles steaming all the escorts had to have their boiler tubes cleaned. To do this they had to go to one of the shipyards around the country. To the sailors it meant two days home leave to each watch, it meant to be back in civilisation, it meant real pubs, and it meant girls; probably the most difficult part of Scapa Flow was never seeing the face of a woman. Amid a flurry of signals, *Myngs* hauled out of station and headed west towards the Pentland Firth to pass along the north coast of Scotland. The cox'n was working out the leave arrangements. One watch would leave on arrival at Greenock for two days leave and on their return the other watch would go. Jim and Dave were hoping that they would be in the same leave party so that they could enjoy their leave together, but it was difficult for stokers as the boiler clean mostly involved them. When the leave lists went up on the Ship's Company notice board they were disappointed to see that Dave was in the first leave party and Jim was in the second, but nothing could change the light-hearted feeling throughout the ship as they got nearer to civilisation.

As evening closed in they were approaching the Minch Channel on the west coast of Scotland. This was a channel marked with navigation buoys and the lookouts were all warned to keep very vigilant, as there had been incidents where German E-boats, fast torpedo patrol boats, had secured to the navigation buoys and waited for passing ships. The approaching ship would pick up the echo on radar, but assume that it was the buoy that they were looking at, until it was too late.

As the ship passed the E-boat would cast off from the buoy, and attack the ship, launching its torpedoes and then speeding away. Several ships had been lost in this way.

Next morning they entered the Clyde and steamed up the river to Greenock where the shipyard workers were ready for them. Greenock had also received the attention of the Luftwaffe and lots of the burnt-out shells of gutted buildings could be seen from the river.

Once secured alongside, the ship became a hive of activity. A large boiler cleaning vessel secured on the outboard side, while the first leave party got ready to depart. Two hours later they were on a naval bus, on their way to Glasgow Central Station, all chattering and singing, whistling at girls, and enjoying the sights of a city again. The people, the traffic, the towns, made Dave realise what made Scapa so depressing. One thought hung heavy on everyone's shoulders; before leaving they had been warned that 'the ship is under sailing orders': this meant that anyone returning late from leave would not only be charged with overstaying their leave but that it would be an aggravated offence, much more serious. They had also been told, to their surprise, that the ship would be on its way to Russia again when she sailed.

Dave's parents were delighted when he arrived home in his colliery village about tea time. He had sent a telegram from Glasgow but they hadn't received it.

He was given the hero treatment and feted in the village; he wasn't allowed to pay for a drink anywhere he went. That evening his father talked to him about some of his experiences and he said, 'You left here as a boy, now you are a man.' Later, looking in the mirror in his room, he could see what his father meant; his face looked a bit gaunt and different.

He had another task which was not so pleasant, and which he was not looking forward to. His mother had a friend in the next village, whose son had been reported 'killed in action' on a Russian convoy. He had been serving on HMS *Lapwing* and she had heard from Dave's mother that he had been on the same convoy. She wanted to hear from someone who had been there about the last moments of *Lapwing*, and her son. She was very composed and calm, but Dave couldn't find it in his heart to tell her about survivors sitting on the boom buoys, or about six bodies from *Lapwing* that had slid into the sea, from under the White Ensign, at a burial at sea ceremony, the day after they sailed from Polyano.

He just told her that *Lapwing*'s sinking had been very quick and she seemed content in the knowledge that she had spoken to someone who knew where her son's body lay.

The two days leave passed only too quickly and soon he was back on board *Myngs*. The second leave party were straining at the bit and that afternoon they were gone, leaving the ship strangely deserted. Besides the boiler clean, there were many other minor defects that had to be put right. Dave got the job, from the Buffer, of going around the ship, with three other ABs, to strip and grease all of the shackles on board, from the biggest on the anchor cables to the smallest on the guard rail wires. This ship husbandry was a never ending job on the ship. Lots of fittings, almost permanently immersed in salt water, soon rusted and seized up, unless they were cleaned and greased as they were doing. For instance, the sea-boat's disengaging gear was designed to slip the sea-boat two or three feet above the surface of the sea; if one end was to 'hang up', the crew would be in real trouble.

That evening Dave had his first 'run-ashore' in Greenock; all the watch ashore libertymen went ashore. Nobody knew when their next run-ashore would be, and no one was going to miss out on the last run-ashore in civilisation; besides, tomorrow would be duty watch on board and the next day they would be sailing.

They all had a real wild night ashore, drank too much, sang until they were hoarse, and chatted up the local lassies, even if they couldn't understand their broad Scottish accent. The local civilians ashore were quite used to a lot of sailors descending on them from time to time, and they were quite friendly and ready to make sure that they had a good run-ashore.

Next morning it was back to work, many nursing hangovers. The second leave party's leave expired the next day at 0900 and the ship was due to sail at 1000.

Dave was duty on board that night The libertymen revellers were returning on board, making a lot of noise, and all during the night the second leave party came back in dribs and drabs. He kept a lookout for Jim, to ask how he got on at home, but he couldn't see him.

The next morning at nine o'clock, when all leave had expired, they piped 'Clear lower deck for payment.' This was a weekly occurrence and, in accordance with tradition, all sailors were paid on their caps. 'Clear lower deck' meant that everyone on the ship had to come up from below and fall in by divisions on the upper deck; no one was excused! The cox'n received reports from Divisional Petty Officers that everyone was present, and he reported to the First Lieutenant, 'Lower Deck cleared, Sir.'

Payment then started, each Division coming up to the Pay Officer's table in single file. 'Able Seaman Brown,' the Petty Officer Writer would call out; Brown would step forward, slap his cap down on the table, with his pay book on the top and call out, 'Able Seaman Brown, Sir, PJX618755.' 'One pound, twelve shillings and five pence, sir,' the PO WRTR called out, the Pay Officer counted out the money onto the cap, and the sailor would carry on below.

This was roughly the amount that Dave picked up each week, although an allowance of six shillings a week that he made to his mother had been deducted. These allowances were compulsory; if you were married, you had to make an allowance to your wife, otherwise, to your next of kin. The amount you allotted was up to you. It's a pity that they couldn't have paid us when we arrived instead of when we are sailing, ruefully thought Dave.

The Pay Muster lasted about forty minutes, after which came the pipe, 'Special Sea Dutymen to your stations, hands prepare for leaving harbour,' and soon they were moving down the River Clyde towards the open sea. It was then that a terrible 'buzz' started going around the ship. This rumour said that twenty-eight men had failed to return to the ship before it had sailed, twenty-eight men had 'jumped ship', and it was an aggravated offence as the ship had been under sailing orders. They would, in fact, be treated as deserters, and when caught they would be subject to a Court Martial.

A thought struck Dave, and he rushed down to the Stokers' Mess, where his worst fears were confirmed. To his dismay and disappointment, Jim was one of the missing men. Why? he thought, the convoys to Russia were bad and very dangerous; was it fear that stopped them coming back? but everyone was afraid, anyone would be a fool not to be afraid after watching burning ships go down.

The feeling of sympathy for the men who had failed to return began to change to one of anger later in the day when the Ship's Company realised that there were twenty-eight Action Stations that had to be covered by the men who were still on board; in other words, the ship was undermanned in every department.

The ship turned north as they left the Clyde and shortly afterwards turned towards the rugged west coast of Scotland, and sailed into Loch Ewe. This was the assembly point for the next convoy, and as they entered, to the usual brisk flashing of Aldis lamps, they could see about fifty merchant ships at anchor and several escort vessels over in one corner, including four of their flotilla. After dropping anchor close to the other escorts, they lowered the boats and lots of activity started. All Captains were called to a meeting on board a large tanker which was flying the flag of the Convoy Commodore, the senior officer of the merchant ships. There were numerous tactics and subjects to be discussed, navigational courses, zig-zags, actions in case of different situations, pre-planned signals, etc. The meeting went on for the rest of the day, whilst more escorts arrived, frigates, sloops and corvettes. There was a pleasant surprise for everyone on board when a boat from *Zealous* came alongside and up the accommodation ladder came Knocker White with all of his kit. After his release from the Iron Duke he had been ordered to rejoin his ship but found that *Myngs* was at sea, so he had been accommodated on *Zealous* to re-join his own ship at the earliest opportunity and this was the first time that the two ships had got together. There was a big reunion in his mess. He had been very popular on the ship and his shipmates came from every part of the ship to slap him on the back and give him a big welcome. Even the First Lieutenant visited his mess and said that he was glad to have him back on board. He said that he regretted that Knocker had had to go to Detention Quarters but under the circumstances, the Captain had no other option. At the end of the day, a tired but happy Knocker was glad to reclaim his hammock billet and say how happy he was to be back 'home'.

At 0700 the next morning, the escorts moved out of Loch Ewe and waited for the convoy to start coming out. Then there was about two hours of organised chaos as the escorts shepherded the merchant ships into their designated columns, snapping at their heels to urge them into their allotted stations. Then they all moved off north towards the North Cape of Scotland.

As they passed to the west of the Orkney Islands two cruisers came out of Scapa and took up stations in the centre of the convoy.

So again started the four hours on, four hours off, routine. As they progressed further north the weather deteriorated until it became a full gale; it was back to the swinging 'pot-mess', the bouts of sea-sickness and the forever damp clothes that they wore day in and day out. This convoy was noted for the atrocious weather rather than the activities of the enemy: the real enemy was the sea, the ice and the fog. The lookouts found that they were more occupied in watching for friendly ships than for U-boats. Because of the terrible visibility, it was impossible to see other ships of the convoy. If you sighted one you reported it quickly because it meant that you were too close for safety. Station keeping was maintained by radar. The only good thing about it was that it was far too rough for submarines to operate near the surface, so the chances of a torpedo homing in were reduced considerably.

Two days before arrival at Murmansk, a merchant ship was hit and went down in four minutes. This was to be their only casualty on this convoy.

Kola inlet and Polyano hadn't changed. There was more snow and the ice was a bit thicker in the bay but that was all. Everyone's intention was to have a good hot shower, do some washing, which was all draped around in the boiler room, then get as much sleep as they could. Very few sailors bothered to go ashore, except to the end of the jetty and back to stretch their legs, and in no time they were on the homeward leg with a new convoy, back into the gale ridden Arctic Sea. The ship was small enough in normal circumstances, but when travel was restricted between for'd and aft, you could go for days without seeing a mate.

Dave never thought that the bleak, treeless shoreline of Scapa Flow could look so good, and they settled down to wait for the next convoy, but that wasn't to be. Three days after arriving back they were under way again, the entire flotilla and many other escorts, nearly forty altogether. Outside the Flow, it was obvious that something big was on as they joined the capital ships, five aircraft carriers, including three Woolworth carriers, and five cruisers. They were told that this was to be a long operation against the *Tirpitz*. The intention was to lie off the coast of Norway where she was holed up and fly air strikes against her daily until her smoke screen gave up.

It started as soon as they arrived off the coast of Norway. The sky was full of aircraft every day, either leaving or arriving from a strike. The escorts kept a tight screen around the capital ships, with the Asdics pinging constantly but without a sonar contact. Everyone waited for a German air attack on the force, as German airfields were not many miles away, but it never came.

They carried on the operation for fourteen days, air strikes being launched every day, and at the end of that time the smoke screen was still effective as ever, and no assessment of damage could be made.

The strike force had started to leave the Norwegian coast, when there was a big explosion and a column of water alongside one of the Woolworth carriers. The escorts on that side started depth charging, but no one got a good contact on the target. The U-boat must have fired, then dived deep, even before the torpedo had hit. HMS *Nabob,* the carrier that had been hit, by this time had taken on a ten degree list to port, but she also made a signal saying, 'Magazine flooded but able to proceed under own power,' and the force continued towards the west. The *Nabob* must have been struggling to pump out all of the water that was coming in from the torpedo damage, as on arrival at Scapa, she had to beach herself, to prevent herself from sinking.

About eight hours after the torpedo struck, there was a flurry of signals, by flag and by lamps, and they all turned 180 degrees back towards Norway, except *Nabob* which continued towards Scapa with three escorts. The captain told the Ship's Company that the reason for the turn was that *Tirpitz* was at sea, and the force was racing back to intercept her; the battleship *King George V* had also left Scapa to try to cut her off.

However even before they sighted the Norwegian coast, they received a second signal saying that *Tirpitz* had gone into another fjord several miles south of where she had been, and telling the force to return to Scapa.

Only a few days after this, the RAF bombed and hit *Tirpitz* with thousand-pound bombs, the *Tirpitz* turned turtle and sank in the fjord and was not to take any further part in the war. The men on board *Myngs* liked to think that they had played a part in the destruction of *Tirpitz* because perhaps it been the fourteen days of constant air attacks that had made the Captain of *Tirpitz* decide that his present position was too hot to remain there. Unfortunately, for them, the fjord that she moved to was much more open and bombing was a lot easier than her previous berth. Maybe also they had not yet got the smoke screen properly organized at that time.

So the convoys went on, with strikes off Norway usually between convoys, the losses of ships and men seemed to be growing fewer with each convoy, probably owing to the success of the hunter/killer groups whose number of kills against U-boats increased each month, and probably the realization in Germany that the war had turned against them. The second front had opened in France, and German forces had been pushed back to the Rhine; on the Russian front they were receiving demoralising defeat after defeat, while the homeland was being bombed increasingly by US Flying Fortresses by day and the RAF Lancasters by night. It really came as no surprise when Germany surrendered unconditionally in 1945.

Myngs and three of her flotilla were ordered to sail to Wilhelmshaven, and it was without regret that they watched the low shapes of the Orkney Islands fade behind them. It was novel to have upper deck lighting switched on, all navigation lights on and to see lights on the shore of eastern Scotland which had been darkened for so long.

When they arrived in the vicinity of the Hook of Holland they were amazed at the buoyed channels everywhere. Square miles of sea mines had been laid in this area, both moored and ground mines. The RN minesweepers had been working incessantly since the German surrender, sweeping and marking the channels.

As they came closer to the port of Wilhelmshaven, they could see that the city had been devastated. During the war years they had grown accustomed to seeing bomb damaged cities, but this was different, there wasn't a single building that stood undamaged. You could see from one side of the city to the other; it had been flattened.

In the port, the Russian Navy were sailing out with German E-boats, and the Americans were taking cruisers (which were later to become targets in Bikini Atoll where they tested atomic bombs). The French were taking destroyers, and the RN crews had already been told that they would be taking U-boats to Londonderry where they would be scuttled in a deep trench called Herd Deep to the west of Ireland. 'To the victor, the spoils,' thought David. He also thought that it was such a waste, as each U-boat had a generator that could supply a small town with electricity.

There was a very strict 'no fraternisation' rule between Germans and the Allies, but it was almost impossible to impose, the German people looked so thin and ill and were so desperate for food. A black market had begun where German civilians bartered the contents of their homes for tins of food, bicycles, furniture, old medals and coins; women would swap their wedding rings for a tin of coffee, and even their bodies, so it was rumoured. That evening the whole of Dave's mess went ashore to have a drink in defeated Germany and discovered for themselves the power of barter. After a long search, they found a pub in the cellar of a bombed building, and the killick of the mess threw a packet of twenty Navy cigarettes on to the bar and said, 'Keep the beer coming all night for that.' They didn't know whether the bar man would accept it or not, but he seemed delighted with the bargain and kept the beer coming. When it came, they realized why, it tasted like onions! It was ersatz beer, like most of the food in Germany during the war. For example, coffee in Germany was made from roasted acorns.

Later on three German sailors came in, one with a crutch and a leg missing, and they asked them to have a drink with them. They all got very merry, even with the onion beer, and later on they found that the sailor with the crutch had lost his leg on the battleship *Scharnhorst*, sunk by the Royal Navy earlier in the war. He was lavish with his praise about the British gunnery and Dave wondered if the situation was reversed, and he was standing there with a leg missing, blown off by the people he was drinking with, whether he could be so magnanimous.

Some French Canadian soldiers came in. They were huge blokes, wearing sheepskin waistcoats over their uniforms. They had an arrogant air about them and obviously took exception to the British sailors being on what they considered was their 'turf'. The rumour was that these troops had overrun Wilhelmshaven and they had been pretty ruthless and rough with the townspeople. The evening ended with a few fights between the sailors and the soldiers, much to the amusement of the Germans.

The four destroyers moved further up the harbour the following afternoon, to an area of the harbour where U-boat pens had been constructed to protect U-boats from air raids. These were huge enclosed docking areas made of concrete twelve feet thick. Two had received direct hits from thousand-pound bombs and had collapsed into the water but the remainder were intact and full of scores of U-boats. One at a time the submarines started to come out, flying no flag, with a British naval liaison officer and a signalman in the conning tower of each boat, but otherwise still manned entirely by German sailors. When the first three were clear of the pens, *Myngs* signalled 'Follow me,' and started leading them out of the harbour in line ahead. Each destroyer would escort three U-boats to Londonderry, and they would sail under the guns of the escorting destroyers.

Out at sea they continued to sail in line-ahead until they passed Dover on the starboard side, then the destroyers positioned themselves on the beam of their three U-boats and ordered the course and speed to take, their guns turned towards the U-boats.

To the British sailors, who had spent many hours scanning the sea for a glimpse of a U-boat, it was a novel experience to look across the water and see twelve submarines on the surface, helpless under the guns of the three destroyers.

They rounded Land's End and headed into the Irish Sea and by mid afternoon they had turned into Lough Foyle towards Londonderry. They could hear faint cheers from the shore, from the people who realized what was happening. Before they reached the town of Londonderry they started to pass dozens of U-boats, secured alongside, and the U-boats that they were escorting were told to tie up at designated berths. The destroyers carried on into Londonderry and secured to a jetty in the town.

They had time for a run ashore in Derry before they were due to sail back to Wilhelmshaven for another group of submarines. They found that the pubs didn't open on Sundays in Derry so they caught a bus into Moff in Eire and had a good night.

CHAPTER 4

South-East Asia Command

As they steamed back up the English Channel, *Myngs* received a signal ordering her to proceed to Portsmouth, and on arrival there, the Captain cleared lower deck to address the Ship's Company. They all mustered on the fo'c'sle and he told them that the ship had been ordered to 'the blue water war'; she was to sail to join the South East Asia Command Fleet, where the war against the Japanese was still continuing.

Many of the crew who had been on board for a long time would be leaving and their replacements would be joining. Dave himself had been on the ship for nearly two years, but nothing in the world would prevent him from going to the Far East; he volunteered and was accepted to stay with the ship, as did many of his mates. Everyone had to go into the barracks to be issued with tropical uniform. The ship itself had to take on board different types of stores, awning stanchions were fitted along the upper deck and the seamen rigged the awnings to check that they all fitted correctly and that all of the wires, tackles and fittings were correct. Everyone was hoping that some form of air conditioning would be fitted but it was an optimistic hope. Where they had suffered with the extreme cold of the Arctic, they would now have to put up with living in a hot tin box in the tropics. On board, more attention was given to the radio news broadcasts about the war in the Far East. It was not going too well for the Japanese, who had suffered some big naval defeats in the Pacific, but there was lots of talk about kamikaze air attacks, suicidal operations where the pilots just flew their aircraft, packed with explosives, into the Allied warships. The atrocities carried out by the Japanese soldiers and the inhuman way that they treated their prisoners of war was discussed quite a lot; they were a fanatical and dangerous enemy.

Finally the sailing day arrived. Lots of relatives were at the dockside to see them off, and there was even a Royal Marine band to play them out. With the end of the European war, they were able to observe some of the niceties of peacetime.

The ship looked spick and span as they slipped from South Railway Jetty, the crew fallen in for leaving harbour in their No. 1 suits and to the strains of 'Auld Lang Syne' they headed out into the Solent. Bugles sounded and bosun's pipes trilled as they passed the naval shore establishments of HMS *Vernon* and HMS *Dolphin*, the submarine base, and there were lots of cheers from Fort Blockhouse, where many more relatives had gathered for a closer look at the ship, and their loved ones, as she faded into the Solent's morning mists.

They settled down on board to what they were hoping would be a pleasant voyage. It would take four to five weeks to reach their destination, which was Trincomalee, the SEAC naval base in Ceylon. They immediately felt the benefits of sailing in peaceful water. They closed up at cruising stations, which was four hours on and eight hours off, much more civilised than the energy sapping defence stations which they had grown used to.

After the Bay of Biscay they were sailing in a cloudless sky and as they entered Gibraltar it was really hot. There were a lot of RN ships in the base.

They stayed overnight in Gibraltar, while the ship re-fuelled and took on fresh provisions and fruit which they hadn't seen for a very long time. The Captain observed all the formalities of calling on the Governor and the Senior Naval Officer.

Dave and a few friends made their way to the beach, swam in the Med and basked in the sun for a while. Their lily white bodies looked weird in the red hot sunshine. They all wanted to start their Far Eastern tan to show off on their return, but they all had to be very careful, particularly Dave, who was a bit red headed and burned easily. Getting sunburned to a state where you were unable to carry out your duties was an offence, for which you could be charged. The Navy looked on it as a self inflicted wound.

They went ashore that night and found Gib a pretty rowdy place. The main street had loads of pubs, all very busy; with the large number of ships in the base, the RAF base, and the Army garrison, they were all full. They all had 'all girl' bands playing on a stage, all Spanish girls, that many a serviceman took a fancy to, but they were out of luck; all of the girls were bussed back over the border into Spain, at La Linea, at midnight. The shore patrols and the Redcaps were very busy breaking up fights that started.

The town looked very foreign, Spanish even, but when you walked down the main street and saw Woolworths, Marks & Spencers, British Home

Stores and policemen with British helmets, you could imagine yourself to be still in England.

They were under way the next morning, with a lot of sore heads and a handful of First Lieutenant's defaulters. They travelled at an economical speed of twenty knots and their next stop was to be Malta.

One of the peacetime routines that they started was appreciated by everyone. This was 'Hands to bathe' at noon each day, providing the conditions and weather permitted. The ship hove to for thirty minutes to allow anyone who wished to dive over the side for a swim. This morning was the first of many; the sun was high in the sky, the sea was blue and flat, mirror calm. In the water you could look down and see the sun's rays shafting down into the depths and imagine that you might have a thousand feet beneath you. It was the opportunity for many to show off their diving skills, diving from the wings of the bridge. Some of the watch on deck were detailed as lifeguards, sometimes the seaboat was lowered and rowed around the swimmers, and on each side of the bridge a rifleman was posted; sharks were very rare in the Mediterranean, but not unknown.

In the evenings, during the dog watches, they piped 'Tombola is now being played on the quarterdeck.' This was like Bingo, and was the only type of gambling that was allowed in the Navy. It was very organized; there was a Tombola committee with the Cox'n as chairman, they had to keep the books, the number of games was limited, and the stakes were controlled. Ten per cent of the takings went into the ship's welfare fund, the rest went in prize money.

When it was dark, they set up a projector screen on the quarterdeck and showed a movie for any off watch personnel, life was easy. Dave wondered how much it would cost for a Mediterranean cruise like this.

Malta appeared as a yellow smudge on the horizon which gradually got bigger to become sandstone buildings of cathedrals, churches, castles, fortresses and tenements. They approached the two entrances, the left one going into Valetta Grand Harbour, where the battleships and aircraft carriers could be seen moored to buoys in the middle of the harbour. They moved into the right hand entrance, which was Sliema Creek, the destroyer anchorage. Just before the creek narrowed, there was a wide area where the ship had to turn 180 degrees in her own length. While this was going on the motor cutter was lowered and slipped. Dave was in this, of course, and their job was to steam up Sliema Creek, past all the double line of destroyers moored there, and put two seamen, called 'buoy jumpers', onto the for'd buoy in their berth. At the same time, the sea boat was then lowered to the water line, with the after buoy jumpers ready to get onto their after buoy.

Once the ship's stern was lined up, pointing up the creek, the ship went half astern, passing the other destroyers quite close. This was an evolution that was carried out every time a ship entered harbour. It was timed to the nearest second, and the critical eye of the admiral and all of the other ships present was on them. As they passed each ship, the junior ship sounded the still and made 'Attention on the upper deck, face to starboard/port,' followed by the same from the senior ship, then both sounded the 'carry on'.

So the ship raced up the harbour, pushing a huge stern wave in front of her. As she reached her berth, the course was adjusted so that the stern was pointing directly towards their stern buoy, whilst passing as close as possible to the for'd buoy, where the buoy jumpers were already on and waiting. The idea was to bring the ship to a shuddering stop just a few feet from the stern buoy, by putting the engines half ahead. On board it looked like pandemonium as anything was happening at the same time. The sea boat was slipped and pulled around to the stern to put the buoy jumpers onto the buoy; they immediately caught a heaving line from the ship and hauled in a wire which they shackled to the ring of the buoy. Even as the ship was still passing the for'd buoy, a heaving line was thrown to the buoy jumpers sitting there; they caught this and started to haul in a picking up wire which was rove through a large fairlead called the 'bullnose' right for'd in the bow. This wire was already turned around the capstan, and as the buoy jumpers clipped their end onto the buoy ring, they started to haul in on the steam capstan. All this happened in seconds and as the first wire was secured, the Tannoy sounded 'Out all ladders, spread awnings.' The Union Jack went up on the jackstaff, the pennant numbers came down from the yardarm, denoting that the ship was no longer under way, and the watchers stopped their stop watches.

There was lots of work still to do. The anchor was secured in the hawsepipe, broken from the anchor cable which was paid out through the bullnose and secured to the buoy, hauled in taut, and the picking up rope was removed. The accommodation ladder was down on the starboard side and the Mediterranean ladder was on the port side; fenders were put alongside these to prevent damage to ladder and boats coming alongside. The boat boom was rigged starboard side at the break of the fo'c'sle, for the motor cutter and whaler to secure to, with a Jacob's ladder for the crews to man their boat.

When everything had been done to the First Lieutenant's satisfaction, the crew could then relax and look around them. About twenty destroyers were moored in two lines the length of the creek, and further up near Manoel Island a big submarine depot ship was secured with about a dozen submarines tied up on either side. The water was very smooth and mirror like, but a bit smelly, and they were surrounded by churches and monasteries whose bells were constantly ringing out. The land of 'Hells bells and smells', was how the old sailors described Malta, and the quayside was only about two hundred yards away, with a line of inviting bars. Rickety buses plied backwards and forwards, going to different parts of the island, while gondola type boats, called *dgaisos*, criss-crossed the harbour, rowed by the boatman standing up and facing the direction that they were going. One of these had attached itself to their ship, and considered itself their ship's boat for the duration of their stay. It would ferry libertymen and officers ashore and to other ships for a few pennies.

The heat was overpowering, beating down from a clear blue sky, and the sandstone all around seemed to reflect its intensity.

They remained in Malta for four days. Everyone, of course, had to visit the infamous Straight Street, known by everyone in the Navy as 'The Gut'. It was a dark and narrow street consisting of nothing but bars, where sailors could buy bar girls sugar water, going under the name of whisky, in exchange for company and unspoken promises that rarely, if ever, materialized. Most of these bars were owned by wealthy London homosexuals, going under such names as 'Sugar' and 'Honey'. They were quite famous throughout the Navy and although Dave and most of the sailors had no time for homosexuals, nicknamed 'brown-hatters', he had to admit that they had an amusing sense of humour, were good company, and didn't force themselves onto anyone. Many a sailor who was broke still found his beer coming up freely, with no strings attached.

These bars all had touts outside trying to tempt passing sailors in, calling such slogans as, 'Big eats inside, Jack, all your Ship's Company inside.' Needless to say, there were always plenty of shore patrols and they were kept quite busy. In the bars at Sliema, the local beer was called 'Hopleaf' and 'Blues', and behind each bar was a framed certificate naming a sailor who had drank ninety-six Hopleafs in one afternoon, and there were always plenty to try and set a new record. Lots of libertymen never got any further than the bars in Sliema Creek.

For those who went to Valetta, where the Gut was, they had to catch one of the rickety buses. There were lots of priests around and they seemed to be the law; it shook the sailors to see a pregnant woman get up and offer a priest her seat, which he took.

After a night of drinking, some of the libertymen would find themselves back at the jetty at Sliema Creek, just in time to have missed the last liberty boat, and then there was a mad scramble for a *dgaiso* hanging around. A lot got fed up with waiting and decided to swim back to their ships, in white suits! The officer of the watch and the duty petty officer were not amused, neither was the 'Jimmy' when he saw them as defaulters the next morning.

They found it much easier to keep the ship clean in the fine climate they were having. Most of the crew were beginning to go brown and only a couple had been seriously burned. Parts of the city were a mass of rubble as they had been heavily bombed by the Germans; in fact they were under siege for months, constantly under attack, and most of the civilian population had lived underground. Despite heavy losses, the convoys still got through to Malta and in the end the Germans gave up the idea of taking the island.

Everyone enjoyed the four days rest in Malta, then they were off again, heading east towards Alexandria in Egypt. One of the things that surprised Dave was the number of RN ships that there were around the world. Very rarely did a day go by without meeting another British warship. He thought that at the end of the war the Navy was stronger than it had ever been and that all of these ships were scattered in all corners of the world. When one did appear on the horizon, the Aldis lamps would start flashing and the gossiping would go on until she disappeared astern. Apart from official signal traffic, the bunting-tossers would join in when the ships were close enough, using semaphore flags. Of course one of them was always the senior ship and they always seemed to take a great pleasure in picking up something to complain about on the other ship, something like, 'I observed on passing that a fender was hanging over the starboard quarter.' This was a serious admonition which no one liked to receive, but sometimes the signals were humorous and cryptic. One that a ship received said, 'I observed in passing that a number of your crew sunbathing on the Bofors sponson were – *Greek Mythology*, Chapter 7, page 86.' This caused a mad scramble to find the right book, and when they did, they found that it referred to a Greek God called Aristarcus.

The other formality that restarted with the end of the war, was to challenge all merchant shipping that they met at sea with, 'What ship and where bound?' The ship in question would respond with, 'SS *Lynx*, Durban to Amsterdam,' and this was entered into the ship's log as 'Spoke SS *Lynx*, longitude and latitude,' and all of this information used to get passed to Lloyds of London and entered into the register of shipping. As the merchant ship got closer, she would dip her ensign, the warship would dip her ensign in return, then haul the ensign up again, followed by the merchant ship. One of the watch on deck was always detailed to stand by the ensign staff during his duty for this purpose.

As they approached Alexandria, it still looked like a country at war, with the British Army present in great numbers. Alexandria had been used as a British naval base during the war. A British battleship had been sunk in the harbour by Italian frogmen, but the enemy never knew, because she sat on the bottom of the harbour, as though still at anchor. All the normal ship's routines were carried out such as the Royal Marine Band parading each morning for hoisting the colours, as though everything was normal. So the Germans and the Italians thought that there was a battleship, ready to put to sea, if any enemy ships appeared in that part of the Mediterranean.

Going ashore there was a bit more dangerous. The Arabs wanted to barter for everything and were a lot more menacing and aggressive if things weren't going in their favour. Young Arab boys would approach you with a cheerful smile and a shoe shine box, and say, 'Shoe shine Johnny?' but in the other hand they held a bottle containing black shoe cleaning liquid. The message was very clear: 'Either you have your shoes cleaned or your nice white uniform will turn black.' Some sailors had their shoes cleaned as many as six times in one night. The place of ill-repute in Alexandria, where all libertymen were warned not to go and where all of them usually ended up, was called 'Seven Sisters Street', Alexandria's answer to the Gut. The difference was that it was filthy, the menacing atmosphere was always present, and the bar-girls were more pushy and were willing to go with a sailor for a few coins. Quite a number of sailors were robbed on their way back to the ship; the Egyptians, or Gypos, as everyone called them, were not a nice lot. Maybe the sailors who were just robbed got off lightly, because during the next few days, a growing number of men reported to the sick-bay. They had 'caught the boat up', the Navy's description for anyone who had caught venereal disease, mostly gonorrhoea, but another punishable Navy offence, as a self inflicted wound, which meant stoppage of leave, and swelled the ranks of Jimmy's dog-watch working parties. They were off again the next morning and soon they entered Port Said only a few miles from Alexandria; this was the northern end of the Suez Canal. They were directed to two mooring buoys to secure, among quite a number of merchant ships, to await the arrival of the north bound convoy through the canal. The canal wasn't wide enough for two ships to pass each other so they had a system of north and south bound convoys.

As soon as they had secured they were besieged by scores of bum-boats, each manned by an Egyptian who wanted to barter his wares: things like earthenware vases, camel skin hand-bags, wood carvings, leather goods of all kinds, and even dirty photographs (which the sailors called Egyptian AFOs, after the Admiralty Fleet Orders, issued by the Admiralty with new instructions, rules, navigation changes, and anything you could think of). All of this bargaining went on between the crew and the bum-boats, over the ship's side and through the lower deck port holes, although it was strictly illegal according to Navy regulations. As the haggling got hotter, arguments developed and tempers frayed, each side accusing the other of stealing from them, and the noise reached such a pitch, that the first lieutenant decided to put a stop to it. First he told the bum-boats to clear off and when no one took any notice of him, he told the duty petty officer to rig the fire hoses and drive them off. So the Egyptians suddenly found themselves soaked to the skin, with all of their wares floating around in the bottom of the boat, and pulled away, cursing the Royal Navy. While all of this confusion was going on, somebody dropped a cable shackle from the bridge wing into a bum-boat whose owner was haggling through a lower deck port. It was a heavy shackle which went straight through the bottom of the boat, which immediately filled up with water. The Gypo had to jump over the side to prevent the boat from sinking, whilst his goods floated all around him. They never found out who had dropped the shackle but it was probably some sailor who had been robbed and had caught the boat up in Alexandria. Dave, watching all this chaos and confusion, thought, 'No wonder they hate us so much.'

An hour later they were passing through the canal at about five knots, having first watched the northbound convoy emerge from the canal. Each ship had to embark a pilot who took charge of the conn and took the ship the whole length of the canal. It was an interesting trip. Most men stayed on the upper deck to see the sights, although there was not very much to see, miles and miles of sand-dunes, and an occasional Arab dhow with its distinct sail on a river running parallel to the canal in places.

Just before leaving Port Said, they had hoisted inboard one of the trader's boats. He was called the 'Gully Gully' man and he had papers to show that he was an official trader. It was the custom to take one of these traders the length of the canal, and they would return on another ship. So bargaining went on in a more civilised manner, and he also did tricks to amuse the sailors. He got his name from keeping on saying 'Gully, Gully, Gully,' which must have been a sort of Egyptian Abracadabra. They anchored in the 'Bitter Lakes', which are natural salt water lakes halfway down the canal, where north and southbound convoys were able to pass each other, then they were under way again through the southern section of the canal to Port Suez, the Red Sea entrance to the canal. They paused there briefly to drop the pilot and the Gully Gully man, then they were off again through the Red Sea. The heat was oppressive; day and night, it was almost unbearable below decks, sweat streamed out of everyone and several outbreaks of prickly heat started among the crew. This was a very nasty looking red rash that started under your arms and between your legs, and spread over the rest of your body; if you scratched the spots, they broke and turned into scabs. The sick-bay was working full out to try to treat and contain this complaint, but there were only four cots in the sick-bay, which had to be occupied by the worst four cases. Jimmy had the quarterdeck awning spread, and the bridge awning, where people could get a bit of relief from the scorching sun. You had to be careful when touching any part of the ship's structure as it was so hot it could give you a bad burn. Everyone missed the daily 'Hands to Bathe', but it had had to be curtailed because several sharks had been sighted around the ship. Several schools of dolphins had also been seen which were always playing around the bow of the ship. Instead they rigged up a canvas bath amidships and filled it up with salt water from the ship's fire main, so you could at least cool down a bit, by sitting in it; it was also good against the prickly heat. It was so hot below that some sailors started sleeping on the upper deck, bringing up camp beds or slinging a hammock wherever they could. This was much cooler than sleeping below but they had to be up very early, as soon as the hands were called, to clear all their bedding from the upper deck. There was also the risk of being hit by a flying fish, which used to fly inboard during the night; many a sailor would wake up to find a flying fish in his hammock.

After two days they arrived at the southern end of the Red Sea. They were due to fuel at Aden, and the harbour suddenly appeared out of the heat haze, surrounded by black volcanic mountains and rocks. There were three frigates alongside in the harbour which were permanently based in Aden. Dave couldn't help thinking, what a terrible place to spend a commission, which usually lasted about eighteen months. The Royal Navy hadn't really got around to air-conditioning, which would have made life a bit more tolerable. The shopping area, which was called Crater City, was a ramshackle town where you had to haggle for everything that you bought, although you could buy watches and electrical goods quite cheaply there. There was a servicemen's club with quite a decent swimming pool, where you could lie in the sun with a glass of beer. Both the Air Force and the Navy based in Aden looked after them very well during their short stay there, they seemed genuinely glad to see some new and different faces, but it was only a short stay and soon they were under way again, through the Arabian Sea and into the Indian Ocean.

The day dawned when they crossed over the invisible line that meant that they had entered the theatre of operations of war in the Far East, and they had to assume Defence Stations once again, of four hours on and four off. It meant that they had entered the operational range of Japanese submarines and surface ships, so the incessant pinging of the sonar started again. They didn't have to start zig-zagging again, as their speed made them a difficult target for any submarine, and a submarine submerged couldn't hope to get ahead of them, unless she was in the fortunate position of being dead ahead of their track. Of course, they didn't have a slow moving convoy to hold them up.

War seemed so far away and unrealistic, as they steamed along through a flat calm sea on a beautiful sunny day. It reminded Dave of a story that he had been told. It was about a sloop passing through these very same waters in 1939, on the month that the war had started in Europe. The Captain was sitting in the captain's chair on the bridge and the First Lieutenant was Officer of the Watch, when the Yeoman of Signals came onto the bridge and handed the Captain a page from a signal pad. 'Priority signal from the Admiralty, Sir.' The Captain looked at the signal for a moment, then said, 'Commence hostilities against Germany, Number One.' The First Lieutenant, looked around, and said 'Aye-aye, Sir,' then leaned over the voice-pipe and said to the wheelhouse, 'Starboard 15.' Now the situation has changed, thought Dave; it's peace in Europe and war in the Far East.

As they got closer to Ceylon, they began to meet more Navy ships on patrol from the naval base at Trincomalee and finally they sailed between two headlands and into Trincomalee Bay. Dave looked at all the ships at anchor, the wide sandy beaches, the palm trees and the mountains in the misty distance, and his first thoughts were, 'It looks like a tropical Scapa Flow.' This was even more so when he went ashore that night and lined up at the NAAFI bar, and watched scenes reminiscent of Scapa. Instead of sea-boots and duffel coats, everyone was wearing flip-flops and white shorts, but otherwise it was much the same. At least there was some local civilian population here, and there was a village with stores where you could buy souvenirs. The best buy in Trincomalee was semi-precious stones, for which Ceylon was famous. The most common of these stones was the moonstone, and you could get a good deal by haggling, and Dave bought a moonstone pendant in the form of a cross for his sister. You could also get ripped off by the many con artists offering you all sorts of wares. They would sidle up to you, glancing furtively around, as though to see that no one was watching, and whisper, 'Want to buy a Rolex, Johnny?' or whatever it was that they were selling, giving the impression that they had some stolen goods that they wanted to off-load cheaply.

Dave found out, to his regret, how clever these street traders could be. One furtively showed him a large cut diamond wrapped up in a grubby handkerchief, it must have been about four carats, and he mentioned a sum, about twenty pounds in the local currency. 'Beat it,' said Dave, 'It's only glass.' 'No, no, Johnny,' the man insisted, 'real diamond, truly,' and with another shifty glance around, to make sure that no police were watching, 'Can I show you?' He led Dave to a filthy corner of the road and there he produced two coins from his pocket, about the size of a penny. He put one of the coins on the kerbstone, placed the diamond on top of it, then put the other coin on the diamond then, looking around, he picked up a large rock and bashed it down onto the coins. The diamond didn't splinter, as Dave expected. The man picked up the coins and the diamond and handed them to Dave, who looked at them and was quite amazed. Not only had the diamond not broken, but the pointed end had pierced one of the coins and had made a hole right through it. 'OK,' said Dave, 'I give you five rupees,' equivalent to about eight pounds. The haggling started and Dave finally got it for ten pounds. When he tried to show his mess mates the trick later on, back on board, with two coins, the diamond unfortunately shattered into hundreds of pieces: a sleight of hand trick somewhere.

There were lots of exhibitions going on, the Indian rope trick, a snake charmer, a fight to the death between a cobra and a mongoose, both natural deadly enemies. Of course, none of these exhibitions could start until the trader had persuaded a few spectators to hand over a few coins. With the cobra and the mongoose the exhibition never really reached the end; always he would see some policeman approaching and he would quickly have to collect up his wares and make a hurried exit. Over the next couple of weeks, Dave was sure that he saw the same cobra and the same mongoose about to fight 'to the death'. All in all, a run ashore here was a lot more exciting than any of the other foreign ports that he had been in.

As it happened, they were lucky to have had their drinks in the NAAFI that first night in Trinco, as at four o'clock the next morning, the duty watch were called and ferried ashore with fire-fighting equipment to the NAAFI club, which was a mass of flames. Fire-fighting parties were landed from almost every ship in the harbour, but despite the large numbers of fire-fighters and all of their equipment, it took fourteen hours to put out the flames, by which time the club was just a smouldering shell. No lives were lost, but about 150 sailors, who had been billeted in the club while their ship was being refitted in a floating dock, lost all of their kit and personal gear in the fire. There were lots of rumours about how the fire had started; the official line seemed to be that it was sabotage.

Dave saw the duty-watch return on board about eight o'clock the next evening. They were exhausted and black with soot, reminding him of the miners in his home village coming home at the end of their shift.

During the next few days, a large number of troop-ships started to arrive, all packed with soldiers, and when beach landing ships also started arriving, everyone knew that something big was about to happen. The buzz had been going around for some time, that the invasion of Japanese-occupied Malaya was on the cards; after all, it was the only way that we were going to force the Japanese to give up their occupied territories. All of this was confirmed a couple of days later when the entire fleet put to sea and turned towards the east, towards Malaya. Once again *Myngs* was escorting a convoy, but never one as huge as this. This was not a convoy of merchant ships, but more warships and troop carriers than Dave had ever seen. In the centre of this massive Task Force was the battleship HMS *King George V*, six aircraft-carriers, ten cruisers and more escorts than he could count. The whole fleet covered several square miles of the ocean. There were several troop-ships and tank landing ships, big ships with bow doors that would be opened when the ship ran up onto the beach. There were a number of Royal Fleet Auxillaries, carrying stores of all descriptions including ammunition, tankers capable of fuelling the fleet whilst still under way. Dave particularly liked it when they had to go alongside a RFA, or one of the troop-ships for a transfer of stores or bread, when a barrage of ribald remarks, whistles and cheers would come from the soldiers lining the guard-rails. He couldn't help comparing this convoy with the notorious Russian convoys, always freezing cold and wet, always, it seemed, in rough seas, while here there was a calm blue sea and cloudless skies with the sun beating down.

They were at sea for about a week, and one morning they were informed that Malaya was just over the horizon to the east. The landing was to take place in two areas, Port Swettenham and Port Dickson. Before the landing started, the warships would move in and carry out a coastal bombardment, and on every ship preparations were being made for their part in the landing. On the troop ships, big landing craft were turned out on their davits, ready to ferry troops and their vehicles to the shore.

While all these preparations were going on, the startling news came that the Americans had dropped a new bomb, called an atomic bomb, on the city of Hiroshima on the Japanese mainland. The radio news broadcasts said that this bomb had totally destroyed the city, killing thousands of the occupants. This was big news and while everyone was still discussing it, a second bomb was dropped on Nagasaki. After these two atomic bombs, it was announced that the Japanese had surrendered unconditionally, and the Emperor had ordered that all of the armed forces of Japan should lay down their arms.

Everyone was flabbergasted. The war was over! It was difficult to comprehend. Everyone had felt that the noose was tightening around Japan, but no one expected that it could end so suddenly.

There must have been a big discussion on what should happen next, but it was decided that the landings would go ahead as if the war was not over. It was a logical decision. The Emperor had ordered his Army to lay down their arms but it had been proved how fanatical, and even suicidal, the Japanese soldier was. There was a patriotic feeling in every Japanese soldier that made them consider that surrender was a cowardly act: the stories of the inhuman way that they treated POWs was part of this; they had no respect for a soldier that had surrendered. So, would they obey their Emperor? Or would they fight on until the end?

So at dawn the next morning, the warships had closed the Malayan coast. The destroyers and smaller ships were closest in and the crews, at Action Stations, could see the palm fringed coast, with its white beaches. The cruisers were further out, and the capital ships even further still. Their task

68

was to lay down a bombardment on the landing beaches, to soften up the landing areas, and destroy any resistance. The bombardment commenced, with the ships moving in line ahead in a northerly direction. In a few minutes the coastline was covered in a pall of dust and black smoke, but there was no answering fire from the shore, no plumes of water among the ships from enemy shells as expected. At the northerly end of their run, the ships turned and re-traced their course, still firing at the shore. At the end of three hours, there had been no air attacks on the fleet, the troop carriers had appeared from over the horizon and closed the shore and in no time, the sea was full of troop-laden landing craft, heading in orderly formations towards the beaches. The ships' guns fell silent, the landing craft reached the beaches and soldiers could be seen running up the beach and into the trees.

The larger landing ships beached, disgorging tanks and other vehicles. No small arms fire could be heard, and soon the signal came back: 'No opposition, Japanese have withdrawn.' The landings went on all of that day, the Army securing a bridge head and striking inland; there were no air attacks, but the aircraft carriers kept a protective air cover above the fleet and the beaches the whole of the time. By the next morning no contact had been made with the Japanese, and the main force of warships was ordered to proceed to Singapore.

The huge war fleet swept down the Straits of Malacca and in the late afternoon sunlight they entered Singapore roads, a majestic sight as they entered in line ahead, led by the British battleship HMS *King George V*. The British had returned to Singapore. They carried out a formation anchorage, all the ships releasing their anchors at the same time. Some ships landed their landing platoons to restore law and order and it was declared that the next two days would be days of ceremony, when the Japanese generals would formally sign the instrument of surrender in front of Lord Louis Mountbatten, the Supreme Allied Commander and the Admirals of the British fleet. At the same time there would be a victory parade as the Allied forces formally marched back into the city of Singapore.

For two days *Myngs* swung around her anchor in Singapore roads, while her landing platoon was ashore carrying out patrols and generally restoring some sort of order with the other landing platoons.

On Victory Day, everyone gathered around the radio to listen to the commentary on the Parade and the March Past, where Admiral Mountbatten took the Salute. Up on deck you could hear the military bands playing from the shore, and the cheers of the Singapore residents; at least they seemed to be happy to have the British restored as the rulers of Singapore. The Japanese had given them a hard time. The official ceremony of the Instrument of Surrender was also broadcast, taking place in Government House, the Japanese generals on one side of a table, Admiral Mountbatten and the British Admirals on the other. Singapore was formally handed back to the British.

Later that evening *Myngs* was ordered to sail the next morning to Singapore naval base, in company with another destroyer, HMS *Rotherham* and an aircraft carrier. The naval base was on the northern side of Singapore island, and their task would be to restore order at the naval base, to get it fully working again and to evacuate 40,000 Japanese troops that had been assembled there.

The three warships weighed anchor the next morning and threaded their way between the scores of merchant ships at anchor in Singapore roads. Already the temperature was very high; Singapore was only three degrees north of the Equator and the temperature rarely altered during the year. *Myngs* led the three ships; she, in fact, was the senior ship, as, although the commanding officers of all three ships were four ring captains, their Captain was the senior among them. They turned down the Malacca Straits, then into the Straits of Johore, a channel that separated Singapore island from the mainland of Malaya.

On the port side they could see an airport, with Japanese fighter aircraft standing on the tarmac, and even as they watched, six RAF fighters flew overhead and one by one came in to land. This was Changi air station, a military air base, and quite close to the infamous Changi Jail, where so many of our POWs had been incarcerated. The Straits got narrower and also on the port side they could see the high dockside cranes of the naval base, and just beyond that, the Johore Causeway which linked Singapore and Malaya. This had been blown up and breached by the British during the Japanese invasion in a futile attempt to slow down the advance of the Japanese forces.

Also at anchor, and alongside each other, were two Japanese cruisers, one with the entire after part of the ship blown off. Dave remembered reading about this even before he had joined the Navy. Four British midget submarines had carried out an attack on Japanese warships at anchor off the naval base. Two midget subs had sunk and one just disappeared, but one had succeeded in getting under a Japanese cruiser. A diver then had

had to exit the sub, hang a large explosive charge under the cruiser, and get back into the sub again. It had taken so long that the ebbing tide had allowed the cruiser to trap the sub between it and the sea-bed. It was only good seamanship that allowed them to escape, but they did it and got clear. The Captain was awarded a VC and the other three crew members were decorated, and now Dave could see the results of their valiant efforts.

The three warships turned in towards the dockyard, and as they drew closer to the jetty, the shore seemed to be moving, surging one way then the other and, as they got closer still, they were astonished to see that there were thousands of Japanese soldiers milling around over the entire surface of the dockyard. They were in full uniform with haversacks which obviously contained their kit, everything except weapons, which they could see stacked up in an open sided shed. This was filled almost to the roof with rifles, bayonets, pistols and machine guns.

It was quite scary, seeing all of these faces staring inscrutably back at them, and when they remembered that there were supposed to be 40,000 of them, it made the hair stand up on the back of their necks. What if they suddenly decided, there's only a handful of British sailors here, we've still got all of our weapons over in that shed, we could soon swamp this lot? However, they never got the opportunity. As soon as the ships were secured alongside, the first job was to get all the soldiers under lock and key and under armed guard. They were split up into groups and billeted in dockyard stores and sheds, and then they discovered a big military barracks near the dockyard at a village called Nee Soon. This was a former British military barracks, and the Japs were packed into huts with an armed sentry on the entrance to each building. It took about four days to make sure that the Japs were secured somewhere, and during that time the British sailors didn't get very much sleep. To their surprise they found that the Japanese seemed to be more scared of them than the other way around, and it became clear that they had been expecting the same sort of treatment as the Allied POWs had received. In fact, they found out later that the Japanese soldiers had been told by their superiors that they would be tortured and killed if they ever became prisoners.

After a week some semblance of order began to take place. Rosters were drawn up for sentry duty over the Jap prisoners. Patrols had to be started when it was found that the local civilians were systematically looting anything that they could in the dockyard. Also in the nearest village, which was called Sembawang, they found quite a lot of looted goods when they searched village houses, including bales of silk from warehouses, tools from dockyard workshops and stolen vehicles; a number of people were arrested. The rosters also allowed the sailors to have some time off duty, to rest and to have a look around. There were abandoned vehicles all over the place, lorries, trucks, jeeps and motor cycles, most of which only had flat batteries, but soon they had a large selection of vehicles around the ships, as sailors who had set out exploring on foot had returned with a vehicle.

One morning two large troopships came in and secured alongside. The evacuation of the Japanese troops was about to begin. Another duty roster was started, this time of searchers who would screen every Japanese soldier before he boarded the troopship. Everyone detailed for search duties had a lecture from a high ranking army officer before the process started.

Three large open sided sheds had been earmarked as the 'search sheds' and each had a row of about twenty trestle tables. There would be a sailor, the searcher, at each table, and there would be a single file of Jap soldiers with all of their kit in front of each table. They would be called over one at a time to each table, empty their kit bags and haversacks onto the table, empty their pockets onto the table, and then would be body-searched by the searcher, before he turned to the kit. This officer had told them which items of kit could be given back; his instructions went something like this: 'After the Japanese soldier has been searched, he will be taken to a troopship with the kit that you have allowed him to keep. When the troopship is full it will sail to Burma, where the Japanese soldiers will complete the infamous Burma railway, and when the railway is finished, they will return to Japan, mostly on foot. The kit that he is allowed to keep is the uniform that he is wearing, two shirts and vests, three G-string underwear, three pairs of socks and three pairs of shoes (they need the shoes because they have a hell of a long way to walk), his personal ablution kit, his mess tin and mug, his wallet and photographs. There is to be no looting. If he has a watch, cigarette lighter, or any jewellery of western manufacture, you can take it off him; the chances are that it came from one of our POWs. Everything else will be taken away and destroyed by burning. The search will go on twenty-four hours a day until the last Japanese soldier has been evacuated.'

Dave found himself on a search table that first day. His first Japanese was a small young man, bowing and smiling, and trembling like a leaf. When Dave body-searched him, he giggled and pretended that he was being tickled but it was obvious that he was scared out of his wits; this would be his first close encounter with the enemy, as indeed it was Dave's, and there

72

was no way that he was going to antagonise Dave. After the body search he looked at the kit on the table. He picked up an empty haversack from the table and passed it to the soldier, then he passed over the items of kit that they had been instructed to return. He looked at a watch on the table; it was of Japanese manufacture so he handed it back. He opened the wallet; there was a lot of money, Japanese yen, now useless as with the surrender the Japanese economy had collapsed and also quite a bit of Singapore occupation money, also now quite worthless, but good for souvenirs. In a pocket of the wallet, there were a couple of photographs of a Japanese lady dressed in a kimono with two children. He turned to the Jap, pointed to the photos, then to him; the man nearly fell over himself, nodding furiously, bowing and smiling. Dave put the photographs back in the wallet and handed it back. The money he threw under the table, then he signed for the man to pick up his gear and leave, and called up the next one in line, and the process started over again.

Over the next few days he got used to the never ending Japanese faces that appeared before him. Most of them were afraid, but some were openly hostile and others just ignored their captors. The searchers got used to finding where the Japs hid things that they tried to hang onto. Some who had European watches hid them in the cooked rice in their mess tins; others hid things bound up in their puttees. The piles of discarded Japanese uniforms grew bigger, and a Jap POW working party was detailed to take it away in hand carts to an open area in the dockyard, where bonfires were burning continuously.

After a week of this, most of the sailors had lots of souvenirs, and almost all of them had a complete Japanese soldier's uniform, including helmet and horn-rimmed glasses. At a sod's opera held on board one night, almost everyone turned up in a full Jap uniform which was hilarious.

They also had some visitors to witness the searching in the sheds. These were Allied POWs released from the jail at Changi, Australians and British; they looked like walking skeletons. They watched silently for some time then gave their verdict. They said, 'You guys are far too easy on the Japs; we went through all of this routine when we were captured, only we used to get our faces slapped, they used to make obscene remarks about our photographs of wives and loved ones, then they would tear the photos up into little pieces and throw them into our faces.' It explained the fear that they saw in the Japanese's eyes. They also told them that the only way you could get through to the Japanese was to make them lose face, and taught them two words in Japanese to use; one was the Japanese word for 'double up' and the other was 'bow'.

When Dave and his chums were off duty they used to get up to all sorts of mischief. There was no such thing as liberty leave, as there was nowhere to go, so they used to explore around. On one trip they found about thirty kamikaze speed boats which had been designed as suicide craft. The bows were packed with explosive and they were designed to be rammed into enemy shipping, blowing them up, including the driver. They quickly got a few of them in working order, and when they had an afternoon off they would take sandwiches and go off into the Johore Straits, and up a river on the Malayan side, where they would collect wild bananas and coconuts. They never gave a thought, at the time, that wild animals, including tigers, roamed that part of the jungle. Dave got some very bad bites from red ants which dropped from a banana tree while they were chopping it down. These bites later turned poisonous and he had to have the venom burned out in the sick bay; they took a long time to heal. On their way back from one of these trips, a small coastal vessel came up the Straits, flying a Japanese flag and in a fit of daring, they decided to board it, as the official boarding party. They realized that the ship had probably been at sea when the war ended and had not yet seen the 'enemy', so they followed it up the Straits until it dropped anchor, then boarded it. They were dressed quite reasonably in clean white shorts and white navy T-shirts and the crew accepted them as the boarding party. By sign language they made them all lie aft on the poop deck, then they searched the ship. They got a few interesting souvenirs and a nice pair of binoculars, then they got off before they were rumbled. After that, they pulled this trick a few times. On one occasion Dave was going along a dark corridor on the ship when someone leapt on his back. He almost had a heart attack, imagining that the Japs had tumbled to the hoax, and he was almost relieved to find that it was a pet monkey that had jumped onto him.

There were always heavy jobs that had to be carried out in the dockyard, moving very heavy machinery from one place to another, but they had a huge labour force in the Japanese POWs. Whenever they rounded some up and herded them to where the work was, Dave felt that there was always a certain reluctance to go, and he realized that a lot of them thought that they were being taken around the corner to be shot. He also wondered, in this place where there was no law and order, if anyone would care.

On one of their leisure meanderings around the base, four of them decided that they would take some war photographs to impress their girl-friends and people back home. One of them had 'acquired' a good German camera, so they went to the jetty where two troopships were secured alongside. Rows of Japanese prisoners were staring down at them from high up on the deck. They went up to a bored looking sailor, who was the sentry standing at the foot of the gangway. He was dressed in uniform, wearing a helmet and carried a rifle with a fixed bayonet; his job was to stop any Japs that tried to come ashore. 'OK if we borrow four Japs, to take some photographs?' Dave asked him. The sentry was quite used to Japs being borrowed for work parties, so he said, 'Sure, but don't keep them too long.' So they went up the gangway, picked out four Japs, and signalled them to follow them. Once again Dave saw the look of fear come into their eyes, and he wondered if they thought that they were going to shoot them.

When they got ashore they led the soldiers to the stern of the ship where there was an area of mangrove trees growing into the water. One of them nipped back and borrowed the sentry's rifle and helmet, then they made the Jap soldiers wade out up to their waists in the water. One of the sailors put on the helmet and pointing the rifle towards the Japs, he made them raise their hands in the air whilst Dave took photographs. Then they changed around so that all four of them had their photograph taken 'capturing' some Japanese. Much later, when they had the film processed, the pictures looked very realistic, with the mangrove trees in the background. Dave remembered the look of relief on their faces when they took the Japanese back and they scurried up the gangway.

Two of the most coveted souvenirs that everyone was always on the lookout for were a Japanese flag and an officer's ceremonial sword. In fact, the trade in ceremonial swords became so fierce that a signal was issued to all units in Singapore, from the Supreme Allied Commander, South-East Asia Command, Admiral Lord Louis Mountbatten, declaring that the practice of taking swords from Japanese officers was to cease. But about a week later, Dave, off duty and at a loose end, was wandering around the dockyard on his own, when he noticed three LCPs, landing craft personnel, approaching the jetty from the direction of the Johore straits, and, always curious about the goings on, he watched with his hands in his pockets. The landing craft ran up to a sloping concrete ramp and beached, lowering its for'd ramp, allowing dozens of Japanese officers to disembark. As they milled around on the jetty, he noticed that they were all carrying long silk covered objects. 'Swords,' Dave immediately thought. He looked around. The usual sailor sentry with the helmet and fixed bayonet was there. He went across to him and said, 'Any chance of getting a sword?'

'Sorry, mate,' said the sentry, 'You've seen Mountbatten's order about swords; it's more than my job is worth to let you take one,'

Sadly, Dave wandered off, but about fifteen minutes later, on his way back to the ship, he was passing the same area when he saw the same sentry scurrying along carrying a silk sheathed sword which he hid in a stack of water pipes. At the same time, he noticed that Dave was watching him and as Dave came up, he said, 'OK, get a sword, don't let anyone see you; if you get caught I don't know anything about it.'

Dave made his way into the group of Japanese officers. Most of them had their swords in white silk sheaths and only a few carried purple silk sheaths, so he thought, they must be the best ones. He looked around. A haughty looking Jap officer was close to him with a purple sheathed sword. He walked straight up to him and grabbed the sword with both hands. The officer looked shocked and pulled the sword close to him. Dave with a look of determination, pulled it back again and the Japanese's resistance seemed to collapse; he pushed the sword towards Dave and he was off with it.

He returned back on board, and in his mess, with a curious crowd of messmates watching, he took the sword from its silk sheath. It was beautiful; the blade was inscribed with a Lotus flower pattern and Japanese characters and the scabbard had a purple sheen. No wonder the Japanese didn't want to give them up; they were family heirlooms, handed down in the family from father to son. Dave had won his trophy of the war. He lashed it carefully in his hammock, a good place to keep it, considering its length.

Everyone worked very hard during those first few months. Slowly the numbers of prisoners remaining got smaller, and the naval base began to look more like a naval base. The Navy reclaimed HMS *Terror*, the RN barracks in Singapore, and some of the crews were allowed to sleep there, when not on duty watch on board. It relieved much of the overcrowding in the mess-decks too. In spite of all of the patrols, searching, sentry duty, and other work details, shipboard life had to go on as usual; ship husbandry and maintenance had to be kept up, rusty patches on the ship's superstructure had to be tackled with chipping hammers, red lead undercoating and re-painted. There were weekly routines, such as Captain's rounds every Saturday morning, when the Captain and his staff visited every compartment which had to be spick and span, decks and tables scrubbed, all brass work polished, all of the mess traps shining and not a speck of dust to be seen. It was quite a ceremony, with the bosun's mate leading the way, blowing the 'still' on his pipe, followed by the cox'n, then the Captain, the First Lieutenant, the heads of departments, divisional officers and the chief Bosun's Mate. Someone was always detailed to stand by for rounds, and he would salute the Captain, and report, 'One mess ready for rounds, sir.' Then they would all look around for something to pick up. Sometimes the Captain wore white gloves which he would run along the tops of fan-shafts, and everyone waited with bated breath to see if there were any dirty marks on his gloves. The Captain would say, 'Very good,' or 'Well done,' but if he picked anything up it meant another inspection, a re-scrub, during the Dog Watches by the First Lieutenant. The Jimmy used to look at all of the kit piled along the sloping ship's side, and complain, 'This mess will have to get rid of some of that rubbish.' 'That rubbish,' of course, was all of the Japanese uniforms and other 'rabbits' that they had 'acquired'.

The other weekly routine was Divisions, held every Sunday morning, when everyone fell in by Divisions in their best uniforms, their No. 1's. Fo'c'sle Division fell in on the fo'c'sle, Quarterdeck Division fell in on the quarterdeck and the Irondeck Division fell in amidships, and they were all inspected by the Captain. After that they all moved for'd onto the fo'c'sle for compulsory church service, after the Roman Catholics had fallen out: they had their church on the quarterdeck.

On a Sunday afternoon, when he wasn't duty, Dave used to enjoy going up to *Terror* and having a long soak in a real bath, that was really luxury after the tiny confined and cramped shower cubicles that they had got used to on board the ship. On this particular day, after a long, hot bath, he was on his way back to the base and the ship, and he decided to have a look into a bungalow on the water's edge, in HMS *Terror*. It was, in fact, the club house for the RN Sailing Club, or had been until the Japanese invasion. Now it was falling into disrepair, but no one seemed to be around, so he wandered from room to room. There was a big wooden balcony overlooking the Johore Straits and, there in the centre of the balcony was a big Japanese telescope mounted on a tripod. Dave held his breath, what a trophy! They were called cruiser scopes on board ship, and he was about to rush in and dismantle it when he heard voices. He tip-toed across and peered around the corner, and there in the next room was his own Captain talking to the Senior Japanese Officer. They hadn't seen him so he withdrew and melted away, thanking his lucky stars for his narrow escape. He could have crept out and disassembled the telescope under the startled eyes of the two officers, much to everyone's embarrassment and, probably, his own court martial.

Shortly after that, the last troopship sailed with the last of the Japanese prisoners, and at that time also a big US Navy supply ship entered the base to re-fuel. The crew came ashore. This was their first port that had been occupied by the Japanese, and they were desperate to get some war souvenirs. They were terribly disappointed to find that all of the good trophies had already been snapped up by the British sailors and it wasn't long before they were coming on board the British ships every evening, trying to barter with the Brits to try to get them to sell their souvenirs.

It wasn't long before an American officer heard about Dave's sword, and he used to come to the mess every evening, bringing bottles of beer and tubs of ice-cream, trying to coax Dave into selling his sword. It took about a week, and a lot of beer and ice-cream, but he gradually wore Dave down, and Dave let it go for all the money that the Yank had, about a hundred US dollars. The US crew hadn't been paid for several weeks and had the US officer had more money he would willingly have paid four times as much. So Dave lost his trophy.

They had been working at the base for about eight months when they were told that the rail link between the base and the city of Singapore had been restored and that they could start giving liberty ashore to the crews of the ships. There was a large crowd of libertymen for that first run ashore. Singapore Island is about the same size as the Isle of Wight, so it was an interesting trip, mostly through jungle, passing villages of wood and straw. The population was a mixture of Chinese and Malay. The city lived up to their expectations of the mysterious Orient. The main street was Orchard Road, and there were hundreds of stalls selling exotic foods. Dave soon developed a taste for these Eastern dishes, although there were many occasions when he didn't have a clue what he was eating. The sailors soon found Singapore's equivalent to the Gut and Sisters Street, which was called Bugis Street, and its claim to fame was the male transvestite. It was a good night's entertainment to sit drinking beer at a street side table watching all these beautiful and glamorous Eastern women parading themselves up and down the street. Some of them were of breathtaking beauty, and it was almost impossible to believe that they were all men dressed up and made up as women. There were the usual bars and usual bar girls ready to relieve them of their money, but after eight months of solitary confinement it made a welcome change. One other place that one had to see was the Raffles

Hotel, called after the Englishman who discovered Singapore island, a swampy and mosquito riddled place which he decided would be an ideal place to develop as a port to trade with the Far East. The hotel was very Colonial and a bit run down, and had suffered from the effects of the Japanese occupation, but it was a bit of England. There was also a big serviceman's club which had been opened, the Nuffield Club, where you could get a good meal and a bed for the night, if you wanted a night away from the ship.

Now that the war was over, the British government found that the country was almost bankrupt, with all of the reserves having been spent in the war effort, and they had tens of thousands of service men in all corners of the world and huge fleets of ships that were no longer needed. They therefore started a plan for demobilization and decommissioning ships.

Myngs found herself caught up in this. She was ordered to return to the UK and to join the Home Fleet on arrival, so almost to the day, a year after she arrived in Trincomalee, she sailed from Singapore to return home.

The return journey was virtually a repeat of the trip out, a relaxing journey. Before sailing, they had all been given forms to fill in, which were their applications for their campaign medals. You had to have served for at least six months in any theatre of war to qualify for a medal relating to that campaign, and Dave found that he was qualified for the 1939-45 Star, the Atlantic Star for service in the Atlantic and North Russian convoys, the Burma Star for the South-East Asia campaign and the End of War medal, which anyone who was serving when the war ended, qualified for.

They also had to fill in forms which would decide when they would be demobilized; this worked on a points system. The men who were already serving when the war started got the biggest number of points, and this figure gradually decreased the later that you joined. Marital status came next; married men got more points than single men, points were added for men with children, and the final figure was worked out as a date for demobilization. So a new phrase was heard quite a lot: 'Roll on my demob.' Ninety-seven per cent of the Ship's Company were still Hostilities Only. One or two would be due for demob on arrival back in the UK, but it would be 1950 before many of them left the service, five years after the war had ended.

Dave was still determined that he would never return to the coal mining villages of County Durham and on the way back home, he put in his request 'to see the Captain to change from HO to General Service and complete

79

time to serve twelve years in the service.' He had a very good Character and Efficiency record, and the Captain seemed delighted to grant his request, so he became a General Service rating and was able to say to most of his mates, 'HOs give me the shits!' He had the option of serving seven years with the colours and five years in the reserves, but he opted for the straight twelve years service. That meant that he would be due for release in 1956, at which time he could opt to serve another ten years service, that is twenty-two years with the colours and retire with a service pension.

When they arrived in Malta, all their medals had arrived, and the Divisional Officers issued them to the men in their Division according to their qualification. It meant that they now had to wear their medals at Sunday Divisions, and there was a busy sewing session that evening as everyone sewed their ribbons onto their jumpers. A lot of ribbing went on, especially of the older members, some who qualified for as many as eight medals, and had to put up with the term 'old bastard'. And there was a lot of 'win 'em and wear 'em' comments, and much hilarity at the expense of the men who only qualified for one medal, and kept being told 'win it and wear it!' amid loud laughter.

CHAPTER 5

Rheumatic Fever and Naval Review

By the time they sailed from Malta, Dave was having trouble with his legs, and they gradually got worse. When they sailed from Gibraltar, he was having difficulty in walking and as he had a very high temperature, he was taken into the sick bay. The Surgeon Lieutenant was a very young officer, straight out of medical school; he became very excited over his new patient and pored over his medical books. He then told Dave that if he had what he thought it was, Dave would be in hospital for a very long time. The day before they arrived at Portsmouth he told Dave, 'You have got rheumatic fever; I have signalled for an ambulance to meet the ship on arrival, and you will be taken straight into hospital.' Dave was really too ill to bother any more, but he realized that the weeks of living in a wet and freezing 'ice box' had caught up with him.

As the ship entered Portsmouth harbour and berthed at South Railway Jetty, to the sound of a Royal Marine band and cheers from loved ones and relatives, Dave was carried down the gangway in a stretcher and into a waiting ambulance, and quickly transferred to the RN Hospital, Haslar. He didn't remember very much about the first three weeks, as he was seriously ill, so ill, in fact, that the Navy sent a rail warrant to his mother so that she could come down and visit him in hospital. His temperature was so high that they were not sure whether he would recover or not, and he could only vaguely remember his mother's visits, but after three weeks he started to show signs of improving. He still had a high temperature, and his legs were so swollen and painful that he had to have a cage over them as he couldn't stand the weight of the blankets pressing on them. But he started to take an interest in things that were happening around him, and he learned more about rheumatic fever. It is not a common illness for adults, but infants were likely to contract it, and when they did they used to wrap them in cotton wool until they recovered. It usually left the person with a weak heart, and the only treatment was, strict bed, lying flat with no pillows, no exertions of any kind, feeding, washing, toilet, all had to be done for him, he was not allowed to do anything for himself. If he stuck to this regime, together with the medicines that he had to take, he might possibly get away with a sound heart.

The treatment hit Dave hard. This was the first time in his life that he had completely lost his independence. The result was that, because he was too embarrassed to ask for bed-pans, he became badly constipated. This led to further complications, as they couldn't move him around very much, and he had to undergo several enemas, all strictly supervised by the Ward Sister, whom everyone was scared to death of, including a lot of the rough and tough sailors who were patients on the ward. Anyhow the enemas finally worked, after some painful bowel movements, and it convinced him that he had better forget his shyness if he didn't want to get into that situation again.

There were about twenty sailors on the ward, all with various illnesses, mostly digestive problems. He was one of four rheumatic fever patients; the other three had been in hospital a long time, and two were discharged a week later. They were discharged from the hospital, and medically discharged from the Navy, he found out later, with weak hearts.

The nursing staff were Navy nurses, VADs, Voluntary Aid Detachment being their correct title (Virgins After Dark, the sailors' interpretation). Many of them had served in the Far East, in a hospital in Australia, and had recently returned to the UK in the aircraft carrier HMS *Formidable*. These were ruled with a rod of iron by the Sister. Dave had a first hand experience of her temper one day when she came onto the ward early one morning and caught the nurse allowing him to brush his own teeth. She gave the nurse a severe dressing-down that made her look about six inches high, then turned on him for doing it himself. 'This is how it is to be done!' she shouted at the nurse, then grabbed the toothbrush and started brushing his teeth so vigorously that, within minutes, he had a mouthful of blood.

In spite of this, it was a happy ward. About one third of the patients were 'strict bed'; the others were 'up patients' and they really worked hard, polishing the floors, helping the nurses to make beds, getting bed-pans and bottles for bed patients, dishing out the food at meal times and feeding patients that couldn't, or were not allowed to, feed themselves.

Dave was amused to find that the Navy routine still went on. There were Commodore's Rounds once a week, when everything had to be ship shape, all of the beds squared-off, pillows in line, and the up-patients did all of the work for the inspection. When the inspection retinue did appear, it was the usual Royal Marine bugler in front sounding the 'Still', followed by the Commodore, accompanied by the Matron, even more feared than the Sisters, then all of the doctors and hangers-on.

After two months Dave was feeling much perkier and it was a momentous day when the doctor announced: 'Allowed one pillow.' About the same time, his doctor came to see him one day, quite a young surgeon-lieutenant, and he said, 'Are you happy in the Navy, Dave? Because if you're not, a word from me will get you discharged on medical grounds; your other three colleagues have all left the Service with weak hearts.'

Dave looked at him for a moment and said, 'Look, sir, I love the Navy, I have made it my life, I have no wish to leave it, and, seriously, do you think that I want to go through life with "has a weak heart" on my medical records?'

The doctor looked a bit taken aback, then, regaining his composure, he said, 'In that case, I have got to congratulate you on being a model patient; you have done everything we asked you to do, and you have come through it with a sound heart.' Dave reflected on some of the evenings when he hadn't been such a model patient, when they had had wrestling matches and races around the ward, and he also couldn't help wondering whether the other three ratings had been discharged because they had weak hearts or because they wanted to get out of the Service.

He gradually got promoted to three pillows, then he joined the up-patients and the work details and after four months, the surgeon-commander told him that he was cured. However, he said, 'You're still not strong enough to return to full duty, so I am transferring you to RN Auxilliary Hospital in Sherborne, Dorset, for convalescence before you are returned to the fleet.'

The hospital in Dorset was more like an army camp. It had been purpose-built as a hospital during the war, but it was more like a holiday camp than a military establishment. The weather was glorious and red hot, and patients were allowed night shore leave at weekends to go into Yeovil to the movies. Although everyone was supposed to be in bed at 9 p.m., there used to be a steady stream of patients and nurses along a well worn path, through a hole in the perimeter fence and into the local pub. It was rumoured that the powers that be knew all about this nocturnal exodus; in fact, it would have been difficult for them not to know, as there was a big mural in the dining hall that a patient had painted, portraying the file of patients and nurses making their way towards the hole in the fence, some nurses carrying bed-pans and urine bottles.

At the end of his convalescence Dave was discharged, with his kit-bag and hammock, to HMS *Victory*, RN Barracks, Portsmouth. On arrival, he noted that it was the usual dismal place, and he swore that some of the rum bosuns were the same as the ones he had seen two years earlier. On starting his joining routine, the chief in the drafting office said, 'What ship have you come from?'

He said, 'No ship, chief, I've come from RN hospital.'

'What was your last ship, then?' the chief asked.

'HMS *Myngs*,' answered Dave.

'Right, we had better send you back there, then.'

Dave was amazed; the last thing that he had expected was to go back to *Myngs*. It was normal to spend about two years on a ship then move on, and he had already done two years on *Myngs*. At the same time, he was delighted at the thought of going back to his old ship, so he didn't argue, and the next morning he was on his way.

The bad news was that he had been told that the Home Fleet was in Scapa Flow, having just finished their spring cruise and exercises. He had hoped that he would never see Scapa Flow again and here he was, on his way back to it. His rail warrant told him to change trains three times and his destination was Thurso, on the north coast of Scotland, then by ferry to Lyness in the Orkney Islands. In fact, it took twenty-eight hours to reach Thurso. Tired and dirty, he was picked up at Lyness by a drifter that shuttled around the fleet and Lyness, and finally he saw his ship again. All tiredness left him as they drew alongside. She looked very smart, now painted in peace time colours of light grey, all camouflage colour having been painted out. A few curious onlookers looked down from above, then there was a shout, 'It's Dave!' and he was dragged on board, pounded on the back, arm almost shaken off, no one had known that he was returning, not even the cox'n, who, like Dave, thought he would have been drafted to another ship. So he had a warm welcome, especially warm with about four tots of rum inside him. Nearly everyone kept a bottle in their locker, against all regulations. Rum mixed with water doesn't really keep, but the sailors got around that by putting raisins in the bottle with the grog, which seemed to absorb the water, leaving only neat rum. He had to listen to where the ship had been for the spring cruise. A lot of the old crew had left and been replaced by new hands, but more than half of the original crew were still on board, so he still had lots of acquaintances on the ship.

The reason that the ship looked so smart was that they were sailing to the River Clyde for the first Naval Review after the war, when all of the ships would be reviewed by the King and Queen. They would be in Scapa for six days, cleaning and painting. At least we won't be sailing for a month of Russian convoy, thought Dave.

The next day he was back at work, not on board, but in a diving boat. Eight sailors, including him, were detailed as 'pumping party', and their job was to turn the big wheels on an air pump which supplied the divers down below. They were working on German warships that had been scuttled in Scapa after the First World War, and at the moment they were engaged on a ship called the *Durflinger*, which was upside-down with her keel above the surface. Dave was intrigued by these tough, professional Navy divers, who worked in the dark, cold water sixty feet below them for hours, and he watched curiously as a diver climbed up the ladder into the boat with his huge lead soled boots. Then the glass visor was unscrewed from his big copper helmet and a lighted cigarette thrust between his lips by one of his mates. He didn't realize it at the time, but the three days that he spent as diving party on that boat was to shape his future naval career.

After six days at Scapa, Dave felt as though he had never left the ship. He had now been given the job of quartermaster on board, which was permanent watch keeping, but a more civilised one where you did one watch on and three watches off, so if you had the middle watch, you had the morning, forenoon and afternoon watches off before going on the first dog watch. In harbour his watches were on the gangway, running the ship's routine, making all of the 'pipes' on the ship's Tannoy, from 'Call the hands' at 0630 until 'Pipe down' at 2200. They also manned the side when officers came on board or left the ship, 'piping the side' for all commanding officers, flag officers and foreign officers. Keeping a check of which officers were on board or ashore, which ratings were ashore on duty or liberty, and keeping the Officer of the Day informed of all other ships' movements in the harbour and of all officers approaching the ship. At sea he kept his watches in the wheel house, steering the course and speed ordered and carrying out all helm orders from the bridge. He had a junior sailor to assist him with all of these duties, who was called the 'bosun's mate'.

On the seventh day this massive fleet weighed anchor or slipped their buoy, all at the same time, and began to move out into the Pentland Firth. It was a magnificent sight: four huge battleships, six aircraft carriers, twelve cruisers, six fleet auxiliary store ships and tankers, and countless destroyers, frigates, sloops, corvettes and mine-sweepers. Dave thought: this is only a small part of the British fleet; there was a Far-Eastern fleet, a Mediterranean fleet and numerous ships spread around in South Africa, West Indies, Antarctica and other corners of the empire. British sea-power must have been at its peak at that time.

This great fleet swept into the Clyde the following day and carried out a formation anchorage just west of Glasgow, all ships letting go their anchors as a pennant fluttered down from the yard-arm of the Flagship. There were many ships already anchored in their berths, eight submarines in an immaculate straight line, and other small craft like motor torpedo boats and inshore mine sweepers. As the anchors were slipped, all ships 'dressed ship', flags and bunting running up the jack-stays, so that each ship had flags and pennants flying over the ship from the jack-staff to the ensign-staff. They would 'dress ship' each day from 'morning colours' at 0800 until 'sunset', for the next six days, when the Naval Review would be over.

Glasgow became a naval port during the next week, with thousands of libertymen streaming ashore and carousing through the city each evening. Dave was able to renew acquaintances that he had made during their boiler clean, and generally the Glaswegians seemed quite happy to have all these sailors in their city.

Meanwhile, on board, the duty watch worked until dark every night preparing the ship for the inspection, especially when it was announced that *Myngs* was one of the ships that the King would come on board to inspect. From 'call the hands' until 'hands to tea' at 1600, everyone turned to; after that, the non-duty watch could go ashore, while the duty watch carried on working.

Dave, on the gangway, watched whilst the iron deckmen started to polish the iron deck. The same iron deck that had been burnished by the waves during the big convoy storm, so that it shone like stainless steel, was now being black-leaded by sailors with soft brushes, and it now gleamed like ebony.

The great day of the Fleet Review arrived. Everyone was up early making last minute adjustments and by 9 a.m. everyone had changed into their No. 1 uniform, including medals, ready to fall-in by Divisions. Dave would be on watch on the gangway and the piping-party who would pipe the King on board comprised a commissioned gunner, the cox'n, two quartermasters, including Dave, and four bosun's mates. The captain walked around the ship and saw, to his displeasure, a dirty mark on one of the guard-rails at the top of the accommodation ladder, where the King would come on board, and someone was dispatched quickly to get a pot of white paint to put the matter correct.

At 0930 they piped 'All hands man ship' and all the sailors lined the guard-rails from for'd to aft on both sides of the ship, standing up to the guard-rail with their arms spread out grasping the guard-rail with their hands. At 1000, in the distance they could hear cheering, regularly getting closer, then they could see a sloop approaching between the lines of ships, with a huge Royal Standard flying from the mast-head, a huge white ensign on the ensign-staff and an enormous Union Flag on the jack-staff. They could clearly see the King and Queen on the bridge with their family and the Royal Party. As it drew near to their ship, the First Lieutenant ordered over the Tannoy, 'Ship's Company, Shun, Off Caps.' Everyone's right arm came up across his face, gripped the rim of his cap, counted . . . 2 . . . 3, and held the cap up at 45 degrees. 'Three cheers for his Majesty the King, Hip, hip . . . Hoorah.' As he said Hoorah, everyone shouted it out at the same time and waved their cap in a circle. Dave smiled to himself as he remembered the Jimmy's briefing: 'On Cheer Ship, you have to say Hoorah and not Hooray, Hoorah sounds much bettah and travels much furthah.' But he had to admit it looked very impressive as he watched the ship opposite to them, as the Hoorah rang out and all of the white caps moved in a circle together. The Royal Party moved out of sight along the lines of warships and the Ship's Company stood at ease, but only for about twenty minutes as, in a flurry of piping and bugles, the Royal Barge appeared heading straight for the *Myngs*.

The Ship's Company fell in once again, this time by Divisions, and were called to attention as the Royal Party came alongside the accommodation ladder amid shrill piping from the side party and some fancy boat-hook drill from the barge's crew.

The King appeared on the accommodation ladder, again to the shrill sounds from the bosun's pipes as they 'Piped the side'. The King was followed by the Queen, Princess Elizabeth, Princess Margaret and Prince Philip, Princess Elizabeth's fiancé. The Royal Standard was broken at the mast-head.

The Captain, First Lieutenant and the other officers were standing at the Salute as the King stepped on board, smiling and also saluting, when, to everyone's horror, he put his left hand on the top of the guard-rail which had been freshly painted that morning. He gave a cursory glance at his hand and the Captain stepped forward offering him his handkerchief, then it was all smiles again as the King wiped his hand and was introduced to the other officers. The King, dressed in the uniform of an Admiral of the Fleet, moved to the fo'c'sle with the rest of the Royal Party to commence his inspection of Divisions. He showed a keen interest in every aspect of the ship. He spoke to many of the sailors, asking how long they had been in the Navy, where they were serving when they got that medal, where their home was, and he gradually moved aft, taking about half an hour to reach the quarterdeck.

Then they were back at the gangway again and Dave heard him say to the Captain, 'I am very impressed with the smart appearance of the ship and the immaculate turn-out of the Ship's Company, very well done,' and they disappeared down the ladder. Again to the shrilling of pipes and the lowering of the Royal Standard, the Barge headed off to the next ship nominated for inspection.

When the Barge was out of sight, it seemed as if a big sigh of relief came from the ship and everyone on board. The Captain turned to the First Lieutenant and said, 'Very well done, Number One, pipe "Hands to make and mend clothes".' This meant that everyone was being given the afternoon off for all of the hard work that they had put into the preparation for the inspection.

Down in the mess decks, the story soon spread, with much chuckling about how the King had got wet paint on his left hand. Some people decided to go ashore, as they were already dressed in their number 1 suits; others started to sling their hammocks, 'micks' as they were commonly called, opting for an afternoon snooze or 'Egyptian PT' as some of them called it.

Later that evening they had another reward for their efforts. A general signal was received which said, 'From His Majesty the King to all ships in the Clyde Review, well done, Splice the Mainbrace,' which meant an extra tot of rum would be issued. This was a tradition from the days of sail. The largest rope on board the sailing ships was the mainmast brace, which held the mast up against the force of the wind filled sails. On the rare occasions when the Mainbrace parted, sometimes in heavy weather, sometimes in battle, it was an extremely difficult and hazardous task to splice the rope together again. The men involved in this job were always rewarded by an extra tot of rum, hence the derivation.

The next morning the fleet started to disperse to various tasks. *Myngs* with her flotilla and two cruisers headed towards the North Sea to take part in exercises with the Norwegian and Dutch Navies. As both of these countries had been occupied by the Germans during the war, they hadn't yet managed to build up a very large Navy, but the ships that they had were ex-RN ships. They had, in fact, been Free Norwegian and Free Dutch ships during the war, serving as part of the Royal Navy, so were very familiar with Navy procedures and exercises.

During the next fourteen days they escorted convoys, being attacked by 'enemy' aircraft and submarines, cleared minefields, carried out live firings at battle practice targets, and then dispersed to various ports on official visits, or 'showing the flag' as they were called.

Myngs went to Oslo in Norway first. The fjord leading up to Oslo was littered with wrecks of ships, many of which had been attacked by our Beaufighters and had run aground before settling on the bottom. They found Oslo very expensive, too expensive to buy beer. The ship was open to visitors every afternoon and there was a huge queue of people waiting to get on board at the gangway during the time that it was open. The duty watch was kept busy as guides, showing groups of people around the ship. The next two ports that they called at were Antwerp and Rotterdam, which were not so expensive, and the night life was exciting enough to satisfy everyone.

Certainly the crew had some wild runs ashore there, and when a libertyman staggered into his mess, the first thing that he was asked by his mess mates was 'Did you get a bit?' It was a waste of time answering the question because if you said 'Yes,' the reply was 'Dirty bastard,' and if you said 'No,' it was 'Lying bastard,' so you couldn't win.

Now that the war was over everyone had to wear a white lanyard with their No. 1 suit, which everyone hated.

The ship then proceeded to Portsmouth, which was to be its home base, and the home base of all of the sailors living on board. The Navy was divided into three home bases: Plymouth for West Country and West Midlands, Chatham for North Country and Scotland, and Portsmouth for everyone else. Although Dave was a Geordie, somehow he had ended up in the Portsmouth home base, which meant he would always return to Portsmouth RN barracks between ships, for advancement courses, leaves etc. His official service number started with P/ . . . the others were D/ . . . for Devonport and C/ . . . for Chatham. All the ships in the fleet were also divided between the three home bases and would always return there for commissioning, paying-off, leave periods and refits.

They spent six weeks in Portsmouth, during which time everyone had two weeks seasonal leave, the ship had its maintenance period and several ratings did courses. Dave went to Whale Island, HMS *Excellent* again, where he qualified as a RC2, Radar Control rating, second class. He found that the Gunner's Mates, now called Gunnery Instructors, still put the fear of Christ up him.

He got to know the low dives of Portsmouth. Queen Street was the area where everything happened; almost every other building was a pub, some with reputations so bad that you had to avoid them like the plague unless you wanted to end up with a broken nose. The naval shore patrol was very, very active there; they had to be, breaking up fights, and dealing with drunken liberty men. Their aim was to keep the sailors out of the hands of the local police, although the resulting naval penalties were just as severe. No self-respecting woman would walk down Queen Street, there were so many prostitutes plying their trade and a lot of queers, called 'Brown Hatters' by the sailors, preying on young sailors.

There were many naval tailors in Portsmouth. Bernard's was probably the largest, and most sailors bought their No.1 uniform from one of these tailors. The tailors' uniforms were made from much superior material, not the rough serge that 'pussers' uniforms were made from. If you wanted to be a real Jack you had to have a tailor-made uniform; the cap was better shaped, and the bow on the cap ribbon was just to the left of the HMS, and you wore the cap with the bow just above your left eye and not over the left ear as per regulations. The gold HMS, as with all of the other gold badges worn on the arms, was made from gold wire and not gold silk like pusser's badges. The jumper part of the uniform was made skin tight; it fitted like a glove and it was impossible to get it off without the help of a buddy. It had a wide U-shaped opening at the front, not the narrow V-shaped front of the service issue. Blue jean collars from naval tailors were a light Mediterranean blue and the colours didn't run; the Service issued collars were almost black when new, and it took years of washing to get them to a nice light blue, and the black dye ran into the three white tapes that ran around the edge of the collar.

The tailors' trousers had much wider bell-bottoms than the service uniform, and some tailors sewed in a chain inside the outer part of the bottom hem, to make the bell-bottoms swing as you walked. To finish it off, the tailor sold black shoes with silver buckles, so someone stepping ashore in this rig looked like a real 'jack me hearty'. It didn't matter how long you had been in the Navy, if you wore the pusser's uniform, you looked like a rookie.

On weekends in harbour, Saturday afternoons and Sundays, the tailors' reps would descend on the ships, finding their way into various mess-decks. Sailors knew them by their Christian names or their nicknames, and usually, by about 1 o'clock, the reps were half drunk, with the 'sippers' of rum that the sailors forced on them. Then they got involved in games of cards and, quite often, they left the ship with less money than they had come on board with. They all carried a small suitcase that they carried their wares in: collars, shoes, silks, white-fronts, but they never seemed to broach the subject of selling. Dave felt sorry for them at times and wondered how they ever made a living. They were ribbed mercilessly by the sailors; one would come into the mess and say, 'Hey, Bernards, have you got any blue jean collars left?' With a gleam of excitement in his eye, the rep would eagerly reach for his suitcase, saying, 'Yes, as a matter of fact I have,' only to have the sailor reply, 'Serves you right for being so greedy then, you shouldn't have brought so many.'

When they sailed again out of Portsmouth it was to a pleasant surprise. They were told to proceed to the River Tyne, to Vickers Armstrong shipyard, where they would go alongside a brand new ship, HMS *Agincourt*. They were to pay-off *Myngs* and transfer completely, crew and stores to the new ship and bring it into commission.

CHAPTER 6

Agincourt

Dave looked at his new ship. He remembered his first sight of the *Myngs*, greyhound of the sea; he remembered, and sad as he was to leave his first ship, the *Agincourt* filled him with admiration. She really looked businesslike. Larger than *Myngs*, she had two twin 4.5 inch turrets for'd and two aft. The guns crews were totally enclosed inside of the turrets, so no more getting soaked as the seas came inboard, or during heavy rain storms, as the loading numbers stood behind in the open. She had several Bofors guns in strategic positions, and on the quarterdeck she was fitted with ahead throwing anti-submarine mortars instead of depth charges. This made attacking a submarine much more accurate as the mortar bombs were fired before the ship reached the submarine's position and fell about 300 yards ahead of the ship, so the ship didn't have to pass right over the submarine to place the depth charges. The accommodation on board was much superior to the *Myngs*; the mess-decks were more spacious and there was much more room in the showers and bathrooms. *Agincourt* was a 'Battle Class' destroyer, she was still the flotilla leader and the rest of the flotilla were all called after famous naval sea battles, *Aisne*, *Solebay*, *Trafalgar* and *Jutland*.

In two days the transfer was completed and they had to sail again under the Red Ensign to carry out acceptance trials, then, as before, there was the ceremonial lowering of the Red Ensign and the hoisting of the White Ensign as she was commissioned and became part of the fleet.

From there they sailed directly to Gibraltar for the spring cruise and exercises, rendezvousing with other units of the Home Fleet in the Bay of Biscay. Dave remembered the last time that he had sailed from the Tyne; it had been flat calm but he was as sick as a dog. He had by now grown used to the motion of a ship at sea and he was never sea-sick. He never made fun of any sea-sick sailors, though; he knew exactly how they felt and he really felt sorry and sympathised with them.

Gibraltar was really choc-a-bloc with ships. All of the alongside berths were full, with ships secured alongside each other in threes, and some of the big ships even had to anchor in the bay outside the harbour. The reason was soon obvious: the Mediterranean fleet, the Home fleet, the US fleet and some French ships had all gathered there for the exercises. Ashore, the Main Street was full of sailors of different nationalities; the bars were full to bursting point, every table taken, and people standing everywhere. There were the usual girl bands, the usual drunks flaked out on the floor and the usual shore patrols rushing in, hitting someone on the head with their batons and carrying them out. Dave had seen lots of 'sailors ashore' scenes in different movies, but, he had to admit, nothing compared to the real thing.

He got chatting to an American sailor, sitting next to him at the bar. The Yank said, 'Say, what badge is that on your arm?' Dave told him that it was a radar badge, and the Yank replied, 'You mean to say that you guys have got radar too?' Dave didn't have the heart to tell him that radar had been invented by the British during the war, and that it had played a big part in winning the Battle of Britain. He was also introduced to American humour. There was a Spanish singer on the stage, trying to make herself heard above the din, she looked very sexy, and the Yank said, 'If that dame had as many pricks sticking out of her as she has had sticking into her, she would look like a godamned porcupine.'

He ended up inviting the American to come on board the next lunch time for a tot of rum. The Americans loved being invited on board the British ships at 'tot time', as all of their ships were 'dry' and they were really envious of the British sailors with their traditional rum ration. Besides it usually meant that you got invited back to their ship in return, which meant southern fried chicken, and ice-cream machines on every messdeck.

After Gibraltar there were seven days of strenuous exercises, then 'showing the flag' again. The first port for *Agincourt* was Lisbon, where they had a tremendous reception. There were big banners across the streets, bearing such notices as, 'After the war, Peace!' and 'Welcome to the victorious Royal Navy.' Portugal, of course, had been a neutral country during the war.

After that, it was Casablanca and Oran. In both ports they hated the British, because, when the French capitulated to the Nazis during the war, the British fleet lay-off Casablanca and Oran and sank the French fleet at their moorings inside the harbour, to prevent them falling into the hands of the Germans. Whilst they were in Oran, a lot of the crew were invited to the HQ of the French Foreign Legion at Sidi-bel-Abbès. It was a fort out in the desert, exactly like the kind you see at the cinema, and they met three English boys who had joined the French Foreign Legion, whom they invited back to the ship but they said that they were not allowed to leave the Fort. They said that they were doing fine but they watched longingly as the sailors left.

On arrival back at Portsmouth, they found that their next task was to be quite pleasant. The King, the Queen and the Princesses were to carry out their first official visit since the war had ended; it was to be an official visit to South Africa. They would travel on HMS *Vanguard*, our latest battleship, and four Battle class destroyers would be their escorts. They were to sail in three weeks.

HMS *Vanguard* was a very modern warship which had not been completed in time to take part in the war, so she had never fired a shot in anger. She was a magnificent looking warship, the world's latest battleship, and a good choice for conveying the Royal Family on their official visit to South Africa.

In due course the ships left Portsmouth amid great pomp and ceremony and after fuelling at Gibraltar were soon heading south into the South Atlantic in hot calm weather. As the ships neared the same latitude as the Gold Coast, a British colony in West Africa, reports were heard on the BBC World Radio broadcast of disturbances in the colony and riots in Takoradi, a port on the western side of the colony where strikes were being organized by the workers.

Agincourt was detached from the group and proceeded to Takoradi, and the very next morning at sunrise she entered the port of Takoradi and berthed alongside. Dave thought that it must have come as a great shock and surprise to the organizers of the dissent in the colony, that the very next day after the riots this powerful looking modern warship had arrived in the port, demonstrating the long arm of the British government. Many political discussions and meetings must have been going on in the background, but that day, the ship was opened to local visitors, the ship's football team played a game with the Takoradi town football team, and libertymen were allowed to go ashore to sample the local beer amid a friendly reception, the result being that the disturbances were over, the strikes were called off, and the ship stayed only one day before leaving to catch up with the *Vanguard* and the other ships.

They were now approaching the Equator, and all ships were preparing for the 'crossing the line' ceremony. This was an initiation ceremony that everyone who was crossing the Equator for the first time had to go through. It started after dark the evening before reaching the Equator. Over the Tannoy was piped, 'Clear lower deck, all hands muster on the fo'c'sle, King Neptune will be visiting the ship to prepare for the crossing of the line ceremony.'

All of this had been organized by senior ratings and sailors, all of whom had crossed the line on previous occasions. On the fo'c'sle, right for'd, a hose had been rigged, playing a fine spray of sea water directly upwards, and, from the bridge, two 20-inch signal lamps were aimed at the stem of the ship, creating a rainbow effect with the spray of water. Then over the side of the ship climbed King Neptune and his retinue, called 'bears'; they must have been crouching on the anchors on the bow. Neptune was wearing a seaweed skirt, a gold crown and a sea-shell necklace and he carried a trident. The bears were covered in hair made from unlayed rope and growled aggressively. Neptune shouted up to the bridge, 'What ship is this that dares to enter into my domain?' and the Captain replied, 'His Majesty's ship *Agincourt*, Portsmouth to Cape Town.'

Neptune replied, 'I command that all seamen on board who have never entered my domain before, will muster amidships at 1000 tomorrow, to be initiated into the band of sailors who have crossed the line. Anyone who dares to refuse will be hunted down by bears' (much growling and clawing from the bears) 'and brought into my presence. God save the King.'

Everything had been prepared by 1000 the next day; an awning had been spread amidships, and the canvas swimming pool had been rigged and filled with sea water. At the side of the pool, Neptune's throne had been positioned so that he could see all of the proceedings. Opposite to Neptune, a platform had been built. On it was a wooden chair, facing away from Neptune, with hinges on the bottom of the rear legs so that it could be tipped back into the pool. This was where the candidates would be initiated.

At 10 o'clock, King Neptune and all his retinue filed down from the fo'c'sle, the King, with his red beard and hair, looking remarkably like the chief bosun's mate. There was already a crowd of volunteers to be initiated, or maybe they just wanted to get it over with. Four bears climbed into the pool, another grabbed one of the volunteers and slapped him down into the chair, then a barber stepped forward and with a huge brush proceeded to lather the face of the volunteer from a bucket that looked like whitewash. The barber then produced a cut-throat razor, about three feet long, and proceeded to shave his unfortunate victim. He then pushed a 'pill', which tasted horrible, into his mouth, and tilted the chair backwards so that the victim fell into the pool, where he was grabbed by the bears, who dunked him several times under the water. They finally let him up, gasping for air, and he was released, initiated.

All morning the initiations went on. Dave got his over with by mid-afternoon. Neptune's policemen were searching all of the nooks and crannies of the ship for those who were reluctant, or afraid, to be initiated, but there was no escape; somehow King Neptune had got hold of a list of those who hadn't crossed the Line.

Looking around at the other ships, Dave saw that the same ceremony was going on aboard them. The King and Queen had both crossed the line before but the two princesses had to go through it.

At the end of the day, the cox'n handed out 'Crossing the Line Certificates', signed by the Captain. It had the person's name, name of the ship, latitude and longitude, and date of the ceremony. Dave stowed his away with his 'Blue Nose Certificate'; he thought he only had to cross the Antarctic Circle and he would have a grand slam.

In due course the group arrived off Capetown. Dave was impressed by the beauty of the place, a fantastic bay. Capetown itself was a magnificent city but the background took your breath away. Table Mountain was directly behind and overlooking the city, with Devil's Peak and Lion's Head on each side. The reception too was overwhelming. Of course, everyone wanted to see the Royal Family, but people were queuing in their cars, at the gangway of each ship, to invite sailors to their homes for the weekend. South Africa, of course, had sent their forces to fight in World War II, but the country itself really hadn't been affected by the war. The shops were full of merchandise that the British sailors hadn't seen for years, and some that they had never seen. Dave went shopping and filled up a kit-bag of stuff to take home to his mother: tinned fruit, tinned butter and tinned meats.

Agincourt took on board ten sailors of the South African Royal Navy Reserve, to get some sea-going experience. They came from Johannesburg and had never seen the sea before. They were to live on board until the group departed for the United Kingdom once again. They soon made friends with the sailors, going ashore drinking with them in the towns that stretched along the Cape coast. They saw for themselves the segregation between the blacks and the whites, benches on the railway stations were marked 'Whites only', blacks had to travel in different coaches and buses, and there were lots of places where they weren't even allowed into. This didn't affect the British sailors too much, but they discovered that the Cape Coloured girls were very attractive. They were the results of liaisons between blacks and whites, although intermarriage and even intercourse was strictly against the law. They used to discuss this around the messdeck table and they noticed that even just talking about it seemed to make the SA sailors physically sick; they had been brought up from birth to believe that it was wrong for blacks and whites to mix. The Brits decided among themselves that they would get one drunk and he would wake up in the morning with a Cape Coloured girl in his bed, but they never succeeded!

The destroyers left Capetown and went up the east coast to East London, Port Elizabeth and Durban. In Port Elizabeth Dave nearly got into a fight with a Boer who hated the British. He came up to Dave with a pound note on his shoulder and said, 'Knock that off.' Dave didn't even know that he was trying to pick a fight until the other South Africans dragged him away. Apart from a few incidents with the Boers, the hospitality was really amazing. In Durban, as they sailed through the harbour entrance, they were serenaded by the Lady in White, who was a legendary character who had sung to every Navy ship and troopship that had entered Durban for a great number of years.

Durban was Zulu land, and there were many of them around in full tribal costume. Some pulled a kind of rickshaw for tourists and sailors, and made quite a living at it; people used to pay them just to take their photograph. There was a big prison near to where they were berthed, and lots of convicts, dressed in sacks, used to sweep the dockside every morning, guarded by Zulu guards, armed with assegais, a short stabbing spear.

Whilst they were in Durban, Dave had his twenty-second birthday. He had been in the Navy four and a half years, four years since he was eighteen, that meant that he now qualified for his first good conduct badge. This was awarded every four years, provided that your conduct had been good during that period, so he saw the Captain as a requestman, had it granted, and sewed his first chevron onto his left sleeve.

It was an uneventful journey back to Portsmouth. Dave knew that he was leaving the ship on arrival, as his draft orders had come through in Capetown. He was going back to HMS *Excellent*, his alma mater, for a 2nd class course in radar gunnery. He knew quite a number of the gunnery staff at Whale Island, and he had no problems with his course; it went quite deeply into the theory side of gunnery and soon he was back in RN barracks waiting for a draft to another ship.

It wasn't long in coming. He had been in barracks for about two weeks, when he was told that he was being drafted to HMS *Cheviot*, a destroyer in the Mediterranean fleet. A commission abroad usually lasted for about two years. He reported to the clothing store and was issued with a full tropical kit: white cap, white shoes and stockings, a full white uniform and white shorts. He was given two weeks draft leave, and he went off to Durham to spend it with his parents. He was looking quite an old hand now, with his gold good conduct badge on his left arm, his second class crossed guns on his right arm and his campaign ribbons on his chest. His recent divisional officers had pressed him to take the course for advancement to Leading Seaman, as he had had lots of experience, but he had decided to wait until his next ship.

He joined the troopship *Empire Windrush* at Southampton, on its way to the Far East; he would take passage as far as Malta. There were Navy, Army, and Air Force personnel on board and a large number of service women and families of armed forces. Most of the personnel were destined for Singapore and Hong Kong; a small number would be disembarking at Gibraltar and also at Malta.

It was an uneventful trip. Dave had to carry out some watchkeeping duties. The males and females had been segregated on board, but nature being what it is, they had to carry out anti-vice patrols, and he got caught for these.

CHAPTER 7

Mediterranean Commission

It was a baking hot day when they sailed into Grand Harbour, Valetta, Malta. Dave had already changed into his white shorts and white front and he had passed the burning stage and had managed to start a tan on the way out. The troopships secured to a buoy and lighters arrived alongside, one marked NAVY, and the other two ARMY and RAF. Dave struggled down the ladder with his kit-bag and hammock, sweat pouring out of him; there were only about twenty Navy personnel, and their lighter was off first, landing at HMS *St Angelo*, a stone frigate which was RNHQ. There patrolmen dealt with them quickly, finding out which ship that they were bound for and supplying road transport to get them there. They found out that all of the Mediterranean fleet were away on the summer cruise, so most of the sailors, including Dave, were sent to HMS *Ricasoli*, to await their ship's return.

Ricasoli was a very old Fort, overlooking Grand Harbour. Dave found that he had two months to languish there, which was very pleasant; not much work to do, swimming every day, living it up ashore every night.

However it soon became boring, and one day he saw a notice on the ship's noticeboard which said that the fleet were very short of diving teams, which every ship was trying to form. The notice was asking for volunteers to do a shallow water diving course at Manoel Island Diving School, which was at the far end of Sliema Creek. Despite all his training, which told him 'never volunteer for anything', Dave remembered how intrigued he had been working with the divers in Scapa Flow, so he put in his request to take the course and after having to take a strict medical examination, he was accepted. He did notice that the surgeon-lieutenant, after reading his medical records and seeing 'Rheumatic Fever', spent a long time in listening to his heart, but in the end he seemed satisfied.

The course started the following Monday, six of them, with a CPO Diver and a PO Diver as their instructors. The first two days they were put through strenuous exercises: running, push-ups, jumping from a height into the water,

99

swimming long distances, with or without fins. Dave realized that they were being tested to see if they had the stamina for what was to come; in fact, by the end of the second day, two had already chucked their hands in. If you made a mistake or you weren't quick enough you got punishing extra exercises and God help you if you called a fin a 'flipper'.

The rest of the week was devoted to diving theory and instructions on diving equipment. Dave was surprised to learn that breathing pure oxygen, because that is what they would be doing as shallow-water divers, was toxic at one atmosphere, that is about 33 feet. This would govern the depth that they would operate, as deeper than that they would start to suffer from oxygen poisoning. The air that we breathe every day on the surface is about 20 per cent oxygen and 80 per cent nitrogen. If you breathe this as you dive, as the divers in Scapa were doing, the partial pressure of the oxygen increases, and around 180 feet it is the same as breathing pure oxygen, and oxygen poisoning will occur. The breathing set that they would be using was called a Salvus Breathing Apparatus, which had been designed for fighting fires in smoke filled compartments, and Dave had used it before in Damage Control exercises on board his ships. Now it had been converted for use as a diving set. The suit that they would wear was a dry suit called the Sladen diving suit, nicknamed 'clammy death' by the divers. It was made of canvas, with a rubber helmet welded onto the collar. It had an opening at the front waist where you got into it, pulling your legs down into canvas feet; you then put your arms into the sleeves, and pushed your hands through tight rubber seals and pulled the helmet over your head. The front had a skirt that was folded up and clamped to prevent water entering; this was pushed inside and covered with canvas straps. The rubber helmet had a hinged visor which was screwed down when you went onto oxygen. You wore a nose clip, the oxygen mouth-piece went into your mouth and was gripped by your teeth, and a tube on the outside was screwed onto your breathing equipment. There were two small oxygen bottles that allowed oxygen, at a pre-set flow, by a reducer, to bleed into a counter-lung that fitted over your head and around your neck. The breathing tube went into a canister filled with a carbon-dioxide absorbent. You breathed in pure oxygen but when you exhaled there was a higher amount of carbon dioxide in your breath which was absorbed by the contents of the canister. This was necessary because a build up of carbon dioxide in the counter-lung would eventually lead to the diver losing consciousness. The CO_2 absorbent was renewed before each dive.

The following Monday they were to start diving. They were led out onto a large pontoon alongside Manoel Island, and the two instructors, assisted by two qualified divers, started slowly to dress two of the candidates, explaining each step of the way, as they did it. Dave and the other students helped, watching everything very closely. It would be their turn next.

Everything went smoothly, and soon they were fully dressed, but not yet on oxygen and their visors were still open. They were sat down on a bench, and the huge, heavy diving boots were put on and laced up with rope which was secured around their ankles.

They stood up and a life-line was passed through a ring on their shoulder and secured around their waist with a bowline knot. 'Put the divers on oxygen,' said the chief diver, and one of the attendants opened the valves on the O_2 bottles. The hiss of the gas going into the counter-lung was heard and the counter-lung started to inflate and deflate as the divers breathed in and out. 'Check the diver,' said the chief and the two attendants gave a thumbs up to their respective divers who replied with a thumbs up. 'Diver reports well,' said each attendant. 'Screw down the visors,' ordered the chief. The attendants closed down the visors and started screwing down on the wing nuts to make the suit watertight.

One of the divers immediately started showing signs of distress, fumbling to unscrew the visor and stumbling away from the water, waving his hands across his face to say, 'No.' 'Open his visor and take him off O_2,' said the chief. They did this and when the visor was opened, the diver took the breathing tube out of his mouth, and said, 'I'm sorry, chief, I can't go on; as soon as you screwed down, I went into a panic.'

'That's OK, son,' said the chief. 'You are suffering from claustrophobia. Many people don't realize that they have it until they are enclosed like that; get him undressed.'

The chief had seen it all before. This sailor would never make a diver, but they didn't treat him unkindly; it wasn't his fault, and better to find out now than when he was under the water. So now they were down to three. 'Put the other diver in the water,' ordered the chief. The other diver, looking a bit apprehensive, was led to the edge of the pontoon and guided onto a steel ladder which led down into the water, and he started to walk down the rungs. As he went lower there was a hiss of air from a valve on the top of his rubber helmet. This was a one-way valve which let air out but wouldn't allow water to come in. When he was waist deep he started to float because the air trapped in his suit wasn't escaping fast enough. 'Pull up on the pepper pot valve,' shouted the chief, and when the diver did this, the air went out with a rush and the diver started to sink quickly. You could see a moment of panic flash across his face and he splashed with his arms until he realized that he wasn't sinking any more and was floating with his visor level with the surface. Then he gave a thumbs up.

There was a jackstay on the side of the pontoon which went down to a sinker on the bottom about twenty-six feet below, and the diver grabbed hold of it, as he had been instructed before the dive. 'Send the diver down,' said the chief, and he left the surface, adjusting the pepper pot valve as he went. The lifeline jerked once. 'Diver reached bottom,' reported the attendant, repeating the signal on the lifeline to the diver.

They left him down about half an hour to get used to the new environment.

'Call him up,' said the chief; the attendant gave three pulls, which was repeated, then one pull from the diver, 'Diver left bottom.'

He appeared on the surface, gave a thumbs up and began to climb the ladder. They sat him down and opened his visor, 'It's great,' he said with a huge grin.

Dave and the other student were then dressed. He felt a tinge of fear as his face visor was screwed down and when he went down the ladder into the water, his ears popped as all the air in his legs was forced into the top part of his suit and the pressure rose. He remembered the chief shouting, 'Pull up on your pepper pot valve,' and he did that. The air went out with a rush, and he started to sink. He had a moment of panic as the sea level rose to his face visor, but he gave a thumbs up and entered a world that was entirely foreign to him, and he was too busy looking around to be afraid. He went down the jackstay hand over hand, clearing his ears as they popped. Above him he saw the bottom of the pontoon, covered in huge barnacles. On the other jackstay he saw the other diver going down alongside him, and they gave the thumbs up to each other. Looking down he saw lots of empty beer cans and other debris, and there was the concrete sinker that he was descending to. As his boots touched the bottom, a cloud of mud arose and surrounded him. He gave one tug on his life line, meaning, 'I have arrived at bottom,' and received a reassuring tug in return. As the mud cleared he saw that the other diver had also reached bottom. There were quite a lot of fish swimming around and he saw one squid scuttle along the sand. It was all so fascinating and different. He looked at the concrete sinker; it had a length of chain shackled to it, and a coil of rope secured to the bottom of the jackstay. He was almost disappointed when he received three pulls on his lifeline. He repeated them back to his attendant, then gave one tug as he left bottom, pulling himself up the jackstay. He looked up and saw the pontoon with the ladders sticking down into the water. He surfaced, gave the thumbs up, climbed out, and soon the three students were chattering away excitedly about their dives.

From then on, the diving started in earnest. They had to do three dives a day, and started off by learning all the lifeline signals whilst they were down: 'Go down', 'Come up', 'Go out to the end of your shot line' (which was the rope secured to the bottom of the jackstay), 'Go left', 'Go right', 'Stop', 'Start the search'. They were also taught the emergency signals. A series of tugs on the lifeline from the diver meant, 'I am in trouble, get me up quick'; from the attendant it meant: 'Return to the surface as quickly as you can.'

They had to start working underwater. Dave found the reason for the chain shackled to the sinker; he was sent down with a hammer and chisel and told not to come up until he had chiselled the end link off the chain and brought it back to the surface. It was very difficult; there was a knack, you had to pick up the sinker, put it between your legs, sit down on the sea bottom, put the chain link on the base of the sinker, and start to chisel. Even then it wasn't easy, because as you swung the hammer, it aquaplaned and went off in a different direction from where you were aiming. Dave found that you had to hold the hammer right up near to the head, and not the end of the handle, to make it go in the right direction required. It took an hour to get through a link. Their next task was to saw through a piece of angle iron with a hacksaw. They were taken to another pontoon and on the seabed below it they found a steel bench with a vice and an angle iron in it. This task was a bit easier, but after that it was a baton of wood and a wood saw, a bit more difficult.

One evening they were kept back after dark and had to carry out these tasks in a night dive, with a headlamp attached to their helmet. They went on to carry out bottom searches for lost objects, the instructors throwing things in like a 6-inch shackle or a boat's rudder, which they had to find. On the last week they were taken by boat to one of the reserve fleet destroyers in Sliema Creek, which had a 'bottom line' rigged under the hull of the ship. This went down one side, under the keel and up the other side, and was hauled taut. There they were taught how to search a ship's bottom for suspected limpet mines. They started for'd with the bottom line, and gradually moved it aft until all of the hull had been searched. It also gave them the opportunity to look at the underwater fittings, such as inlets and outlets, the log, the sonar dome, rudders and screws, places where they might have to work in the future, after they had qualified. They carried out bottom searches by day and by night.

The course lasted six weeks, at the end of which they received their qualifications as Shallow Water Divers, from the officer in charge of the Diving School. He gave them their diving logs, in which they would record every dive that they did, their annual diving medical examinations, and any other qualification that they might receive. They were also given their qualification badge, a red diver's helmet with the letters SW beneath; this was to be sewn on the right cuff of their jumpers. They also now had a rise in their pay, diving pay. To keep it they had to do at least 120 minutes per quarter underwater and remain medically fit.

A few days later Dave stood on the ramparts of Ricasoli and watched the Mediterranean fleet return to Malta, big ships into Grand Harbour and small ships into Sliema Creek. That afternoon transport took him with his kit to Sliema front, and he saw *Cheviot*'s motor boat approaching from the lines of destroyers. He was made very welcome on board, especially by the man that he was relieving, who had been waiting for weeks for his relief to arrive. He would be demobilized when he got back to England. *Cheviot* was very similar to *Myngs*, another Emergency class destroyer, but she was in a much better condition, having spent most of her life in the tropics. There was a full flotilla in Malta, each with its name starting with Ch: *Chevron, Chivalrous, Charity, Chieftain*; the leader, Captain D, was the *Chequers* and Prince Philip was the First Lieutenant on board that ship.

He met one able seaman that he already knew, a gunnery rating who had been on the same course as him at Whale Island. His Action Station would be in the Gunnery Control Centre, and his duties on board would be as quartermaster. He also found that they would be sailing within a week on an operational patrol off Haifa. This patrol had been going on for some time, with the object of preventing illegal Jewish immigrants from landing in Palestine.

Dave was fair skinned and a red-head, so he had to be very careful with the sun, which was extremely hot in Malta, but his skin had hardened considerably after his time in the Far East and the trip to South Africa, so he already had the makings of a good tan. They sailed a week later and headed east towards Palestine. On the way, his new messmates told him of some of their exploits on previous Haifa patrols. When they approached one of the illegal ships, abuse was hurled at them besides the various missiles coming from the ship. They had to board the ship in order to 'arrest' it; the Jewish immigrants knew this, and their guard rails would be lined with women brandishing weapons like knives and broken bottles. They worked on the principle that the boarding party would not hurt a woman to get on board. When they arrived they relieved HMS *Chevron*, who quickly, after receiving her mail from them, disappeared over the horizon and for three days, they patrolled up and down the Palestine coast. It was boring, but of course, there was always the ship husbandry to be carried out. Dave was already into his watchkeeping duties, carrying out his 'tricks' on the wheel. Generally the work was much easier in the pleasant Mediterranean weather, the ship gleamed, there was less rust, and rust-stained paintwork, which Dave had got used to in northern waters.

On the seventh night they picked up a radar signal of a ship moving very slowly but heading in towards the shore. They shadowed her until dawn, when they saw that she was a small, filthy coastal vessel, crowded with people, so laden that the water-line was well below the surface. They ordered her to stop, first by Aldis lamp, then over the loudhailer. Dave saw what his mate had meant about the noise and the missiles: everyone on board was screaming at them and throwing things. However the ships on these patrols had everything down to a fine art. The boarding-party were piped to muster on the flag-deck which was just below the bridge. This consisted of a lieutenant, a petty officer and ten sailors, who were dressed in uniform, helmets and webbing gear, and armed with automatic rifles and pistols; they also carried batons. *Cheviot* slowly closed on the immigrant ship, which turned away and tried to avoid them but it didn't have the power and manoeuvrability to escape. With all of her fenders out the destroyer crunched alongside; they had their fire hoses rigged and turned on to drive the people back from the guard rails. Nominated sailors, for'd and aft, threw grappling hooks, and hauled them in tight so that the two ships were locked together; there were also marksmen at strategic places, just in case someone on board produced a firearm. It wasn't expected, no firearms had been used in previous arrests, but you had to take all precautions.

Dave then saw the training that the boarding party had done come into action. Constructed on the side of the flag deck was a drawbridge, which, once the two ships were secured together, was lowered onto the bridge wing of the immigrant ship, and the boarding party stormed across, immediately taking possession of the other ship's bridge. From there four stokers went straight down and took possession of the engine-room, two sailors went for'd to the bow and two went aft to the poop deck, braving the thumps and blows they received from the immigrants as they forced their way along the deck.

Within five minutes, a signalman in the boarding party flashed that the ship was in their hands. *Cheviot* cast off, and both ships turned together to the north-west, and Cyprus, where they were bound. It was a very smooth operation; it had been rehearsed many times, and in fact, some of the boarding party had done it many times for real.

There was no further incidents. They arrived at Famagusta, in Cyprus, twenty-four hours later and the immigrant ship was turned over to the port authorities and the British Army. Quite a number of illegal immigrants were being held there in internment camps.

Another ship had taken over the Palestine patrol and *Cheviot* headed back to Malta. They berthed in Sliema Creek, making their usual impressive, high speed, stern first, run up the creek where they berthed alongside the leader, *Chequers*. Dave, on the forenoon watch, quite often used to watch the First Lieutenant of *Chequers*, Prince Philip, having his First Lieutenant's requestmen and defaulters, and seeing sailors standing at the table with their caps off, he wondered how many in future years could boast that they had once got '14 days stoppage of leave' from the Duke of Edinburgh.

He struck up a friendship with another AB in his mess, 'Bagsy' Baker, who became his 'run-ashore' oppo. Bagsy was a three badge AB who had been in the service for over twelve years; he was married with two kids and lived on the Isle of Wight. Although he was a seaman, he worked with the supply branch and was responsible for all the store-rooms, getting victuals up to the galley daily for meals. He attended all 'issues' to the messes including the rum issue. Although the war was over, food was still rationed, and he was responsible for issuing the rations of sugar, tea, coffee, flour and frozen meat to the messes. He was called the 'tanky' and he was excused all other musters, except 'clear lower deck'.

They used to catch a *dgaisa* to Sliema and drink and talk in the bars along the front. Dave was watch keeping of course, and after a middle watch he was entitled to a 'make and mend', an afternoon off, and sometimes he would sling his hammock to try to catch up with lost sleep. Quite often, at weekends, he would have just dozed off when a face would appear over the gunwale of his hammock, and Bagsy would say, 'Come on, get the old suit on then,' and it was no use arguing with him.

The Mediterranean fleet was due to sail on their summer cruise shortly, and *Belfast*, a cruiser, was having her annual inspection by the C in C Mediterranean, Admiral Lord Louis Mountbatten. This reminded Bagsy of an inspection on a ship that he had been on; he swore it was true. He was on the *Edinburgh*, a cruiser in the Mediterranean, about 1936, and they were due for their annual inspection. Everyone was optimistic about it because they had been preparing for weeks. In charge of the naval stores was a three badge AB called Smokey and on the day previous to the inspection he had terrible pains in his stomach, which was diagnosed by the surgeon-commander as appendicitis. An ambulance was ordered to take him to the RN hospital at Bhigi, and before it arrived he sent for his assistant, a two badge AB, and asked him if he would be able to cope with the inspection.

'Don't worry, Smokey,' his assistant said, 'you have taught me everything I know about naval stores, and I know where everything is, and all of our books are in order; you just get off to hospital and get better,' and Smokey left the ship feeling that the naval stores were in good hands.

The next day the C in C's barge came alongside and the inspection started. It soon became apparent that everything was going well, by the smiles and laughing of the senior officers. Smokey's assistant waited in the naval stores, in his number 1 suit, for about two hours, spending his time dusting in inaccessible places, and squaring off all the bins and coils of rope, until he heard the Bugle sounding the 'still', getting closer. He stood to attention just inside the door of the naval stores and, as the Admiral entered, he chopped him off a smart salute and reported, 'Naval stores ready for your inspection, sir, Able Seaman Jones reporting.'

The Admiral returned his salute, looked around and said, 'Well, everything is looking ship-shape and clean in here.'

Over the Admiral's shoulder, Jonesy could see the captain beaming at the Admiral's remarks. The Admiral walked up to the desk and said, 'These are the naval stores ledgers, I suppose; now let's see,' he opened a page at random, pointed a finger at a line which said, 'Shackles, steel, 4-inch . . . 6 in number,' and he said, 'Show me these.'

'Yes sir,' said Jones, he knew the exact aisle, and the exact bin that they were in, and he was back in less than a minute with the six shackles.

'Very good,' said the Admiral, and opened another page. 'Lamps, Aldis, 4 inch . . . 2 in number, show me them!'

Off Jonesy shot and in no time was back with the two Aldis lamps. The

Admiral was pleased. 'One more,' he said and opened another page, ran his finger down the column, and stopped at 'Shovewood . . . 1 in number.'

'This one,' he said.

Jonesy looked at the book and a cloud crossed his face. He looked again then went down one of the aisles. He was away a long time, they could hear him rummaging in the bins, the captain and staff officers started to fidget, the Admiral was tapping the deck with his cane.

Jones came back with nothing and looked at the book again.

'Well, come on, man,' shouted the Captain, 'Where is this Shovewood?'

The Admiral's face had turned black.

'I can't find it, sir,' bleated Jonesy.

The Admiral exploded. 'Can't find it!' He turned to the captain, 'It's obvious to me that this ship is not ready for its annual inspection, and how can a ship be on a war-footing without a Shovewood? I am suspending this inspection and I will continue when you inform me that you are ready,' and he stormed out under a thundercloud, and left the ship.

The captain sent for Jonesy, who was beside himself with despair. He had let the ship down and under questioning he had to admit that he didn't know what a Shovewood looked like, 'Commander,' the Captain snapped, 'Meeting of all officers in the wardroom, in one hour.'

It was a gloomy lot that assembled and the captain spoke to, and it soon became apparent that no one knew what a Shovewood looked like, except an old commissioned gunner, sitting in the corner, who seemed to remember that when he was serving in the *Unicorn* in 1928, they had a Shovewood and it used to be stowed on the quarterdeck near the ship's bell.

'Describe it, Guns,' said the Captain.

'Well, as I recall, it was about four feet square, made of oak, and it had wooden wheels, like the ones that used to be fitted on the old gun carriages and . . .'

'Draw it for me,' interrupted the Captain, and Guns was given a large sheet of paper and he drew much the same as he had described with the addition of handles on the front and the back.

'Shipwright officer, can your men build this?'

'Yes, sir,' said the Chippy, and the Engineer Officer said, 'I'll get my artificers busy on the handles.'

That afternoon there was the sound of sawing, hammering and a lathe turning, and finally finished, the Shovewood was wheeled down to the quarterdeck, where the Bosun's party painted it with two coats of varnish, highly polished the handles and decorated them with Turks Head knots. The Gunner's party, not to be outdone, screwed on each side, in brass letters that they had found on an old rum barrel, 'The King, God bless him.'

And, in the end, it stood in all of its glory. The gunner declared that it was exactly the same as the one on the old *Unicorn* only much better.

The Captain sent a signal, 'To C in C Med. *Edinburgh* now ready for annual inspection.'

The next morning, the C in C's retinue arrived on board again There were some grim faces and by the way that the Admiral went around the ship, it was obvious that he only had one thing on his mind. Finally he arrived on the quarterdeck, and his eyes went straight to the Shovewood. He examined it closely, felt the smooth sides, noticed the fine work of the Turks Heads, and he turned to the Captain and said, 'In all of my years in the Navy, that is the finest Shovewood that I have ever seen. *Edinburgh* has passed her inspection with flying colours.'

Later that afternoon, the Admiral, sitting in his day cabin, with a gin and tonic, thought of everything that had happened in the last two days, and on impulse, he got a signal pad and wrote, 'To all ships, from C in C Med. Report number of Shovewoods held on board.' He rang for his Yeoman and told him to send the signal.

Within an hour the replies were coming. 'To C in C Med. from *Orion*, Nil Shovewoods held on board.' All of the other ships were reporting the same message. The Admiral was furious. He signalled: 'Executive officers of all ships will repair on board HMS *Edinburgh* to take plans to construct Shovewoods. All ships to report when they have full complement of Shovewoods.' And by the end of the next day every ship in the fleet had a Shovewood.

The fleet sailed the next day for the summer cruise and were away from Malta for two months. When *Edinburgh* entered Grand Harbour and secured to a buoy, one of the first persons to go on board was Smokey, fully recovered from his appendix operation. He made straight for the naval stores, and his first question to Jonesy was, 'How did the inspection go?' Jonesy replied, 'We passed with flying colours, but you nearly landed me in it over that Shovewood. I didn't know that we didn't have one.'

'Shovewood,' said Smokey, 'What are you talking about?'

Jonesy opened the ledger and showed him the entry: 'Shovewood – 1 in number.'

'There!' said Jonesy.

Smokey raised his eyes to the sky, and said, 'That's not Shovewood! it is Shov, wood, an abbreviation for 'Shovels, wooden – 1 in number'; we have it in aisle 3!'

They had been in harbour about three weeks when there was a crisis in the Middle East. Britain owned a big oil refinery at Abadan in Iran, and the Prime Minister of Iran, Mr Mosadequ, suddenly decided to seize it, nationalise it were his words. Britain ordered Iran to hand back the refinery to the Anglo-Iranian Oil Company, the owners, or suffer the consequences. In Malta, a cruiser and two destroyers were ordered to sail immediately to Abadan. *Cheviot* was one of the destroyers.

They sailed within twenty-four hours, at their top speed of around 28 knots. Dave looked at the big bow waves that they were making, and enjoyed the cool breeze from their speed. They had priority in the Suez Canal and two days later they were speeding south in the Red Sea. It got even hotter and shoals of flying fish took to the air, disturbed by their speed and the noise from their screws. They stopped at Aden just for two hours to refuel, then they were in the Arabian Sea and turned into the Persian Gulf.

The Persian Gulf had an infamous name in the Navy. It was probably the hottest place that you would ever serve. Where a normal commission was two to two and a half years, in the Gulf it was only eighteen months because of the conditions.

As they moved up to the north end of the Gulf, most of the sailors took to sleeping on the upper deck, the heat was intolerable below decks. They had spread awnings to attempt to make it cooler, but it didn't make much difference. They began to pass lots of oil tankers, going to or coming from the oil refineries in the area. At night there were numerous glows on the horizon, coming from the oil fields burning off gases ashore. There was a constant smell of crude oil, and by day, the sky looked yellow with the sand-laden air. When you blew your nose, your handkerchief was covered with sand and you could feel the grit between your teeth.

They arrived at the mouth of the Shat al Arab River at dawn, and started up the river in line ahead. At noon they arrived at Abadan oil refinery on the east bank. The frigate that was stationed in the Gulf was already there, moored to buoys in the middle of the river, her guns trained around and pointing at the refinery. Alongside the refinery were three Iranian gunboats, with their guns pointing at the frigate.

The cruiser and destroyers secured to buoys astern of the frigate and trained their guns on the refinery, and everyone settled down to await a political agreement. The options seemed to be: a. Iran would back down; b. Britain would back down; or c. the ships would receive orders to destroy the refinery.

The heat was energy sapping and the ships started working tropical routine: the hands were called at 0500, breakfast at 0530, and turn-to for work at 0600 until 1200, with a make and mend every afternoon.

Dave had been keeping up his diving practice. The Diving Officer on board was the Torpedo Gunner who was a trained diving supervisor and had been delighted when he found that Dave was a shallow water diver. Up to then they had had only two divers, now they had three, and the Gunner occasionally took them for an afternoon of practice diving, so that they could get their 'minutes in', to remain qualified for their Diving Pay. While they were at Abadan, the whaler boat was secured to the stern and one morning they found that the rudder had been lost, and the Gunner decided that they would have a dive to see if it was on the bottom. They put the shot rope down with the sinker; the river was about 30 feet deep where they were. Dave took the first dive, and it wasn't very pleasant; the water was a muddy, yellow colour, and as soon as he left the surface there was zero visibility, he couldn't even see the jackstay that he was hanging onto. It was a very fast flowing river, and he had literally to hang on or he would have been swept downstream. With no visibility your imagination plays tricks with you, and peering through your visor at total blackness, you imagine that you saw something pass in front of you. He arrived at the bottom, which seemed to be covered with huge logs like railway sleepers and as he stumbled and climbed over them, feeling around for the rudder, he knew that they would not find it. With the river flowing so fast it would be somewhere near the Persian Gulf by now. He stayed searching for about thirty minutes then surfaced and another diver went down, although he told the Gunner that they didn't have a hope of finding it. Another unpleasant thing about this dive was that, because it was a fresh water river, there was a worm that could bore into your skin and attack the liver. Originally they had meant to dive in just a bathing costume, but the Gunner had said that they had to wear the full suit. The rudder was never found.

The frigate was sent further up the river to a RAF base at Basra in Iraq for rest and to replenish stocks. The ships all did this in turn, and they spent two weeks at Abadan and in the end the refinery was handed over to Iran. They left there in poor spirit, as they thought, like dogs with their tails between their legs.

On arrival back in Malta, Dave applied to the Captain, to take the seamanship board for advancement to Leading Seaman, which his Divisional Officer had been pressing him to do for some time. Three weeks later all the candidates reported on board an aircraft carrier where the board was being held, at 0800. Each candidate brought an eye splice of two inch hemp rope and a one inch wire splice with a thimble. They had been notified of these tasks twenty-four hours earlier, and had to present them to the board. The board consisted of six officers, and throughout the day the candidates rotated between these officers, carrying out practical tasks and verbal examination. These included Power of Command; taking charge of a body of men for squad drill, Physical Exercises and a small evolution; knowledge of the regulations for prevention of collision at sea; coastal navigation; buoyage in channels; rigging, including maintenance and survey of all ships standing and running rigging; boats' davits; rigging sheer legs, tackles and hawsers; a practical exam on handling boats under oars, sail and power; a practical knowledge of anchors, cables, capstans and moorings; clearing a foul anchor; different types of anchors; practical knowledge of a ship's damage control arrangements; general knowledge of organization of a Ship's Company and the naval storekeeping system; to have a working knowledge of all flags and pendants used in naval and international signals; to send and receive a signal in semaphore and by Aldis lamp.

It was an exhausting day and didn't end until quite late. The candidates then had a two hour anxious wait while the board considered their decision. Out of the twelve candidates, only six were successful and Dave, to his relief, was one of the lucky ones. The Captain of the carrier saw them formally and rated the successful candidates Acting/Leading Seamen. The 'acting' title meant that it was provisional for a year, after which it would be confirmed, providing that they had proved their efficiency.

Dave went back to his ship, sewed an anchor above his GC badge, rolled into his hammock and slept like a log. The effect of his promotion was immediately apparent the next morning. The mess that he was in didn't have a leading seaman in charge, so he became killick of the mess, and everyone started to call him 'Hookey'. The cox'n sent for him and told him that he was having a job change; he was now the cox'n of the 36-foot motor-boat, with a stoker and an able-seaman as crew under him. This was a 24 hours on/24 hours off job. He found that a leading seaman's job was a most unpopular one. You had to be in charge of men that you lived with, and went ashore with, but at times you had to put them on a charge, 'in the rattle' as it was called, such as 'guilty of an act, prejudice to good order and naval discipline, in that he was absent from place of duty, namely cook of the mess,' or 'failed to carry out the lawful command of Leading Seaman Jones, his superior officer,' so he had to walk a tight rope at all times.

A few days later, the fleet sailed from Malta for the spring exercises and cruise. The first stop was Gibraltar. It was the same scene: Home fleet, Med. fleet, American fleet, fights ashore, good runs too. Dave had now got himself in the ship's rugby team, so there was plenty of sport there also. They did ten days of exercises off the Portuguese coast, and then split up for ship visits. *Cheviot* went to Genoa in Italy, and on the way they carried out live torpedo firings. To do this the torpedomen removed the explosive warheads and fitted dummy heads filled with compressed air, in their place. After the torpedoes had been fired, they ran their course until the propellers ran down, then the torpedo was brought to the surface by the air filled dummy head, and a smoke flare, fitted into it, made it easy for the lookouts to spot. The ship raced to the area where the torpedoes were floating, dipping up and down in the swell. They lowered the whaler, and Dave got his first job as a killick: he was cox'n of the whaler under oars to recover the torpedoes. They pulled alongside the torpedo, placed a recovery strop over the nose and allowed it to slide down to the centre of gravity, then they pulled back to the ship, passed the strop line inboard, and went after another torpedo while the torpedomen on the ship hoisted the torpedo inboard, and slid it back into the torpedo tubes. They were soon all recovered and they were under way again.

Genoa was a lively run ashore, and their next port of call was Naples. It was supposed to have the worst slums in the world, and they could believe it; it would definitely be a no go area for any foreign civilian, but their Navy uniform was a passport to anywhere and they were accepted wherever they went. One place that they were in was raided by the police. Dave and his two chums escaped through the window onto the roof, and there was an exciting roof-top chase before they got back to the ship. They also got invited to tea with Gracie Fields on the Isle of Capri; all visiting British Royal Navy ships in Naples were invited to her villa for tea. Vesuvius, the extinct volcano at Pompeii, was another excursion that most of the Ship's Company took advantage of; this resulted in the ship being flooded with the key chain winged phallic symbols that were on sale there.

Whilst in Ancona, Dave almost lost his hook. Bagsy, as usual, dragged him ashore, for a swim he said, so they set out about lunch time with their bathing costumes and towels rolled up under their arms. They had missed lunch on board so they went into a café-bar for something to eat. Everyone on board could speak Italian by now, and Bagsy ordered 'Two-o sandwichios of eggio and baconio,' which came up as ordered and while they were eating it, Bagsy noticed a rum bottle among the liquor bottles behind the bar, only it was spelled Rhum, and he decided that a tot would be in order afterwards, as they would have had on board.

That was the last that Dave remembered about that day. He woke up the following morning locked down in the Tiller Flat, with a splitting headache and a mouth like a vulture's crutch. When he went back to his mess, he got the full story. The quartermaster of the last dog watch had heard an uproar ashore, and when he looked up, along the jetty, he saw Dave and Bagsy running towards the ship with a mob of shouting Italians in full pursuit. He had alerted the duty Petty Officer who had called out the duty part of the watch. When Dave and Bagsy got alongside the ship, they decided to make a stand and take on the whole mob, but the duty watch dragged them on board and locked them in the Tiller Flat.

They were charged with returning on board drunk, and when Dave was up in front of the Captain, he said, 'I don't expect this kind of behaviour from newly rated leading seamen who should be setting a good example to other junior rates. I considered disrating you to able seaman, but your Divisional Officer has told me that this is completely out of character for you, so I will not do this. I sentence you to three weeks' stoppage of leave, two weeks' stoppage of pay, and one week's stoppage of rum.'

So Dave found himself falling in every day with the pipe, 'Men under punishment and stoppage of leave to muster.' They arrived back in Malta before his stoppage of leave had finished, and they found that they were off on another operational duty. Dave thought that even although the war had been over for five years, they were still involved in these small conflicts that seem to erupt all over the world.

This time their operational job had come up because of the Israeli/Egyptian war which had been going on for some time. The Israeli army had pushed right down through the Sinai Peninsula as far as the Gulf of Aqaba. In fact, at the northern end of the Gulf of Aqaba, four countries met at a point on the coast: Egypt, Israel, Jordan and Saudi Arabia. Jordan had a treaty with the UK, and fearing an Israeli invasion, she had asked Britain to station a warship at Aqaba as a communication to the rest of the world.

114

They had sent a destroyer immediately, which had been on station for some weeks and now *Cheviot* was being sent to relieve it. So it was off through the Suez Canal once again. Dave was to find that by the end of his two and a half years commission in the Mediterranean, he would have passed through the Suez Canal twelve times.

Again they travelled at top speed. This time when they entered the Red Sea they turned into the Straits of Aqaba, which was only about one mile wide, with Saudi Arabia to the east and Egypt to the west; sun baked barren mountains were on each side, with no sign of habitation anywhere.

The northern end of the Red Sea is like two horns; the western one leads to the Suez Canal and the Eastern horn leads to Aqaba. When they arrived there they anchored off a beach where half a dozen sand coloured houses seemed to be the only things there. The mountain range to the east and the west continued inland, leaving a parched sand-dune valley between them, stretching away into the distance in the north. On the western bank there was a sandstone fort which looked straight out of *Beau Geste*; this was on Jordan territory. One of the daily highlights was to see the Camel Corps of the Arab Legion ride out on their camels every morning, and disappear up the valley, to return in the evening. This had been formed and commanded by a famous English military man called Glubb Pasha.

The other destroyer remained for twenty-four hours so that the Captains and First Lieutenants could carry out a turnover; then she was off on her way back to Malta.

It was a boring but very relaxing patrol. The weather was always perfect, and they often arranged 'banyan' parties on the beach, a kind of barbecue where they used to land their own beer. The sea was very calm, warm and clear, so they did lots of swimming. Anyone could take the whaler or the dinghy away for a day's sailing but you were prohibited from landing anywhere; the four countries that came together there were all very suspicious of strangers landing in their territory. Israel, in particular, had on two or three occasions arrested British sailors that had strayed into their territory during a back-packing trek ashore. It took a lot of talking by the First Lieutenant to get them released, and on one occasion he had to go to Jerusalem, where the Israelis had taken their 'prisoners' to get them off.

Twice during their stay there, they went on a long trek by camel to the lost city of Petra, a beautiful city that had been carved out of the sandstone mountains, and had quite recently been discovered again. On his way back from Petra, as he rode his camel over the sand-dunes, Dave remembered that this was the very trail where Lawrence of Arabia had led an Arab army to capture the Port of Aqaba.

He thanked his lucky stars that he had taken the diving course, because the diving in the bay was magnificent. The coral was multi-coloured, as were the fish that surrounded you as you went down. The only drawback that made you very cautious and 'swivel-eyed', as they called it, was the large numbers of sharks that used to congregate there. They never bothered the divers, but you were always aware of them circling around on the edge of visibility. The divers on board got their minutes in several times over during the stay in Aqaba.

They spent two months on station before being relieved by another Mediterranean fleet ship and returning to Malta. They returned at a more leisurely pace. Every evening the Captain would work out the crew or his officers of the watch with dog-watch evolutions for officer of the watch manoeuvres, usually around supper time. They would all be sitting around the mess table when the ship would suddenly heel over to port or starboard, all the mess stools would tip over, sending the occupants flying, and all the plates and cutlery would slide off the table and onto the deck. Everyone and everything would end up on one side of the ship. Although they had lost their supper, it was normally treated as a big joke. They said that what had happened on the bridge was: Capt. to First Lieutenant, 'What are the hands doing, Number One?' Number One, 'They are at supper, sir.' Captain, 'Oh good, Wheelhouse Starboard Twenty!'

Another destroyer, HMS *Comet*, had arrived in Malta on her way out to join the United Nations Fleet in Korea, where the war between North and South Korea was being waged. The Commander in Chief was carrying out exercises off Malta at that time and had ordered *Comet* to join in. The final exercise was a 'Grid Iron', where two lines of warships, in line abeam, steam at full speed towards each other and pass through each other's line. The difference was that this time they did it at night, with no lights showing. Ships passed within half a cable of each other and *Comet* collided with another destroyer, causing considerable damage to both ships and several crew members were injured. Both ships had to be towed into Malta and the Admiralty decided that *Cheviot* would sail to Korea in place of the *Comet*. However, as most of the *Cheviot*'s officers, and a lot of the senior rates, had their families living in Malta, it was decided that *Comet*'s crew would take over *Cheviot* and *Cheviot*'s crew would move to *Chevron*, which was just finishing a major refit in dry dock. This news that *Cheviot* would not be sailing complete with its present crew came as a big relief to a lot of the people on board, although several of the younger men volunteered, and were accepted, to stay on board and go to the Korean war. Dave thought about it and decided against it; he was quite happy in the Middle East.

The *Chevron* was towed out of her dry dock and alongside *Cheviot* and they started the transfer, lock, stock and barrel. This is the second time that I have had to do this, thought Dave, first from *Myngs* to *Agincourt*, and now this one.

They had hardly got settled down on their new ship, the *Chevron*, when they were off to Aqaba again; they went twice more during that year. On their second trip out they were relieved at Aqaba and sailed to Port Sudan in the Red Sea; this was an official visit but they didn't think much of it. It was terribly hot, there was dust and flies everywhere, the bars were tumble down shacks, filthy, and the bar girls frightened the life out of them.

The next port of call was across the Red Sea to Jedda in Saudi Arabia. This was the port where all the Muslims landed on their pilgrimage to the holy city of Mecca; all Muslims must try to visit Mecca at least once in their lifetime. The ship arrived off Jedda at about 8 o'clock in the morning. It was a tortuous channel to get in; the temperatures were already up in the nineties and it was impossible to see the shore because of the yellow heat haze. In the radio room they were talking by radio to the harbour master, and it was announced over the Tannoy that here they took their time by the sun and the time now was 1030. The jetty became visible about thirty minutes later, sticking out from the town. As they berthed on one side of the jetty, the pipe was made 'Up Spirits', it was noon! The morning had passed in a few minutes.

On the other side of the jetty was a dirty old tramp steamer. It had two gangways and a stream of people dressed in sacks were going up one gangway, picking up a bag of cement, coming down the other gangway and loading it onto a battered old truck, then returning up the gangway again. They were all the colour of cement. There was cement powder everywhere; it covered the jetty and blew all over, soon their ship also had a film of cement over it. This went on night and day, and after a couple of days the sailors found out that these people were slaves, and many of them were women.

Jedda definitely turned out to be 'not a good run ashore'. Because of religious reasons they weren't allowed to wear shorts ashore or smoke cigarettes ashore and alcohol was not sold anywhere. The libertymen who did bother to go ashore, found a shop that sold photographs of men having their hands cut off, or head cut off, with a sword. This evidently was a weekly occurrence in the main square where sentences were carried out, under Muslim law, on convicted thieves and for more serious crimes. It was unanimously agreed that it was most definitely not the place to get arrested ashore.

After a couple of days an American oil man came and saw the First Lieutenant, and told him that the libertymen were welcome at their club, at an oil field about eight miles out of town, and he would send a bus to pick them up in the evening and return them at night. After that Jedda became a bit more bearable.

Fitting in between their operational duties in the Red Sea, they still managed to carry out exercises and cruises in the Mediterranean. They visited Venice and Trieste, which had been declared an international port, as both Italy and Yugoslavia claimed that it was part of their country. Quite a few warships were based there, mostly American. They also visited Istanbul and then went and anchored in the beautiful Bay of Marmarice in Turkey. The whole Mediterranean fleet assembled here once a year for the annual fleet regatta, when the ships competed against each other in sailing and pulling races. It was a remote part of Turkey, with only the very small village of Marmarice; the rest was sandy beaches and high woodlands of pine forest.

Prince Philip had been appointed as captain of the sloop HMS *Magpie*, his first command. *Magpie* did quite well in the officers' whaler pulling race, winning the trophy. Whilst in Marmarice there were lots of excursions ashore, including barbeques, and on one of these, rumoured to be an officers' barbecue, they started a forest fire which burned for three days. All of the ships landed their duty watch for fire fighting, and they worked shifts to bring it under control, but a large area of the pine forest was destroyed.

After that *Chevron* visited Piraeus, which was the port of Athens. They were always short of money, and on one of his liberty boat trips, Dave, who was cox'n of the motor cutter, was approached by a Greek Navy sailor, who asked if he could buy some cigarettes from them. The boats crew got together with the sailor and, after some haggling, they agreed on a price for several packs of Navy 'blue liners'. They agreed to meet the Greek sailor when they came in to pick up returning libertymen at 10 o'clock, and the sailor showed them a place where they could carry out the transaction before

118

picking up the libertymen. They returned to the ship and started organizing the packs of cigarettes, keeping it all very quiet, as it was all strictly illegal.

They left early for the 10 o'clock pick up. It was very dark, but flat calm, and the lights reflecting from the shore gave enough light to see by. They entered the harbour, which was a small circular bay, and headed for the spot where the sailor said he would wait, and they saw him standing on a wooden pontoon. They came alongside and the sailor came on board. They showed him the packs of cigarettes, and he started counting out thousands and thousands of drachma, the Greek currency, into Dave's hands.

As they were doing this they heard the ripple of a bow wave and, looking up, they saw a dark, unlit launch gliding alongside with lots of uniformed men on board; it was the Greek Navy police. The Greek sailor looked startled. He pushed all of the money into Dave's hands, and jumped onto the pontoon. At the same time, one of the customs officers jumped into the cutter and then ashore, grabbing the Greek sailor.

'Full ahead, Stokes,' quietly said Dave to the stoker, and he pushed the gear lever forward and opened the throttle, and the motor cutter shot forward. Dave pushed over the helm and headed for the harbour entrance and, glancing back, he saw that the customs launch was almost on top of them. The bow man had come aft, and as the launch drew alongside, one of the customs officers jumped from its bow into the stern-sheets of Dave's cutter. Before he could regain his balance, both the bow man and the stoker grabbed him and threw him over the side into the sea; the launch stopped to pick him up, and *Chevron*'s boat shot out of the harbour. 'Switch off all lights, change the appearance of the boat!' said Dave. They knew that they had to go back into the harbour to pick up the libertymen, so they removed the life-belt from the canopy, took off the illuminated ship's name and took down the ensign staff, whilst Dave steered round in a full circle to enter the harbour from the other side, switching on the navigation lights just before arriving at the entrance.

In the harbour there was lots of activity. The Customs launch was alongside the pontoon where they had been, and the Greek sailor was being taken on board. Lots of probing searchlights were flashing around. They headed to the jetty where the liberty men were waiting. Fortunately two other cutters from other ships were already alongside, one just about to leave, so they didn't stick out like a sore thumb. The libertymen filed on board with the usual lusty singing, and they pushed off, heading back towards the ship, and as they passed through the harbour entrance, the crew looked at each other and heaved a sigh of relief. They had also ended up with all of the cigarettes and all of the money.

After a big exercise around the Greek islands, ships were told to go to an island of their choice for a twenty-four hour rest-up period. *Chevron* picked a place called Dragamesti, which was a small and remote island and when they arrived there, they found it to be a small village with only a jetty jutting out into the sea. Because it was so small, they decided only to give leave from 6 p.m. until 9 p.m. At least they can't get into trouble in that short period, everyone thought, and in any case only a few libertymen decided to go ashore.

When Dave took the boat in at 9 o'clock to pick them up, the first thing that he noticed was that half of them were stretched out on the jetty. He found out that they were drunk and had to be carried into the boat. The local booze was ouzo, a clear liquid that tasted and smelled like peppermint. It was the only drink you could buy in the two local bars, and it turned out to be too potent for the British sailors. Several of the libertymen had been sick in the boat before they got them back inboard but it would take weeks for Dave to get rid of the peppermint smell from the bilges of the motor-cutter.

After that cruise *Chevron* was sent to Gibraltar for two months refit in a dry-dock, and during the refit they lived ashore in dock-side accommodation. It was two very pleasant months. Gibraltar was an entirely different place without the fleets in, it was so quiet, and the crew spent their off-time sailing in Algeciras Bay and swimming from the beach. They also did lots of sight seeing, across the border to La Linea, or taking a motor fishing vessel across the Straits to Tangiers in Spanish Morocco, in North Africa. They would usually spend the evenings at HMS *Rooke*, the shore base in Gibraltar, which had a great NAAFI, a cinema and first-class playing fields. Gibraltar dockyard was very old, the naval cemetery had gravestones that went back to Nelson's Navy, and some epitaphs mentioned deaths in the old sailing warships: 'fell from the main top-mast.'

At the accommodation, the toilet blocks were really ancient; they consisted of a long building with a long bench running the whole length on one side. This bench was the toilet seats and had holes cut into it all the way along. It could accommodate about twenty men, and probably, when it was new, it was quite an advanced invention. Every five minutes, water started running along a gutter under the bench seats, which washed everything clean in the toilets. One of the popular gags with the sailors, when the toilets were busy, was to wait until the water started to run, then drop a burning sheet of newspaper into the first toilet and listen to the succession of screams, one after the other, as the burning paper passed under everyone's bottom on its way to the other end.

The refit was quickly terminated when another operational job came up. For some time there had been problems with the Egyptian workers in the Suez Canal, and now they had started a long strike, which had brought all of the traffic in the canal to a halt. The Mediterranean fleet had been instructed to get the traffic flowing again and *Chevron* had been told to proceed to Port Said.

When they arrived there they found several RN ships secured to buoys near the northern entrance to the canal. Merchant ship convoys were again passing through the canal, RN navigating officers were acting as pilots to take the ships through, and ships companies were divided into berthing and unberthing parties. That was the work that they immediately became involved in: working in shifts twenty-four hours a day, meeting merchant ships, whatever time that they arrived, securing them to buoys until the next south-bound convoy was due, then unberthing them. There had been many acts of sabotage ashore by Egyptians trying to keep the canal at a standstill, and on the western mole of the entrance, the statue of Ferdinand de Lessops, the builder of the canal, lay in ruins where it had been toppled off its plinth.

Exhausted as the Ship's Company was, the daily work still had to carry on, and one afternoon the TAS gunner rounded up the divers for practice dives. The ship was moored in about twenty feet of water and close to the eastern bank, an ideal spot for an oxygen dive, and Dave was dressed, his life-line secured, and he was told to go down to the bottom and walk towards the shore and come out there. It was a pleasant dive, a sandy bottom, and good visibility, and Dave was enjoying the coolness as he plodded towards the shore, only about fifty yards away.

He was surprised, as his head broke surface, to see a police Land-Rover with two Egyptian policemen waiting, and as he headed for the shore, the Egyptian police waded in and helped him to dry land. One unscrewed his face visor and, although they didn't speak English very well, he gathered that they were placing him under arrest.

By this time, his attendant on board and the TAS gunner had alerted the

First Lieutenant who jumped into the dinghy and quickly rowed across to the shore and started a furious argument with the police, who were accusing the Navy of secretly planting mines on the sea bed. While the row was going on, the whaler with half a dozen sailors came across and, ignoring the protests of the police, they bundled Dave into the whaler and took him back to the ship.

After three weeks of Canal duty they were relieved and they returned to Malta for a break. Shortly after they got back, the cox'n sent for Dave and told him that his relief would be arriving in a couple of weeks, as he had spent two and a half years on the Mediterranean station. He had been recommended for RC1, and would be going to Whale Island. He felt sad at having to leave all of his friends that he had made during the commission in the Med. especially Bagsy, who had been on the ship when he arrived and whose relief had not yet been detailed. They had a few more runs ashore, and finally came the last one before Dave had to return to England. He was going to miss Bagsy's face appearing over the gunwale of his hammock and his 'get the suit on' greeting.

Bagsy, who was a raconteur of Navy stories, told him one more on this last run. It concerned a quartermaster who had been on the ship before Dave joined. His name was Pincher Martin and he gained the reputation of knowing many of the VIPs in the Mediterranean. It started in Monaco, where the ship was on an official visit. Pincher was on duty on the gangway during a cocktail party being held on board. One of the guests was Prince Rainier, and as he came up the ladder, Pincher was manning the side, at the Salute. Prince Rainier saw him and shook his hand and said, 'Hello Pincher, I haven't seen you for some time, come up to the Palace tomorrow night for a drink.'

Of course the story went around the ship like wildfire and on their next stop, which was in Marseilles, almost the same thing happened when the Aga Khan visited the ship. Pincher was very modest about the whole thing, but he hinted that he did know quite a few of the local personalities, and he became a bit of a celebrity himself. This was strengthened when Winston Churchill, who was on a visit to Malta, spoke to Pincher for quite a long time, and again when, in Naples, Gracie Fields sent him a personal invitation to visit her home.

On board at the time there was a Stoker Petty Officer, who took offence at all the attention that Pincher was getting; in fact he was jealous of Pincher's reputation, and he decided that he would take him down a peg.

So he poured scorn on Pincher's reputation and he would say things like, 'I bet you don't know Gordon Richards,' and other personalities, all of whom Pincher proved that he did, some by writing and receiving a letter, and others by personally inviting them on board. It became an obsession with the Stoker Petty Officer, and he would lie awake at night thinking up schemes to trip Pincher up.

Finally, he thought that he had him. They were due for a visit to Naples in a month's time, and during a movie on the quarterdeck, one evening, during a break when they were changing reels, he announced, 'I'll bet you a month's tot that you don't know the Pope.'

This was serious; no one had ever been known to bet a month's rum ration before, and at first Pincher just smiled and tried to shrug it off, but the PO was insistent, and in the end Pincher said, 'As a matter of fact I do know the Pope, but how can we prove it?'

The Stoker Petty Officer thought that he had him, and that Pincher was trying to wriggle out of it, so he said 'Well, we are in Naples next month; you can prove it then or admit that you are wrong and pay up your month's tot.'

'OK,' said Pincher, 'You are on,' and everyone on board waited with bated breath to see what would happen.

When they arrived in Naples, Pincher went to the Stoker Petty Officer and told him that they would both go up to the Vatican in Rome that weekend. When the weekend arrived, they caught a train to Rome and walked up to the Vatican gates. The PO began to have doubts when one of the Vatican guards shouted, ''Allo there, Pincher.' Pincher turned to the PO and said, 'Look, the guards won't let you in because they don't know you, but in half an hour's time the Pope will be appearing on the Vatican balcony; you go round to St Peter's Square, and if I come out onto the balcony with the Pope, will you agree that I know him?'

With a sinking heart, the PO said, 'I suppose that I will have to,' and he watched Pincher disappear into the Vatican.

He made his way round to St Peter's Square, which was packed with people, all looking up towards the balcony. In about twenty minutes, the balcony doors opened, and the Pope stepped onto the balcony, followed by Pincher Martin! The Pope blessed the people and the crowd went wild, cheering loudly. The Stoker Petty Officer threw his cap onto the ground and jumped onto it; he looked up at the balcony again and, on impulse, he turned to one of the excited Italians and said, 'I suppose that is the Pope up there, isn't it?' The Italian smiled and said, 'I don'ta know about the Pope, but thatsa Pincher Martin standing besides him!'

CHAPTER 8

England Again

Dave flew home the next day, by RAF troop transport aircraft, to Brize Norton in Wiltshire. It was his first time for flying, and this method of transport was being used more often instead of troopships. He stood on a cold and drizzly railway station three hours later, waiting for a train to Portsmouth, and marvelled at the change in the weather.

Portsmouth barracks sent him on three weeks' foreign service leave and he headed up to his colliery village, where his parents were amazed at the change in him. He guessed that he must have filled out, he was very brown and he wore a white cap and white front which was the trademark of sailors that had served on an overseas commission. He met a lot of his old school friends, some of whom had never been out of Durham, and he had been half way round the world.

Back in Portsmouth barracks, he found that he still had some time before his gunnery course would start, and, being tall and of good stature, he was put into the Barracks Guard. This was a body of about sixty men that carried out all of the Ceremonial Duties, such as the Naval Guard for visiting Royals and Diplomatic Dignitaries, Naval Funerals, Parades, Sentries etc. They also carried out security guards for the security of the barracks, twenty-four hours a day, guards and escorts for RN Detention Quarters attached to the barracks, and the Ceremonial Sentries on the Main Gate of RNB and the Wardroom. They were issued with special uniforms, tailor made, which broke all of the regulations taught at Whale Island: their trousers were pulled out of their gaiters, giving a plus four effect, their blue jean collars were all a uniform Mediterranean blue colour, and on parade they all looked very smart. They were issued with 303 Lee-Enfield rifles, where all of the metal work and long bayonets had been chromium plated; they loosened the magazines before going on parade so that when they presented arms, they slapped the magazine and there was a loud metallic click from the guard.

Besides this duty, he had been recommended from his last ship for Petty

Officer, so during the 'dog' watches, he used to go to Victoria Barracks to train for a Petty Officer's Examination Board. This would be similar to the Leading Seaman's Board, with more emphasis on leadership and responsibility.

He also had to get used to cold water diving now that he was back in England; it came as a bit of a shock. To remain qualified he still had to get his quarterly 'minutes under water' in, and to do this he used to go to the RN Diving School at Horsea Island in Portsmouth harbour. Certain days had been allocated at the Diving School for shore based sailors to come and get in their training and practice. To do an hour and a half in the lake at Horsea was really an effort and you came out numb and blue with the cold; it was also a bit different groping around in the muddy water after the good visibility that he had got used to in the Mediterranean.

While he was at Horsea he used to talk to the Clearance Divers, the Navy's professional divers. It was an elite branch of the service, consisting of not more than four hundred officers and men. When the Clearance Divers found out that he was an enthusiastic diver they encouraged him to put in to transfer from the Gunnery Branch to the Diving Branch. Dave gave a lot of thought to this, and decided he would apply to change branches, but when he saw the Captain in RN barracks, the result was a bit disappointing. He was told that Whale Island were reluctant to transfer him, as so much had been spent on his Gunnery Training, so although he didn't get a definite 'no', the Captain said, 'Not at the present time.'

His first class Gunnery Course started. It was very difficult as they went deeply into the theory part of gunnery, for example how the electrical computers solved the fire control problem; they had to learn spherical trigonometry and although he had been a bit thick during his school days, he found that mathematics came easy to him, and he quite enjoyed it. It was a long course, part of it being at HMS *Cambridge* near Plymouth, where they were able to carry out live firings of 4.5 inch guns out to sea, and a week on board a destroyer, attached to Whale Island, for live firings at sea.

He was given a day off, to go to Victoria Barracks for the Seamanship Board for Petty Officer, which he successfully completed, so that when his RC1 course ended, he was not only rated RC1 but also Acting Petty Officer. This again meant that he was on a year's trial before being confirmed, and he also had to continue wearing the sailors' uniform before changing into Petty Officers' uniform. Still, he now received Petty Officers' pay and wore the crossed anchors on his left arm, the Petty Officers' insignia of rank, and he moved his kit into the POs' mess. Life became a lot more civilised.

He met another PO who had just been promoted in the POs' mess, and they became firm friends. The other PO was very keen to become a Branch Officer; they were called Special Duty Officers, and were commissioned officers who had been promoted from the 'lower deck'. His problem was that you had to have four naval Higher Education Certificates, equivalent to the civilian 'O' Level Education Certificates. For a Gunnery Officer, two of the certificates had to be Mathematics and English, and John told Dave that he wasn't very good at these subjects, and also that he found it very difficult to study alone. So he persuaded Dave to study three nights a week, at the Naval Education Centre with him, 'just to keep him company'.

Dave didn't mind, and he found that he rather liked doing mathematics and English, and after three months they both sat the examination. Dave took mathematics, English, navigation and general knowledge, and, much to his surprise, he passed all of them with honours. John passed in three subjects but unfortunately he failed in maths. However he said he would continue to study and try again. When Dave's Divisional Officer found out that he had passed educationally for Branch Rank he sent for him and told him that there was a shortage of Commissioned Gunners and that he was recommending him to take the course for advancement. One of the reasons for the shortage was that candidates didn't seem to be able to achieve the educational requirements. One of the other requirements for the course was that you had to have a certain amount of time and experience as Officer of the Watch in a sea-going ship, and his Divisional Officer told him that he was being drafted to HMS *Reward* to achieve this time and experience.

So Dave packed his kit and was off again. He had to take a ferry across the Channel to join *Reward* which was in Cuxhaven, Germany. He had, of course, found out about the ship before he left the UK, but his first sight of *Reward* surprised him. She was an ocean going tug, painted in Navy colours, flying the White Ensign, a fully commissioned RN ship. She was much bigger than any tug that he had ever seen, and looked very powerful lying alongside her berth in Cuxhaven.

The Cox'n met him and took him straight to the Captain's Cabin. He was a Lieutenant, a bosun who had obviously been in the service a long time, and he made Dave feel very welcome on board. He knew that Dave had joined the ship for bridge watch keeping experience and he assured him that he would get plenty on board this ship. He introduced Dave to the other two officers, both Sub-Lieutenants, one a Special Duty Officer and the other a General List Officer from Dartmouth Naval College. Then the Cox'n took him down to the Petty Officers' mess and he met the other four Petty Officers on board. Besides them, her complement consisted of twelve junior rates.

He found that *Reward* had the best accommodation that he had come across in the Navy. Each of the officers and petty officers had a cabin to himself, and even junior rates were two to a cabin. As the ship had been built to Board of Trade specifications, there were no such things as mess-decks, so it was very comfortable. The largest compartment on board was the galley, so everything seemed to happen there, all the 'clear lower deck' musters, such as evening cinema, Tombola, etc.

The ship was berthed alongside an RN Naval Base called HMS *Royal Albert* and so they enjoyed the shore facilities in the POs' mess. That evening they were having a dance in the mess, nicknamed 'Fräulein Night' where everyone invited a German girl; the 'no fraternisation' rule was obviously over by then.

They sailed very early the next morning. It was still dark and raining as they sailed down the River Elbe on their way to the North Sea. Dave's duty was on the bridge, and he was amazed at the number of flashing lights on beacons and buoys as the Captain navigated his way towards the sea. After about half an hour, still very dark, they left the river. There were still lots of lights flashing on the buoys that marked the channel through the minefield. The Captain turned to Dave and said, 'OK, Guns, you have got the ship, keep to the marked channel', and he left the bridge. Dave felt a moment of panic, as he realized that he was the Officer of the Watch, in pitch darkness and lights flashing all over the place. He spent five minutes orientating himself over the chart table and radar scan and then he knew where they were and he began to con the ship through the channel. Two hours later the Captain came back onto the bridge. It was now light, but there was no land in sight, only the buoys marking the channel and Dave was able to point out to him exactly their present position. 'Well done, Guns,' he said, 'you can now start keeping watches as OOW, with myself and the navigator.'

They went into Sheerness, in the Thames estuary, to pick up a battle practice target, a big barge, almost as long as they were, with a large wooden lattice target about 25 feet high. The lattice was covered with black hessian and it had two radar reflectors, so that it could be seen by eye and by radar. They secured it alongside and sailed again, heading for a spot in the middle of the North Sea where they were to rendezvous with the Home Fleet for live firing exercises.

When they met up with the fleet, they started to tow the target about half mile astern, and Dave found out his other duty on board: he was called the 'Fall of Shot Marking Officer'. He had to position himself on the towing deck, and he had an instrument called 'the rake'. It was a T shaped device with the cross bar having nails equidistant from each other; it had been calibrated using angles and length of tow, so that each nail represented one hundred yards. Dave looked along the sighting bar at the target and as the 'fall of shot' splashed up, usually in groups of four, he would call out, 'Mark.' He had two sailors, one with a stop watch and the other to write down the records. At the call of 'mark,' the stop watch sailor would call out '3 minutes, 26 seconds,' which the recorder would write down and Dave would call out 'Short 200, Over 50, Over 100, Over 150,' as he sighted along the nails, which the recorder wrote down. Although it seemed a crude method the results were quite accurate. The firing ship itself kept a record of shots falling left or right of the target, and stop watches had been synchronized before the firing had begun. So this went on all day, ships coming up in their turn as called.

Reward towed the target for four days. There were some exciting moments, when the fall of shot strayed uncomfortably close to them, but when it was all over, she closed with the flagship and passed over her records by line, then she set a course for Rosyth to leave the target at the Naval Dockyard. The Home Fleet had split up for port visits. *Reward* had her visits too, to much smaller harbours that the big ships couldn't get into; they went to Aberdeen, Great Yarmouth and Exmouth.

Dave spent six months on board *Reward*. It was a happy ship and at the end of that time, he received a Certificate of Competency as a Bridge Watch-Keeping Officer from the Captain.

On return to Whale Island he found that he was starting the course for Gunnery Instructor, a GI, the very Petty Officer that used to instil him with fear as a new recruit. He wondered if he would have the same effect on new recruits when he qualified. He was also informed that he was now a potential candidate for SD Officer, although there was only one course each year. He also saw the Captain, as a requestman, and was confirmed as a Petty Officer, so he said goodbye to his sailor's suit, with the blue jean collar, and he changed into a Petty Officer's uniform, a navy blue suit and peaked cap, white shirt and black tie. He took his jackets to the naval tailor to have his badges sewn on: crossed anchors of a Petty Officer over three GC stripes on his left arm, crossed guns of an RC1 on his right arm and his campaign ribbons.

The Gunnery Instructors' Course was long and arduous. He had to learn all aspects of naval gunnery, and not just the radar control side, all of the explosives carried by an RN ship, and demolition work. There was a big emphasis on parade ground training, because the GI was the naval equivalent of the Army's Company Sergeant Major. He could make his voice heard on the other side of the parade ground, and, he thought, put the fear of Christ into sailors on squad drill, when he shouted, 'Pick up the double!' or 'Hold your head up!'

He completed the course, qualified as a Gunnery Instructor, and was told that his first job would be as an instructor at HMS *St Vincent*, a stone frigate at Gosport, a Boys' Training Establishment where they joined the Navy at 15 years of age. This used to be the normal way to join the Navy before the war, and Dave had met many sailors who had done 'boys' time', but during the war there was conscription, and most men had joined as 'hostilities only', as, in fact, Dave himself had. But the Boys' Training Establishments were still there, HMS *St Vincent* and HMS *Ganges*, and were re-establishing themselves. At first Dave thought it was hard on a boy to commit himself to a life in the Navy at the tender age of fifteen, although in lots of cases it was the parents' decision, as they had to sign the papers.

However, Dave's opinion changed after he started working with the boys. Many of them suffered so badly with home-sickness that they were released after a month, and allowed to return home. At the age of eighteen, they were allowed to sign to serve twelve years with the colours (or seven years active service and five years with the reserve) or they could leave the service at that age if they wished.

The thing that struck Dave most about Boys' Service was the keenness that they all seemed to have to learn. He had got used to HOs moaning about service life, and whose only ambition was to get out of the Navy so it came as a breath of fresh air to teach these youngsters.

Each instructor had a class of about thirty boys for about a year, taking them through a syllabus, and teaching them all aspects of the Service. They were at a very impressionable age, and Dave found that he had to be very careful in the things that he told them, because they believed everything that he said. If he told them that a starboard lamp was red, he felt sure that they would spend the rest of their time in the Navy believing that, even though it was wrong.

At *St Vincent*, the day was a long one. The boys were called at 0600 and had breakfast on a long trestle table while the Divisional Chief walked backwards and forwards along the table, reading out Orders for the Day; which boys were requestmen; or defaulters attending the dentist or doctor; dress of the day, etc.

Divisions were at 0800, when they were all inspected by their instructors, followed by prayers and a march past the Commander, then they dispersed to classrooms for instructions. Lunch was at noon, then at 1300 they started afternoon activities, which could be sport or boat pulling or sailing or a route march. After tea there were more classes and secure was at 1830. The instructors spent the whole of the day with their classes. Six weeks after they had joined they were allowed 'shore leave' from 1900 till 2200; they had to be on their best behaviour or they were in trouble.

Dave became an expert at dinghy sailing after he had been teaching his class for so long. They called their instructor 'Sir'; it was a bit like a miniature Navy, and an outstanding boy would be picked as the class leader and he became a 'Leading Boy', and in the Division, there would be about three Petty Officer Boys. All of these ranks were dropped when they finished Boys' Training, and they all became Ordinary Seamen when they became eighteen.

Punishment was given for minor offences and that usually meant squad drill in the evening. They had kit musters once a month, when they had to lay their kit out in the approved manner.

There was a very high sailing ship mast with yard-arms on the parade ground, and they all had to be able to climb the shrouds, go through the 'lubber's hole' and down the other shroud before finishing their training. For a really dismal kit muster a boy could be instructed to lay out his kit on the 'cross trees', halfway up the mast.

Dave spent eighteen months at St Vincent and felt that it was a very rewarding job, watching young boys turning into sailors, and seeing them off to their ships. Then he received his draft back to Whale Island to start the course for Commissioned Officer. There were ten of them on course and they were billeted in a Nissan hut near the parade ground. They were required to wear white trousers on course, and they found out that this was so they could easily be picked out as Officer Candidates. Of course they were all very experienced senior rates and didn't make many mistakes, but if they did, they found that they were not immune from 'doubling around the island', and there were plenty of GIs lurking, only too happy to give them a few 'about turns' as they went round. In the winter, white trousers were very cold and they took to wearing pyjama trousers beneath them, which was quite a bit warmer. On Divisions, instead of rifles they carried a naval cutlass, and the class looked very smart as they marched past the saluting podium and carried out the 'Eyes Right' with the proper sword drill.

They also started to train to put on a weapons display, for an 'Open Day' at Whale Island. For thirty minutes, they carried out all of the rifle movements on the march, without a single order being given, all carried out in unison. The display included: slope arms; present arms; shoulder arms; order arms; change arms; port arms; slow march with arms reversed; and unfix bayonets; and finished off with a volley of blank cartridges whilst marching. The display received a loud ovation from the crowd.

At the end of the course they were to receive quite a large grant of money, in order to change from ratings' uniform to officers' uniform, and this resulted in 'dog-watch' visiting from various naval tailors' representatives, all anxious to get their custom to provide the uniforms. This included their normal blue uniform with gold braid rings on the arms, caps, overcoat, and mess-dress, with dress shirts, bow-ties, cummerbund etc. They also needed all of their tropical uniform and, of course, the most expensive item, a naval officer's sword. The reps competed with each other, making various offers to get their custom.

Finally, the course completed, they received their Certificates of Qualification, and then a bombshell was dropped. It was announced that, owing to a clerical error, Dave and two of the others had not done sufficient hours of bridge watchkeeping experience, to qualify for promotion to officer, and would have to go back to sea to gain the necessary requirements. The three of them were very disappointed, and in Dave's case it was more worrying because he was approaching the maximum age limit for promotion from the lower deck.

He was sent to HMS *Carron*, a destroyer attached to Dartmouth Naval College. There were three ships attached to the college, known as the Dartmouth Training Squadron. They were manned by new entry cadets, getting sea experience and learning all things nautical. They also carried a small number of regular Petty Officers and sailors, who really ran the ship. Midshipmen from the college, nearing the end of their training, used to join the ship on its training cruises, to learn officers' duties at sea: navigation, anchoring ship, picking up a man overboard and other duties.

When Dave joined the ship, and went into the Petty Officers' mess, he felt that you could cut the atmosphere with a knife. He had an uncomfortable feeling of aloofness. He realized that, through the grapevine, they knew that he had passed for officer, and would become an officer in a few months time, and he was being treated with suspicion, as someone who could be an informer. It took him some time to break down this barrier, but after a few runs ashore with his mess-mates, he was able to convince them that he was still one of them. In fact, the feeling swung the other way and, by the time that he left *Carron*, the other petty officers would shield him and would do anything to prevent him getting into trouble, and maybe ruining his chances for promotion.

The ships used to go on four training cruises a year, and seemed to get the best ports for visits. Dave's job at sea was with the Officer of the Watch, of course, on the bridge, getting in the vital hours of experience; in harbour he carried out the duties of the Gunnery Instructor.

Their first cruise was to the Mediterranean, and in Gibraltar they found that the border to La Linea was closed to ratings, although officers could still cross to Spain as they were allowed to wear plain clothes ashore. The POs used to borrow the cadets' ID cards and go across the border, and there used to be some amusement when they borrowed an Indian cadet's card, with a photograph of a black face and a name like Ali Hamid, but the Spanish police never seemed to be bothered.

Dave did have one bonus by having to go to sea again. Because of the delay in his promotion, whilst he was on *Carron* he qualified for the Long Service and Good Conduct Medal. This Medal is awarded only to ratings who have completed fifteen years of unbroken Very Good Conduct on their Service Records, fifteen years 'undetected crime', as the sailors used to call it, from the age of eighteen. Officers couldn't qualify for this medal, so it was a good medal for an officer from the lower deck to have, and Dave was quite proud of it.

Whilst they were in Gibraltar, a German Navy ship came alongside, Germany, of course, being a member of NATO by then. The POs invited the German POs on board to their mess for an evening's entertainment, plied them with rum, found that they couldn't take it, and carried them back to their own ship.

CHAPTER 9

Commissioned Officer

Dave spent seven months on *Carron* and returned to HMS *Excellent* who confirmed that he was now fully qualified, in all aspects, for promotion to a Commissioned Officer.

They sent him on six weeks leave, to await his first appointment, which would be to the RN Naval College, at Greenwich. He would go on leave as a PO and return as a Naval Officer. After visiting the naval tailors and making arrangements for his new uniform to be delivered to his home in Durham, he went there for his leave.

His appointment as a Sub-Lieutenant arrived, and he reported as directed to the College, where there were further courses on the duties of naval officers. They were introduced to wardroom life, in, probably, the most imposing wardroom in the Navy. Several mess-dinners were held whilst they were there, in the grandeur of the magnificent Painted Hall of Greenwich College.

They had to learn the mystery of tying a bow-tie, and got used to being saluted by sailors and returning the salute. The course that they were doing was nicknamed 'the knife and fork course', and it was to teach you the 'do's and don'ts' of officer life. For example, you never took your sword into the wardroom, it could cost you a round of drinks, and the most heinous crime was to draw your sword in the wardroom.

It was a four week course and they felt much more confident when their appointments came through from the Admiralty appointing them to their first ship as an officer. The appointment was in the traditional flowery language of Nelson's Navy: 'Their Lordships have directed me to inform you, that you have been appointed to HMS *Yarmouth*, as Sub-Lieutenant (SD) (g). You are to repair on board by 1000, 15th February, etc.

This had to be answered in good handwriting to the Captain of the ship in the same manner,

Sir,

I have the honour to inform you that I have been appointed as Sub-Lieutenant (SD) (g), on board HMS *Yarmouth*, under your command. I have been directed to repair to my duties on board by 1000, 15th February.

I am, Sir,

Your obedient servant,

Dave discovered that *Yarmouth* was a brand new frigate, lying in John Brown's shipyard on the River Clyde at Greenock. She was receiving her final finishing touches before commissioning, which would be in one month's time. He reported to the Ships Office, a mobile building on the jetty alongside the ship. The Captain's secretary took him in to see the Captain who chatted to him about his duties on board, then the secretary gave him the address of a boarding house where he would be living until they moved on board.

The next four weeks were extremely busy, then they moved on board. It was sheer luxury having a cabin to himself, even if it wasn't much bigger than a wardrobe. The ship had a complement of twelve officers, the Captain was a four ring captain, the Engineer Officer was a commander, and there was one other SD officer besides himself, an Electrical Officer. Dave found that among his duties, he was the Quarterdeck Divisional Officer, with about 50 men in his Division, he was the Diving Officer with a team of 8 Ship's Divers, Explosive Accounting Officer, Wardroom wine officer and the Laundry Officer.

At the Commissioning Ceremony, he was the Officer of the Guard, the first time that he had had to use his sword. The Flag Officer, Scotland inspected the guard.

They sailed the next morning. Dave's Special Sea Duty was on the quarterdeck, in charge of handling the mooring lines with his quarterdeckmen, then falling them in for leaving harbour.

At sea he understudied the Officer of the Watch, which he would do until the Captain decided that he was competent enough to stand OOW watches on his own.

Their first destination was Portland, where they spent an arduous month 'working the ship up'. They carried out every evolution that a ship could expect during a commission. Things would be suddenly imposed on them at any time of the day or night. This training was organized by Flag Officer Sea Training (FOST) and his sadistic staff officers; they might get sent to find a submarine which had 'sunk' in a certain position, and they would be 'attacked' by RAF fighter aircraft during the search. They had to be able to cope with any situation swiftly and efficiently.

They might have to land a naval shore landing party, 'in aid to the Civil Powers'. Dave found that he was also officer in charge of the Ship's Landing Party. One night the ship was aroused at 0200, to find that they were being attacked by underwater saboteurs, these being the Portsmouth Clearance Diving Team; they had to be alert for anything.

They received a signal from FOST on a Sunday morning telling that the Sheik of Weymouth would be arriving in one hour's time, and that they had to give him the full VIP treatment, and the Sheik arrived in a stretched limousine, complete with bodyguards, all in full Arab dress, including swords and daggers.

On completion of the work-up, they visited Great Yarmouth in Suffolk, as the ship had been adopted by the town. The ship was open to visitors every day, the Ship's Company was entertained by the Civic Authorities and the wardroom laid on a cocktail party for the Mayor and all the local dignitaries.

There followed a big NATO exercise, with European and US Navies involved; a large part of this was a convoy exercise, which brought back memories to Dave of those terrible wartime convoys to Russia.

His Action Station was Officer in Charge of the Transmitting Station, where all of the target information was fed into a computer which controlled the fire power of the ship. The accuracy of the modern warship was fantastic. *Yarmouth* could fire twenty rounds of 4.5 inch shells before the first one landed, and if it wasn't on target, the aim was adjusted, much like a garden hose, so that once you found the target it would be sunk by sheer weight of metal hitting it. There were some amusing 'shoots', although the Captain never saw the funny side of it. They still used towed drogue targets, much like a wind-sock towed by an aircraft, and as it approached, all the relevant information went into the computer, until Dave could report on the intercom '4.5s Radar', meaning that the whole Fire Control system was locked onto the target and the guns were following it. As it got nearer, the Captain would order 'Engage'; the Gunnery Officer would wait until it was within range, and order '4.5s Open Fire.' Dave would check all the instruments in the TS and order, 'Commence, Commence, Commence', the RC1 on the radar console would press the trigger and the twin turrets would fire, left gun, right gun, left gun, etc. On the odd occasion, nothing would happen.

The Gunnery Officer on the bridge, seeing the Captain getting fidgety, would repeat, 'TS Open Fire,' and the Captain would say, 'TS what is the delay?' The chaos and confusion would get worse, until the target passed overhead and the Gunnery Officer would order, 'Check, Check, Check,' meaning stop the engagement. On this occasion, at that moment, A gun opened fire, and everyone went mad, shouting 'Cease fire!' Of course, fortunately this didn't happen very often, and normally there was the satisfying thumping of the guns, and the occasionally shooting down of the target, but when it did happen, the sailors thought it was hilarious, especially when some wag, in answer to the intercom saying, 'What is the delay?' would reply, 'There is no delay, we always take this long.'

Yarmouth was sent for six months detached duty to the Far East. Dave was able to re-acquaint himself with all the familiar places that they stopped at on their way to Singapore and Hong Kong. They stopped at Mombasa in Kenya where Dave and a young Sub-Lieutenant were invited to spend a week-end with a British coffee farmer near Nairobi. The trip up there by sleeper train was very interesting, crossing an endless African veldt with an occasional village, and it was amazing to be woken in the morning by an African steward with a cup of tea and the greeting, 'Jambo, Bwana.'

The coffee farmer, gave them a VW for their own use and they were able to explore a game reserve and the Great Rift Valley.

At the time, Kenya was approaching independence, and there was a lot of unrest and demonstrations, with the Mau Mau carrying out unspeakable atrocities. Lorries full of Africans were driving around shouting, '*Uhuru!*' which meant 'freedom'.

Dave was amused to hear an interview on Nairobi radio, when an African school teacher, supposedly an intelligent man, was asked, 'What difference will *Uhuru* mean to you?' and he replied, 'The British have made us all drive on the left hand side of the road; after *Uhuru* we will be able to drive on whichever side we want.'

When they arrived in Singapore, the Captain sent for Dave, and told him that the ship's Landing Platoon had been invited to take part in an Operational Patrol lasting for two weeks in the Malayan jungle, with a platoon of Gurkhas. It was operational because at that time Malaya and Indonesia were at a state of confrontation, over a dispute of territory, and groups of terrorists were acting in the jungle.

Dave and the Landing Platoon took transport to the British Army barracks at Nee Soon and met the Gurkhas who were to take them on patrol, and

Dave met the English officer of the patrol. He was a lieutenant in the Gurkha Regiment, who spoke the Gurkha language fluently and whose father had been in the Gurkhas before him. It was a family affair; the Gurkhas treated him like a God.

They were kitted out in jungle greens and jungle boots and issued with mess-traps and mosquito nets and ammunition. They had brought their own weapons from the ship; Dave had a Smith and Wesson revolver. Then they were taken across the causeway to Malaya, then several miles inland. They left the lorries and the road, and went single file into the jungle. Simon, the Gurkha officer, had the maps and the compass. It was really rough going. Dave had thought of the jungle as a very dense tropical woods, but this terrain was steep hills and valleys. They had to climb very steep, densely wooded hills, go down the other side, wade through a river, then up again on the other side. It was extremely hot and they were soaked with sweat. It rained quite a lot, making the ground very slippy, but if you slipped you didn't dare to grab a tree or a branch to steady yourself because they all seemed to be covered with spikes.

By the afternoon, the sailors were in real trouble. They had thought that they were fit, but this was energy sapping. Some of the jungle boots, now wet, had shrunk (they found out now that they should have asked for a size larger than they normally take); two of them were so bad that their toes had turned black, and the Gurkhas made a sort of a litter, and carried them. About 1800 they came to a flat clearing. Simon held up his hand, said something in Gurkhali, and the soldiers all started various tasks. Some set up the cooking facilities, some dug latrines and the rest started to build *bashas*. A *basha* was a sleeping platform, raised about three feet from the ground, which was covered with a leaf covered roof, all made from branches in the jungle. Then the mosquito nets were fitted around this platform so that you could sleep in a mosquito free area. The Gurkhas built these quickly, using their *kukris*, the famous Gurkha knives and they showed the sailors how to make them.

They cooked Compo rations, special ones for the Gurkhas which were mainly curry and rice, and the soldiers caught little fish from the river which they cooked with the rice. After supper they cut the sailors' jungle boots, so that they were more comfortable to wear, and the two sailors who had been carried in litters said that they would be able to walk the next day.

Everyone turned in early, because it would be an early start the next day. The *bashas* were surprisingly comfortable and, watching very bright glow flies rising from the river and listening to the jungle noises, Dave soon fell asleep.

And so the days continued, one after another. The Gurkhas were happy, cheerful and friendly, and everyone got on well together; they always wanted to help. Dave saw many carrying two rifles, one belonging to a sailor.

On one day, as they were crossing a stream, he saw a group of excited soldiers gathered around a sand-bank, and when he went across he saw that they were looking at an eight-inch footprint which, they said, was from a tiger which had passed that way only about two hours earlier.

Towards the end of the patrol they did discover the site of a terrorist camp, probably being about two weeks old. Now that they had got used to the life, everyone was beginning to enjoy it; it was certainly an experience that they would never forget.

Two weeks later they emerged from the gloom of the jungle onto a road, where they found the army lorries waiting for them. They spent the last night in Nee Soon barracks, and they had an evening in the bar of the NAAFI with the Gurkhas and their wives, who were covered in gold. If you wanted to know how wealthy a Gurkha was, you just had to look at his wife.

The Gurkhas presented each sailor with a crossed *kukris* badge, which they were allowed to sew onto the cuff of their working rig.

Their next port of call was in the Philippines at a large US Naval Base at Subic Bay. They were lavishly entertained by the US Navy at the Enlisted Men's Club and the Officers' Club, hospitality which they were able to return on board their ship. They played them at soccer and baseball, then went on to Hong Kong.

After that it was Japan, calling at Yokasuka and Tokyo, and the Japanese equivalent of the Dartmouth Naval College. Dave and his friend went to Hiroshima by train and saw the destruction that had been caused by the atomic bomb. The city was well on its way to being rebuilt, but the Opera House, which had been directly below the bomb burst, had been left as a Memorial, and a Garden of Remembrance, which had many photographs and models of the city immediately after the bomb, surrounded the Opera House. They also visited the giant Buddha at Kamakura, and at the Japanese Naval Academy they managed to get some diving in with their Japanese opposite numbers.

They then retraced their course, heading back towards the UK.

In the Indian Ocean, they stopped at the Maldive Islands to refuel, at the island of Gan. This was an RAF airfield, where all the RAF trooping flights used to land between UK and the Far East. It was an idyllic small desert island. The British had moved all the inhabitants off to a neighbouring island in order to build the Air Base, and RAF personnel used to do six months postings to the island because it was so isolated. There were no women on the island, and when off duty, everyone walked around stark naked. The weather there was always marvellous, and everyone was brown all over. The islands formed a huge lagoon, several miles across, and there was a tanker at anchor in the lagoon, where passing RN ships could berth alongside and refuel. There was no crew on the tanker, only a couple of ship keepers, who used to carry out the refuelling. Every few months a Royal Fleet Auxiliary Tanker would visit Gan to replenish the fuel oil in the tanker.

At a dinner in the RAF Officers' Mess, Dave asked one of the officers if they never got bored living on the desert island for so long. He replied, 'Well it may look boring now, but you should see some of the parties that we have in the mess, when the trooping flight lands with your wives and families on their way to Singapore.'

They arrived back in the UK almost six months to the day that they had left England, and Dave thought, what a difference from the two and a half years that they used to do when he was a young sailor.

The officers' rotation system was a bit different to the ratings', where all their drafts originated in a central office at HMS *Centurion*. All officers had their own Appointing Officer for each branch. Dave got in touch with his Appointing Officer and broached the subject of changing to the Diving Branch again and, to his delight, his Appointing Officer was sympathetic and agreed that, because of the acute shortage of Diving Officers, he could take the course for Clearance Diving Officer. However, he said, 'I already have you earmarked as a Staff Officer in the Joint Service Training Team in Ghana, and you will not be able to start the diving course until after that,' but Dave was satisfied with that.

He spent another six months on board *Yarmouth*, now as a confirmed Sub-Lieutenant (SD), and he now had his Bridge Watch Keeping ticket.

He left Liverpool on the Elder Dempster Passenger/Cargo ship SS *Apapa* for Accra in Ghana. It was a pleasant voyage, lasting seven days, calling at Freetown. He landed at Accra, the capital of Ghana, and was met by a Lieutenant-Commander, an ex RN officer, who was now in the Ghana Navy under contract. He found that he would be working in Accra, as Training Officer for the Ghana Naval Volunteer Reserve, and they went to their HQ first, where Dave was introduced to the permanent staff, a Petty Officer and two seamen, none of them in the Ghana Navy but working full time in the Reserve Navy. He was taken to an Army barracks, and shown a bungalow which was to be his home during his tour of duty. He met the Army officers, two of whom were British, the remainder Ghanaian officers, all of whom had done their training in Sandhurst.

Ghana was almost on the Equator and the first thing to get used to was the heat, day and night, all the year round; the temperature only fluctuated within a few degrees. Formally called the Gold Coast, when it was a British Colony it had been called 'the white man's grave'. There were still a number of British businesses active in Ghana; they gave holidays to their employees every six months, and insisted that they spend their holiday in a temperate climate. They believed that the climate in Ghana was so energy-sapping that it affected people's power of thinking and, after a while, they started making wrong decisions, so they needed to get away from the environment for a break every six months.

The main naval base was at Takoradi, and Dave had to visit there regularly. He met the Commodore of the Ghana Navy, the most senior officer. Their Navy was relatively new; the story was that President Nkrumah sent for a Ghanaian Army General and told him that they had decided to have a Navy, and that he was now a Commodore in the Ghana Navy. They had four inshore mine-sweepers, converted into patrol boats, commanded by RN Lieutenants, seconded like himself. He remembered the time, years ago, when he had sailed into Takoradi harbour on the *Agincourt*.

In Accra he was responsible for all of the training of the Naval Reserve. There were about 120 officers and men, and a great many of them went into the regular Navy in due course. The Headquarters was a brand new building on the sea front. The men came from all walks of life, from jungle villages, chiefs' sons, and there were even MPs. All of the training started after 1400, as most of the volunteers had civilian jobs, and went on until about 1900. He found that his was the only white face in the whole organisation.

In the camp where he lived there was quite a social life. There were regular Band Concerts and parties, attended by government officials and even the President himself at times, and he was acquainted with most of them; some of the MPs were in the GNVR. The Minister of Defence, Kofi Barko, was quite a character, who after a few drinks would get up on the stage and give a few songs.

The officer in charge of the Joint Service Training Team, a RN Commander, had quite a difficult job. He was based in Takoradi, when one day three Russian gunboats sailed into the harbour, and he found out that the Ghanaian government had bought these three gunboats from the Russians without him knowing anything about it. And so, at the height of the Cold War, he found himself administering these boats, complete with Russian crews, into the patrol programme.

On another occasion, a Russian Military Delegation arrived in Accra, to sell military equipment to the Ghana government. A party was arranged in their honour, attended by President Nkrumah, his ministers, and officers of the Ghanaian Armed Forces, and including the British officers. Later in the evening, the President excused himself and left, and shortly after he had gone, the other Ghanaians gradually drifted away, until, in the end, only the British officers were left to entertain the Russians.

With the climate so good, swimming was a must; there were some wonderful beaches but they were a bit isolated, and one of the problems was local villagers stealing from the cars whilst you were on the beach. Another officer went swimming with him one weekend and taught him the way to beat these thefts. When they parked the car, he put an empty beer can on the bonnet of the car and arranged some sticks on top of the can in a pattern. He said that this was a 'Ju-Ju' and that none of the villagers would go near the car. Dave found that it worked and he always used it after that.

One of his jobs was recruiting for the Navy, and he flew to many remote parts of Ghana in a light aircraft of the Ghana Air force on recruiting drives. The most interesting town that he went to was called Kumasi, a place in the centre of Ghana. He had to address the High School, explaining all about the Ghana Navy, then interview potential recruits from the volunteers.

In Kumasi was the largest gold mine in Ghana, belonging to the Ashanti Gold Mining Corporation, and he was invited to be shown around the mine. It was very interesting to see the whole process from the digging of the ore to the pouring of the molten gold into ingots, and the storage area where scores of gold ingots were stacked, worth about £100,000 each. There was an English manager in charge and he said to Dave, 'If you can pick one of these up with one hand and hold it above your head and walk out with it, it's yours.' Dave tried it; it was so heavy that he couldn't move it off the bench.

At the end of his tour of duty, he found that he had quite a lot of leave coming to him, three months in fact. Because of the climate in Ghana you earned five days leave for every month that you served there.

He had bought himself a duty-free car, and shipped it to the Canary Islands, spent a month there, then shipped it to Lisbon and spent the rest of his leave driving in Portugal, Spain and France, crossing to Dover at the end.

CHAPTER 10

Diving Training

At Whale Island Dave was told that he would be appointed to HMS *Vernon*, the Diving School, in three months time, to start the Clearance Diving Officers Course. In the meantime, he would take up the duties of Range Gunner, at Tipner Rifle Range, Officer in Charge of the Navy's small arms firing range. This suited Dave perfectly. Tipner was a small island at the north end of Portsmouth harbour, right next to Horsea Island, where the first part of his diving course would be taking place. He knew that this course was one of the toughest courses in the Navy, he also knew that he wasn't 100% fit, after the fleshpots of Ghana, and, as he would be one of the oldest officers to attempt this course he decided that he would be fit before the course started.

So every evening, and sometimes during the afternoon when he could get off, Dave went across to Horsea, donned a dry suit and fins, and started surface swimming the whole length of the lake and back, up and down for a couple of hours. By the end of the first week he could hardly walk because of the pain in his thigh muscles, but from then on it got easier, until it was no effort at all by the time that the course started. But he knew that if he had not done this he would not have got through the first week.

The course gathered at HMS *Vernon* on the first day, and Dave moved into a cabin in the Wardroom. There were twenty-six officers, including a South African, a Norwegian, two Portuguese, two Indians and a Pakistani. They were taken straight to Horsea Island, which, of course, Dave was by now familiar with. The island was manmade from all the excavations of the dry docks in the dockyard, around the turn of the century. It was only about ten feet above the high water mark, and its main feature was a lake about one mile long and 300 yards across, and roughly thirty feet deep. A causeway had been built for motor traffic to cross but this could only be used at low water; otherwise there was a foot-bridge made from scaffolding tubes and planks, which was the normal way to cross. The lake was ideal for diving training, especially with oxygen because of its depth. The lake had originally been constructed for testing torpedo running.

At Horsea they were issued with a rubber dry suit, two pairs of Long Johns, a pair of fins, a neck seal and a clamp, and the course started immediately at a hectic pace that was to continue during their stay at Horsea.

On the first day they were paired off and their partner became their 'buddy' for the rest of the course. They started off with quick dressing into the dry suits. It took two persons to be able to get into the suit, through the tight narrow neck entrance, so, working with your buddy, you had to be dressed in two minutes, including the neck seal and clamp that prevented water getting in at the neck. When the two minutes were up, the instructor shouted, 'Everyone in the water!' and you had to leap in regardless of whether you were ready or not. If you weren't finished dressing, or had been sloppy putting on your neck seal, you got wet and you would stay wet for the rest of the day.

The instructor for the course was a Chief Diver called Norman with his assistant, a PO diver called Reg. They also had four junior rates, qualified divers, as their assistants, and they were known as 'Second Dickys'. These instructors, the course soon discovered, were the most sadistic men that they had ever met. If anyone made the slightest mistake, they were punished, by having to carry out 'push-ups' or 'circuits'. If you were told 'you owe me three circuits', you had to climb a high tower, jump into the lake, swim to the other side, climb out, and run around the top of the lake and back to the tower for your next circuit. These punishments didn't have to interfere with the training; you had to do them in your own time. If you didn't find the time during working hours, you had to do them at the end of the day after training.

That first day would remain in Dave's memory forever. They started with surface swims, the length of the lake and back, then circuits until their chests were heaving, then they were doubled to the end of the island. The Chief Diver pointed to the wreck of a submarine beached on the mud, about a mile out in the harbour, which was mainly uncovered by the tide, and told them to 'Pick up the double' and run out onto the mud, around the submarine, and back. As soon as they got out onto the mud, they were in trouble; you sank up to your knees, and it was an effort to pull your foot out of the glutinous mud, and it came out with a horrible sucking sound. Sometimes you sank up to your waist, and the only way to get free was to fall forward, and sort of swim out. During all of these exercises, the Second

Dickys would be shouting, 'Come on Sir', 'Faster Sir', 'Stand Up Sir'. Mud runs became the most hated part of the whole diving course. When they got back to the shore, lungs screaming, filthy, and stinking with the harbour mud, there was no relief, 'Into the water, sir, swim back to the school.' And the day went on in this vein. It became obvious that this was a thinning out process, separating 'the men from the boys'; they were being pushed to the end of their tether, then a little bit further. There was no lunch because you were not allowed to dive after a heavy meal. The Second Dickys brought out a fanny of soup and bread rolls at noon, but most of them had picked up punishments by then which they had to work off; if they picked up a cup to have soup, the instructor would say, 'You don't have time for that, sir, you owe me six circuits,' so for most of them, the soup just got cold.

Most of them were bursting to 'spend a penny', but they didn't have time to get out of and back into the suit again, and so, although they fought against it, they just had to wet themselves; most of them were soaking wet in any case.

The next day two members of the course failed to turn up for training, confirming their idea that this was a sorting out period and, indeed, after two weeks the twenty-six had been cut down to fifteen. Not one had been removed from course; in all cases the notation on their records said, 'Off course, own request.'

On the second day, the class was issued with their diving sets CDBA, Clearance Diver Breathing Apparatus. This set had been in the service for many years, and could be adapted for breathing pure oxygen, or different percentage mixtures of oxy/nitrogen gases, depending on the depth that you intended to work at. The set was a self-contained rebreather set: when using pure oxygen there were no bubbles released that could give away a diver's position on the surface, so it was ideal for attacking an enemy ship. All of the metal parts were non-ferrous, which meant that a diver could work alongside a magnetic mine without activating it, and it was silent in operation so that they could also work alongside an acoustic mine.

They were to start their diving training using this set on oxygen. None of the others had dived on oxygen before, but Dave had done his first diving as a shallow water diver on O_2. They had never heard of the Sladen Clammy Death suit before, which made Dave feel his age a bit.

The Chief told them that he wanted them to achieve ninety minutes endurance from a fully charged set in each dive, and he wanted them to achieve at least three dives per day, which meant at least four and a half hours under water each day. They started charging their sets; although Horsea Island had modern electric pumps for charging sets, they had to use a hand rocker type pump to charge, to keep them fit, the Chief said.

As soon as their sets were charged, they were in the water to start their swimming around the lake. 'Keep deep', the Chief said, so they kept near the bottom. They had been taught 'pendulum breathing': you took a deep breath, held it for a while, then breathed out, this was to get the maximum endurance from the set but, swimming about two feet above the bottom, when you breathed in, your lungs filled up, you became more buoyant and you started to go up, then, as you breathed out, you became heavy and started to sink. So you went along like a roller-coaster. You had to remember the 'keep deep' instruction, as if you got too close to the surface, an ominous black shadow came across you. You knew that it was the Chief in his boat, and you struggled to get deep, but quite often the blade of an oar would be placed on your back, and you would be pushed to the bottom. You aimed to get your ninety minutes endurance, because if you didn't it probably meant more circuits, but when your gas ran out, you surfaced, raised an arm to signal, 'I am all right', and a Second Dicky would skim up to you in an inflatable dinghy and say, 'Take your face-mask off sir, swim to the shore, double back to the school and recharge your set.' So off they doubled again, with the added misery of having to wear the heavy CDBA; they would start rocking the hand-pump to recharge the set, change the CO_2 absorbent, and they were back in the water again.

Of course the circuits continued. They used to have at least one mud-run each day, but there was no rest; the joke in the class was that the only rest that you got was when you jumped off the high board, you had a bit of a rest before you hit the water. There were always four or five classes training at Horsea Island, and at times it became a bit like Piccadilly Circus underwater. There was a jackstay on the bottom that ran the entire length of the lake and at times, they were told to swim the jackstay. This was pretty easy, but halfway along the lake there was a wire rope that stretched from bank to bank. In the centre this wire rope was hanging under the surface of the lake, and the first thing that the diver knew was when his marker float snagged on the wire and brought him to a stop. He then had to follow his marker line up to the wire, cross the wire, then go back to the bottom and the jackstay. When half a dozen divers were all trying to do this at the same time, they really used to get into a mess, with lines going in all directions.

There were humorous occasions also. There was one class of Nigerian divers, being trained for the Nigerian Navy. They were learning to clear a flooded face-mask under the water. The instructor would call each individual to the surface, pull his face mask off so that it filled with water, then send him down to the bottom, and he had to come up again with no water in his mask. There was one diver who had had several attempts and repeatedly he had come up with his mask still half full of water. The last time that he came up the instructor started to flood his face mask again, and the young diver waved his hands, pulled off his mask, and said, 'I'm sorry, Chief, I don't care if you take me off the course, I can't drink any more of that dirty, salty water.'

They spent six weeks at Horsea Island on oxygen diving. They learned how to swim to a position using a compass underwater, they started doing night diving twice a week, they carried out emergency drills, they learned how to jettison their set on the bottom and make a free ascent to the surface.

Instructions normally finished at 1630, but after that, they had to recharge their sets ready for the next day. They had to put their wet gear into the drying room, so that it would be dry the next morning. If they suspected that they had a leak in their dry suit, they had to find it and repair it, and there were always circuits and push-ups to reduce.

Each night Dave dragged his weary legs across the foot-bridge to the waiting buses, and there was always the doubt that he might not make it through the next day, but he persisted and he got through the oxygen stage.

The training now moved to HMS *Vernon*, the class boarding small diving tenders and sailing out into the Solent, Spithead or up harbour, depending on the type of training they were doing. They were still using CDBA, but this time with 60% oxygen/40% nitrogen that allowed them to dive to about sixty feet and still get endurance. In the Solent, they carried out sea-bed searches, laying a jackstay in an area where it was known that there were practice mines and they discovered three of them. While Dave was down he found a mine and he was just about to give the 'found' signal, when he noticed a black antennae moving in one end. On closer inspection he found that there was a reasonable size lobster there. It was an unwritten law, that if anyone found a lobster, they broke off whatever they were doing and caught it, so Dave used the end of a line to coax it out and when it was clear of the mine, he grabbed it behind the claws, and started up to the surface with it. He was surprised to find out how strong it was. As it flapped its tail like mad, he held it well away from his body; he didn't want one of those claws grabbing onto his breathing tube. As he surfaced he held it up above him, and saw the safety boat racing towards him. 'Well done, sir,' said the Second Dicky, 'chuck it in the boat and go down and complete your task.'

As he went down he felt very pleased with himself; he had just caught his first lobby. Half an hour later, task completed, he surfaced. Everyone on the diving tender was standing around eating lobster sandwiches, and there wasn't any left. To add insult to injury, the instructors made the whole class jump into the sea and surface swim all the way back to *Vernon*, about three miles.

Diving in Portsmouth harbour was different. In most cases the visibility under water was zero; as soon as you left the surface it was bad, and usually on the bottom it was zero. If you could see on the bottom, by the time that you had stirred the mud up, you couldn't see a thing. They started training with CDBA using 40% oxygen/60% nitrogen that allowed them to dive to around 120 feet without running into oxygen poisoning.

They laid jackstay searches on the bottom again, but the actual search had to be done by feel alone as you couldn't see anything. They did compass swims in the harbour. The diver took a bearing on a ship about a mile away, using a compass strapped to his wrist. Then he dived, stayed about 10 feet below the surface so that he could still see his compass, and swam on a compass course. After about fifteen minutes he would slowly surface, so that his eyes were just above the surface of the water, this so that he would not be spotted by an alert sentry on the ship. He would quickly take another compass bearing, dive and continue swimming towards the target ship. He might have to do this two or three times, but when he got closer to the ship he could be able to hear machinery noises and swim towards that. Sometimes they would carry dummy magnetic limpet mines, which they would attach to the hull of the ship before swimming away. They examined underwater fittings of all classes of warships, sonar domes, Chernikeif logs, inlets and outlets, screws, rope guards, 'A' brackets and rudders until they were very familiar with all of them.

On some occasions, they would go alongside a Reserve Fleet aircraft carrier, and the Chief would tell them to run up to the Flight Deck and jump from there into the water. It was frightening because of the height. They were all wearing dry suits and as their feet entered the water, all the air inside the suit was forced up and out through the neck seal. They went very deep after such a high jump, and some surfaced feet first. There were always casualties: everyone was winded with the pressure of going so deep so quickly; one lost two front teeth when his neck clamp hit him under the chin with the force of the air being expelled, others had abrasions under their chins.

This training went on for weeks. One day they went across to HMS *Dolphin*, the submarine base. There they had a 100 foot water tower where submariners were taught to escape from a submarine using a breathing set. The divers had to escape and ascend 100 feet without any breathing set. This was to teach them how to reach the surface in a free ascent, if they ever had to jettison their diving set whilst under water. They all filed into a steel compartment at the bottom of the 100 foot tank. In the centre of this compartment was a circular canvas skirt leading up to a hatch, now closed; the skirt ended about four feet from the deck, and was secured there by lines. They all wore special belts with a short rope lanyard hanging on both sides. The instructor had already briefed them that when they left the compartment into the tank, they had to start blowing gently out through their lips, similar to whistling. The reason for this was, as they ascended, the pressure would decrease and, unless they blew the air out, it would expand in their lungs, and, in fact, burst their lungs if they didn't allow it to come out through their mouth.

They clamped the door closed; the submarine instructer looked around. 'I am going to flood the compartment now, is everyone ready?' The divers nodded and he opened a valve near to the floor. Water came rushing in, rising, above their knees, above their waists and still rising. As it got deeper they had to keep swallowing to clear their ears which were popping as the air pressure rose.

The water rose to their necks and stopped rising; the compressed air that they were breathing would not allow it to rise any further. 'I am now going to open the hatch into the tank,' said the instructor, and he ducked under the canvas skirt and disappeared. They heard the hatch clang open, and he reappeared from under the skirt.

'I am now going to send you up one at a time. You have all been told what to do. As I tap you on the head, take a deep breath, duck under the skirt and exit through the hatch.' He tapped the nearest diver who took a breath and disappeared. A phone hanging on the bulkhead buzzed, the instructor spoke into it, and tapped the next diver who also disappeared.

There was about two minutes between each diver and soon it was Dave's turn. He was tapped on the head, took a deep breath and went up the skirt and out of the hatch. As he came out, a waiting instructor grabbed his belt lanyard and looked him in the face to check that he was blowing out, he decided that Dave wasn't blowing out hard enough, and poked him in the belly with his finger. When he was satisfied, he let him go, and Dave started ascending slowly towards the surface. He looked up; there were three blisters at different depths, each with an instructor in. As he approached the first blister, an instructor ducked out of it and swam to the centre of the tank. As he passed this instructor he put his finger across Dave's lips meaning 'breath out slower'; the instructor turned and headed back towards the blister.

This happened at each blister: a prod in the stomach meant 'breathe out faster', a finger across the lips meant 'breathe out slower'. Dave broke the surface, gave the thumbs up to the instructor and climbed out of the water. The instructor told him to stand next to the last diver and pressed the telephone buzzer, the signal for the next diver. Dave was amazed at how clear it was in the tank. It was floodlit inside and he could clearly see the next diver emerge 100 feet down, watched the instructor grab him and let him go, and his progress coming up, with the instructors leaving their blisters, until he broke surface. They had to stand for four minutes to make sure that they didn't have an air embolism, which could rupture veins.

They stopped diving with CDBA and moved onto SDDE, Swimmers' Deep Diving Equipment; this was an air breathing set, surface demand, which meant that air was supplied by hose from an air bank on the surface; this hose also acted as a life-line. It was a comfortable set, and the endurance was dependant on the depth at which you were working. If you were just working on a ship's sonar dome, you could work on for hours, but if you were working on the sea-bed at 180 feet, you could only stay on the bottom for about ten minutes: longer than that and you would have to have decompressions stops in the water to avoid the diver getting a 'bend'. Of course they still had to do their 'deep dives' to 180 feet, but as they couldn't find 180 feet around the Portsmouth area, that would come later on at Oban in Western Scotland or Falmouth in Cornwall. The other piece of equipment that they used with SDDE was a communication set. It had a bone conductor that you fitted under your Neoprene hood, and the diver and the attendant could speak to each other, even if the diver's words were a bit garbled because of his mouth-piece.

They also started tool training during this period. *Vernon* had a 40-foot water tank, with work benches on the bottom, and they learned how to use an underwater oxy-acetelene cutting torch to burn through steel plates. They also used the Cox's gun which fired a hollow bolt into a steel plate; you could then unscrew the end of this bolt and attach an air hose to pump air through. It had been designed to deliver air to submarines that had sunk to the bottom and had men trapped inside. During tool training they were introduced to the Siebe Gorman Standard Diving Suit, the traditional big copper helmet, canvas suit and heavy lead boots that almost everyone is familiar with. Dave found it very comfortable to work in. You breathed naturally and talked to the surface naturally, but it was extremely cumbersome and difficult to move around in. You had to be very careful not to have a fall to deeper depths, as the change in pressure could prove fatal. There had been extreme cases where a complete human body had been squeezed into the copper helmet by the pressure.

They travelled to Portland for a week's training with a sonar dome exchange unit. Unfortunately their class had been depleted to twelve by now. The dome exchange unit was a device that fitted exactly over a ship's sonar dome, which was about the size of a small car protruding through the keel of a ship. The exchange unit was lowered into the sea alongside the ship, then, using a system of air tanks built onto it, it was made negative buoyant, then neutral buoyant and manoeuvred by the divers over the ship's sonar dome, it was then made positive buoyant and it fitted snugly around the dome. The dome could then be unscrewed from the ship, and, using the unit's buoyancy tanks, brought to the surface. Fitting a new dome was just a reverse of the same procedure: a team of divers could exchange a sonar dome in twenty-four hours. When this was compared to the weeks of work required to dry-dock a ship and the salaries of dockyard workers, the divers saved the Ministry of Defence several thousands of pounds.

Once a week they had a classroom session, where they learned how to work out how long a diver could spend at a certain depth without having to carry out decompression stops, and, if he over-stayed his bottom time, how to calculate the depths, and the time that he must remain at that depth before rising to the next decompression stop. They learned about all of the illnesses that could affect a diver, how to be constantly monitoring yourself and your 'buddy', watching for the symptoms of these illnesses. For example, nitrogen narcosis, beyond a certain depth, can cause a diver to act irrationally, as though he was drunk. In extreme cases, the diver might think that his bubbles were going down, and swim the opposite way, under the impression that he was heading for the surface; it can be extremely dangerous, and all divers had to be aware of how to deal with the situation if his buddy is acting strangely. Its ancient name was 'raptures of the deep'. They all had a copy of the RN *Diving Manual*, which was their Bible and which, by now, they all knew by heart. It contained all the Diving Decompression Tables, and one of the regulations was that diving could not take place unless the *Diving Manual* was with the Diving Supervisor at the site of the dive.

The following week they were to start their Deep Diving at Falmouth in Cornwall, where 180 feet depths could be found outside the harbour. Deep diving training was carried out here in the summer, but in the winter, when long Atlantic rollers made it too rough to operate there, they did it at Oban, on the west coast of Scotland, where 180 feet could be found in sheltered waters. They had been training for these dives at *Vernon* by regularly carrying out 180 feet 'pot dips': that is, going into a decompression chamber and being compressed to a pressure equivalent to 180 feet, then being brought back to surface pressure, sometimes doing decompression stops on the way up. Even in the pot, they could feel the effects of the 'Narks', Nitrogen Narcosis; their voices changed and they sounded like chipmunks, which made them all giggle; anything that they said seemed funny and made them giggly.

They travelled to Falmouth by train. A sea-going diving tender *Ixworth* had sailed from Portsmouth the previous day, loaded with all of their diving equipment, and scores of cylinders of breathing gases. She was fitted with pumps for recharging the sets, but, most importantly she was equipped with an eight-man decompression chamber, with a lock on the end, where a medical officer could be locked in if necessary. Another diving regulation said that diving deeper than 120 feet can only take place if there is a decompression chamber in the immediate vicinity of the diving site.

There was no naval accommodation in Falmouth so the rest of the day was used up in finding 'digs', bed and breakfasts, for the class and the instructors.

Everyone was on board *Ixworth* at 0800 the next morning in Falmouth docks, and they slipped and headed south, watching the depth recorder until they had 120 feet beneath them and they dropped the hook. They started off in SDDE and they were going to work up to 180 feet. SDDE is surface demand but the diver has two small cylinders of air on his back for emergency purposes only. If the air supply from the surface fails for whatever reason, it could be that the hose has fractured or that there is a problem at the Air Bank, automatically one of the bottles on his back takes over, and the first indication that his main air supply has failed is when he has exhausted all the air in the bottle and he can't breathe in. The diver then pulls a lever on the set and equalises the air between the two bottles which allows him to continue breathing and gives him enough air to reach the surface.

Each member of the class took turns in being the supervisor for each dive. The rest were split up into diver, two attendants and line handlers, stand-by diver and attendant, air control panel operator, decompression chamber operator and communication number. They changed rounds after each dive and the whole process was under the eagle eye of the Chief Diver.

The hose line was marked every ten feet, and when the diver left the surface, the attendant called out, 'One-oh, two-oh, three-oh . . .' as these marks reached the water line. The control panel operator repeated these depths and adjusted the air supply on the gauge, so that the diver was receiving air pressure for the depth that he was at. The attendant also reported all signals he received from the diver, such as, 'Diver reached bottom,' 'Diver started task,' etc.

Several times Dave had heard the Second Dickys say, 'Keep a look out for flying scallops,' and he thought that they were joking and were trying to take a rise out of them, until he was down and he saw these things that looked like birds flying around him. They were scallops that moved through the water by opening and closing their shells. From then on, the last job of each day was to gather a bag of scallops, which they opened, put in a dab of butter, and cooked in the half shell on the galley stove. They were the tastiest shellfish that Dave had ever eaten. After this meal they would weigh anchor and head back to Falmouth.

During that week they did 120 feet and 140 feet dives, ready for the next week's 180 feet dives. Occasionally they switched to CDBAs to carry out compass swims. Once they were told to compass swim to the beach and land there. It must and been a big surprise to the holiday makers lying on the beach when half a dozen black suited divers emerged from the sea and walked up the beach. The class comedian went up to a group of holiday makers and said in his best Pakistani accent, 'Excuse me, can you tell me the way to Birmingham?'

They all got several 180 feet dives in on the following week, and their final dives were surface decompression dives. This meant that they spent enough time on the bottom to have to do decompression stops, but instead of doing them in the water, they came immediately to the surface, and, as quickly as possible, into the decompression chamber. The chamber was then pressurized to the equivalent of 180 feet, and then they were brought back to the surface, doing the necessary stops in the chamber.

The reason for surface decompression was that after they had qualified, some of them would be appointed to a mine hunter. These ships carried a team of divers, and the First Lieutenant was always a Diving Officer. These ships found mines with mine-hunting sonar, and a diver would go down to verify that it was a mine. The mine hunter had to get on with the task of finding mines, and didn't have the time to wait if a diver ran into decompression time. So they would carry out the surface decompression routine and the diver could do his stops in a one man chamber whilst the ship got on with its task.

During one of Dave's surface decompression dips, he had rather a bad experience that he would never forget. It was quite a cold day, they were still 'changing rounds' between each dive, and he stood beside the diving ladder, fully dressed with SDDE and on air. 'Put the diver in the water,' said the Dive Supervisor. The attendant tapped Dave on the head and led him to the ship's side, gave him the 'thumbs up', and he jumped into the sea. The attendant reported, 'Diver entered the water.' 'Send the diver down,' said the Supervisor, entering the time in his log. Dave held up his left arm and with his other hand he pulled open the cuff of his dry suit. As the air rushed out he started to sink, and he grabbed hold of the shot rope and started to descend. The visibility was quite good in Falmouth and he could actually see the sinker on the sea bed 180 feet below.

He arrived at the bottom, and gave a tug on his life line to signal 'reached bottom'; the signal was repeated back to him. He began to undo the search line secured to the sinker; he took a breath and there was a clunk from his set, and no air came through. He tried to breathe in again – no air! He felt a moment of panic, then he pulled the equalization lever, he heard the two bottles equalise as the air rushed from the full bottle to the empty one, and he thought, 'The chief is testing me, he has switched off the air to check that I carry out the correct emergency procedure.' He was about to start his ascent, when the air stopped again; he equalised again but after only two breaths it gave out once more. He knew then that this was not a drill, he realized that he had just breathed out, he didn't have enough air to go up the shot rope. He started to give the emergency signal, short tugs on the life line, but each time he tugged, it was paid out to him and soon there were several bights of loose life line all around him. He thought of ditching his set and trying to make a free ascent to the surface, but he knew that with his lungs empty he would never make it. He heard a screaming noise in his ears, and realized that it was him as he tried to breathe in nothing. His vision started to go, the shot rope started fading in front of his eyes and he knew that he was about to pass out. Then, suddenly, he was jerked off his feet and hurtled towards the surface as he was hauled in. His face broke the surface and he jerked off his face mask and took a deep breath of fresh air. He looked up at the row of faces looking down at him.

'My air stopped,' he shouted.

'Never mind about that, get the diver inboard and into the decompression chamber,' the chief ordered, and he was literally hauled aboard, his set was taken off, he was rushed to the chamber and pushed inside, the door clanged closed, air hissed in and he found himself at 180 feet again.

Once he was safely there and the Chief had assured himself that he was OK, he spoke to Dave on the intercom and said, 'Right, we are going to bring you up with decompression stops. It will take about an hour to get you back to the surface; now tell me exactly what happened down there.'

Whilst he was in the 'pot', they had a small inquiry about what went wrong. Dave found out later that the dive had started normally, with the attendant calling 'one-oh, two-oh, etc.' which was repeated by the Panel Operator and applied on the control panel. 'Diver reached bottom,' the attendant reported. What happened after that was that the attendant received the emergency signal, but, thinking that the diver was moving away from the shot rope, he just paid out more line. It took two or three minutes for him to realize that it was the Emergency Signal and he reported, 'Diver giving Emergency Signal.' The Chief Diver rushed to the control panel, looked at it and said, 'Pull the diver up, as fast as possible.' They found that the panel operator had been repeating the depths, 'One-oh, etc,' but instead of increasing the pressure to the diver, he had been increasing it to the 'stand-by' set, which was lying on the deck ready for instant use, so Dave had been breathing from his emergency bottle as soon as he left the surface and had used up half of his emergency air before he reached the bottom. The panel operator was an Indian student who had just completed his dive previous to Dave and all that he had worn was a pair of swimming trunks under his dry suit; consequently he had come out of the water absolutely frozen, and so cold that he really didn't know what he was doing.

With such a mistake, if he had been an RN student he would have been 'off course'.

Dave also found that, while he was still in the pot, the Course Officer had spoken to the Chief Diver and said, 'When Dave comes out of the pot, send him down again,' using the theory that if you fall off a horse, you climb straight back on again. The Chief Diver said, 'We can't do that, sir, he has already spent so much time under pressure today that it would be a combined dive. It will take a long time to bring him back to the surface, and there is a strong risk that he will get a "bend".'

When Dave heard about this, he was glad that the Chief Diver had spoken up, because when he left the pot he felt so shaken that he was sure that he would have refused to go down again.

As Dave walked back to his digs later that evening, he was aware that the flowers seemed to be more colourful, the grass was greener and the birds were singing more tunefully, and he realized that he was seeing everything in a new light, after his brush with the 'grim reaper'.

Back at *Vernon* they had their final diving examinations, both written and oral. They had been assessed weekly on their practical efficiency over the eight months that they had been on course. When they received their results, it was with a feeling of satisfaction that Dave found that not only was he the oldest officer to have got through the course, but that he was the second highest in the class.

They left *Vernon* for Horsham, where the Joint Service Bomb Disposal School was based. As its name implies, it was run by the three services, and had instructors from the three services, to train personnel in disposing of explosive ordnance.

Each branch of the service had its own responsibility for the disposal of unexploded ordnance. The Navy was responsible for all explosives below the high water mark, in rivers, lakes, canals and anywhere that would require a diving suit. In addition they were responsible for UXBs on naval property and all sea mines wherever they were found. The Germans, during World War 2, had found that by fitting a sea mine with a bomb fuse and dropping it on a city, it effectively demolished a whole block. The Navy were the only service trained to deal with a sea mine, so it became their responsibility wherever they turned up. Because, in most cases, a diving suit was required to carry out these duties, all Clearance Divers were trained in Bomb Disposal.

The RAF were responsible for bomb disposal on RAF property and on all crashed aircraft. The Army was responsible for the remainder, and this duty was carried out by the Royal Engineers.

The first few weeks were classroom work: composition of explosives, fuses and their types, and national characteristics of bombs: for example, the Russians used square headed bolts, the German method of hanging bombs on an aircraft was different from other countries, some nations used fuse pockets on the side of a bomb, while others had nose fuses, and the tail fins could be quite different. All of this information was very useful at 60 feet depth in a river, where there was zero visibility and you were trying to identify a bomb by feel alone.

They used to go to Lydd demolition range on the south coast, where they learned how to counter-mine unexploded pieces of ordnance. They used all types of demolition charges: shaped charges which could punch a hole in a steel plate; instantaneous explosive cord which could cut a steel railway track in half. They learned about detonators and how to treat them with respect, and how to withdraw them from a bomb, how to trepan a bomb, that is, to cut a circular hole in the steel case so that a steam hose could be inserted which would liquify the explosive and it would run out, later to be burned.

They learned all about electric fuses: some would explode on impact, some would have a timing device so that they could pass through several floors of a building before exploding, some had an anti-disturbance fuse, which would not arm itself until after it had come to rest. Any subsequent movement of the bomb would activate the striker mechanism and the bomb would explode. One of the simplest methods of dealing with these fuses was to immunise them. You had to drill a small hole in the fuse casing into which was pushed a hollow tapered needle. This needle was attached to a rubber hose, which went to a three-way valve marked 1, Off and 2. You put the switch to position 1 and used what looked like a bicycle pump to suck the air out of the fuse, creating a vacuum inside it; you then put the switch to Off. Leading from position 2 was another hose leading to the bottom of a glass beaker. A very strong saline solution was poured into the beaker and the switch was turned to position 2. The vacuum in the fuse sucked in this saline solution and, after about two minutes it set hard into a block of salt. The fuse had now been immobilised: none of the mechanism would work, the striker could not hit the detonator, and the bomb was safe to work on.

They studied books which listed explosives from all parts of the world, with their dimensions, shape, what explosive they were filled with, types of fuses fitted and national characteristics, so that they could identify them without looking at the captions. The Navy students were taken to a lake which had ropes leading into the water, and each rope was secured to a stake. These stakes were all around the shore of the lake, about forty altogether. They donned dry suits and CDBAs and dived in the lake, following the rope, where at the end they found a piece of ordnance: mines, bombs, torpedoes, shells etc. Some were British and some were foreign. They were allowed to swim around and examine these objects, and they were told that at the end of the course they would have to identify several of these items by feel alone, they would not be able to see them.

They went to Lydd several times, did a full explosive demolition course, and in the sea there were several underwater obstructions, designed to prevent landing craft from beaching, and they were taught how to blow them up.

Finally it was exam time again. It was really a tough one, both written and oral. Then they went to the lake. This time when they put on the CDBAs they found that masking tape had been stuck on the inside of their face masks, and they couldn't see a thing when they put it on. The instructor led them blindly around the lake, put their hand on one of the ropes and said, 'Swim out and identify this object.' Each diver followed a rope, came to the device, then by feeling alone, they had to guess the dimensions, shape, nationality, type of fuse, tail fin, etc. then return to shore. The instructor said, 'Describe it to me, what do you think it is? How would you dispose of it?' They each had ten devices to examine and identify. They all passed their exams, and Dave was content to remain second in the class. They were all now Clearance Diving Officers.

CHAPTER 11

First Diving Appointment

Back at *Vernon* their new appointments were waiting for them. Dave had been appointed as 2nd in Charge of the Portsmouth Clearance Diving Team, based at *Vernon,* on the staff of Flag Officer Portsmouth. It was the job he would have chosen if he had been asked.

One of the good points of his new job was that he didn't have to move anywhere; he kept his cabin in the wardroom of HMS *Vernon*. The headquarters of the PCDT was situated in a corner of *Vernon* and his office, the workshops, stores and transport were all in one building. The team consisted of the Officer in Charge, a lieutenant commander, a 2i/c, a Lieutenant or Sub Lieutenant, which was now Dave, a Chief Petty Officer CD1, a Petty Officer CD1, two Leading Seaman CD2s and ten Able Seaman CD3s. They were divided into two smaller teams, each consisting of an officer, a CD1, a Leading Seaman CD2 and five Able Seaman CD3s. They were called A and B teams. While one of the teams was responsible for all the port diving, the other carried out all the bomb disposal duties, and they changed over every week.

There were three such teams in the United Kingdom. Portsmouth was responsible for the area from Hull on the east coast to Poole on the south coast; one team based in Plymouth covered Poole to Carlisle; and the other, based in Rosyth, covered all of Scotland and Northern Ireland.

A report of proceeding was forwarded to Flag Officer Portsmouth every month, and Dave was surprised to see that the incidents of unexploded ordnance averaged out at about one every day, World War 2 sea mines were dealt with at least one every month, some months as many as three.

During their bomb disposal week, Dave had to keep Flag Officer Portsmouth's Duty Commander aware of where he could be contacted at any time, and the members of his team had to keep him informed of where they would be. It was very popular with the sailors because it usually meant that they would be travelling around in the area, moving from one incident to another, staying in pubs or digs overnight, wherever the incident was. They had a long based Land-Rover, painted in dark blue Navy colours, with red wheel arches, the Bomb Disposal colours; it was fitted with a blue flashing light and a two tone horn, for use when they had to get somewhere in a hurry. They carried an inflated diving dinghy on the roof, diving sets and equipment, explosives for counter-mining, and all the manuals for identification of ordnance.

During the diving week they dealt with the diving tasks in the port and immediate vicinity, such as underwater inspections, screw changes, dome changes, foul screw and lost items. One of their best customers was the submarine base HMS *Dolphin*. They would receive a signal from submarine HMS *Grampus*, requesting a screw inspection. The team had their own diving boat so they could quickly be alongside the ship requesting assistance. The subs were forever losing things over the side and the signal was quite often just an excuse to get you there, and while you were inspecting their screws, the First Lieutenant would appear and say, 'Oh, while you are here, we lost a jar of rum over the side this morning, would you mind having a look for it?'

They quite often got requests for assistance from the police. Dave had only been in the team for a week when Southampton police requested assistance, to find a woman feared drowned in a river at Swaythling. They went to the local police station and the Inspector told Dave that this lady had disappeared, they had found her shoes and handbag on the river bank, and they thought it could be a suicide. They searched the river all day: it was really a large stream. At first, there were lots of policemen who had come down to watch the diving operation, but they gradually drifted away. After about six hours searching, Dave and the Chief had a discussion about the search tactics. It was quite a fast flowing river and they had searched for about a mile downstream from where the handbag had been found. At that point the stream went through a culvert, under a road, and continued on the other side. They decided to start searching on the other side of the road. First a diver was sent through the culvert. He found nothing, but said that there was a very deep hole where the water came out of the culvert. Dave told him to search the hole, and he had hardly left the surface when he gave the '5 bells' signal, that is 2-2-1, which means 'task completed'. He came to the surface holding a woman, who had been in the water for two days, Dave had seen many bodies in the water during his Russian convoy days, but this was the first woman that he had seen. They carried her up the bank and covered her. Some things that they noticed, were that her wrist watch was full of water, and her jacket pockets full of stones. Dave called the police station on his radio, and when they arrived, they turned over the body, made a statement whilst they waited for the coroner, and then the team returned to their base in Portsmouth.

The same week there was a request from the Gosport police. A lady boarding the Gosport ferry had dropped her wedding ring over the side; could the diving team help? This really wasn't a service job, but they put it down as diving training and went across to the ferry terminal. The water was only about twenty feet deep alongside the jetty, and the lady was there to point out the exact spot where the ring had gone into the water. All of the divers knew the condition of the bottom in Portsmouth harbour, thick slimy mud, so the diver who went down was told not to touch the bottom, but to stay a few feet above it so that he would still have some visibility. He went down, and looked at the bottom where there was the usual mud, but there were two or three holes in it. He poked his finger into one of the holes and, to his amazement, it came out with a gold ring on it. All the passengers waiting for the ferry were amazed when he surfaced with the ring, and they all started to clap. Even the other divers could hardly believe it.

Dave had his first call-out for a bomb disposal job at 3 o'clock on a Sunday morning. The coastguard at Lee-on-Solent had found a canister washed up on the beach below the high water mark, marked 'Danger – Do Not Touch', and they gave him a description. He guessed that it was a submarine smoke candle, and he told them that he would be right out there before high water, which was at 6 o'clock. He went across to his office, took the Land-Rover, and went out to Lee-on-Solent. There was a policeman keeping a watch on the canister, which had been roped off, and 'Unexploded Bomb' notices had been placed. He examined the device through binoculars, and, as he had thought, it was a submarine smoke marker. They could still be dangerous if they had not been fully expended, and it was with a fluttery stomach that he approached this, his first incident. To his relief it was an expended device and he was able to take it back to the Land-Rover. They had a sand-bin at HQ where they kept non-dangerous items until they could take them to a range and blow them up.

Some of the diving and bomb disposal tasks that they had to undertake needed the whole team effort to complete and that month they received an 'Action Immediate' signal that had the whole team moving to Chatham with all of their diving equipment and transport. The 'boss' had been on the phone to MOD and was told that the Thames sludge carrier *Sir Joseph Rawlinson* had sunk in the Thames estuary and eleven crew members were missing. She had been sailing out to sea about 3 a.m. to discharge sludge and, in heavy fog, she had collided with another vessel off Sheerness. She had taken on a list and the crew had gone to emergency boat stations. They decided that she would have to be towed back into harbour, but as the tug would not arrive for about another two hours, the crew were stood down and many returned to their cabins. At this point the ship suddenly settled by the stern and sank. A number of the crew who had been on the upper deck were picked up by small boats in the vicinity, but eleven were unaccounted for.

They arrived at RN barracks in Chatham and were briefed on their task, which basically was to search the ship and recover as many bodies as possible. They would operate out of Sheerness, where a boom defence vessel was waiting to take them out to the area where the ship had sunk. They would be accommodated in Chatham barracks until the task was completed. Because of the flooding and ebbing tides in the area, divers would only be able to operate for about two and a half hours around high water and the same around low water. On the way to Sheerness, they stopped at Greenwich, where the sister ship to *Sir Joseph Rawlinson* was berthed, so that they could see the lay-out of the ship that they had to search. The first thing that Dave noticed was that the entrance to the cabins was through a bulkhead door amidships at upper deck level. This passage went right through the superstructure and came out on the other side; in the centre another corridor went for'd, and the cabins were on either side of this corridor. As the ship had settled by the stern, this passage could have been flooded, preventing anyone from getting out of the cabins. He also noticed that although each cabin had a large square window, they were fixed windows and there was no way of opening them.

They carried on to Sheerness and boarded the vessel that was waiting for them, loaded all their diving equipment and left for the area where the ship had sunk. It was easy to spot the place where she had gone down, as bubbles of oil were coming to the surface. The boom defence vessel anchored as near to the position as she could. Dave decided that he would make the first dive, which would be to take a rope down to the wreck and secure it in a suitable position onboard. This would be the datum for the search.

He got dressed and climbed into the Gemini dinghy, and they crossed the few yards to where the oil bubbles were rising. In the dinghy was the Diving Supervisor, the stand-by diver, and two other divers, one to attend Dave and the other to tend the stand-by diver, should he need to go in.

When they were ready, Dave rolled backwards off the dinghy and into the water. The end of the coil of rope was passed to him and he left the surface and swam down. The visibility was reasonable for that area and he could vaguely see the ship sixty feet below. As he got nearer, he saw that she was lying on her port side, and that there was no sign of any damage. The closer that he got the better the visibility became and when he could see the whole length of the ship, he was amazed at the gleaming paintwork and all the highly polished brass tallies. One of the things that had impressed him when he had looked at her sister ship, was how smart and clean the ship had looked, for a ship with such an ugly title as 'sludge carrier'; she looked like a small cruise liner. In fact the crew hardly ever saw any of the sewage that they carried. In port, they attached hoses from pipes ashore, and it was pumped directly into their tanks on board, and at sea, it was discharged straight into the sea.

He saw the amidships bulkhead door that led to the cabins. It was open and directly below him, and the passageway went straight down into the ship. This would be a good position to secure the rope, he thought: later on they would have to go into the ship to search the cabins, and the rope would lead them straight to the entrance. It was difficult to get orientated, with the ship lying on her side. He secured the rope onto the guard rails, which of course were above the door. After he had done this, he signalled to the diving boat to let them know, and he knew that they would be securing the other end onto a green marker buoy, marking the wreck and the position where the divers would enter the water.

Having done that, he turned to have a look around the ship, and he got such a shock, he could feel his heart thumping. Right next to him was a dead man, only a couple of arms lengths away. He had been trapped under the gunwale of the ship, which would normally have been off to the side, but now that the ship was lying on the side it was above the door. Dave imagined what must have happened. He had managed to escape from the passageway, which must have been underwater by then, and had done everything correctly; he didn't inflate his life jacket until he got through the door, thinking that it would take him to the surface. But it didn't, it took him straight up and under the gunwale. He hadn't been able to free himself before he drowned; in fact, his life jacket had killed him. Dave pulled down on his legs to roll him out from under the gunwale, and as he turned over he saw a stream of bubbles emerge from his mouth, body gases. He held onto the dead man and slowly ascended to the surface. The dinghy came alongside him as he broke surface.

The stand-by diver leaned over to grab the body. It must have smelled pretty bad because Dave saw him turn his head away as he got close to the dead man. At least I am wearing a face mask, Dave thought. He went down again, deciding to swim for'd and look into the cabins through the windows. The water inside the cabins didn't come right up to the glass and he could see paperback books, cigarette packs, clothing etc. floating on the surface. In the third cabin he saw something which could have been a body but it was in the shadows and he wasn't quite sure. At that point he received the 'Return to surface' signal and he went up.

The rest of the day was spent in searching the ship's superstructure and the bridge area but no more bodies were found. They returned to Chatham barracks for the night with the intention of making an early start the next day. At dinner in the wardroom that night, Dave was approached by a naval padre who said that he had heard that they were engaged in a rather unpleasant task, and could he come along with them the next day, to offer some moral support to the divers. Dave told him that he would be welcome.

They started diving at 0700 the next day. The first job was to smash all the cabin windows on the starboard side, the side facing the surface. They worked two divers together, using a sledgehammer. It took a few blows to shatter the thick, armoured glass, and a huge bubble of air rushed out as the sea poured in. This brought most of the loose stuff to the window area, but no bodies were found in the first cabins that they tried. Then in the for'd-most cabin, which was the one where Dave thought there might be a body, two bodies were washed up to the window and, after knocking out all of the glass, they got them out and brought them to the surface. Dave helped to pull them into the dinghy and he found out why the other diver had turned his head away. He looked up to the bridge wing of the diving tender and saw the padre being violently sick over the side: so much for moral support, he thought.

The next day they went into the ship, or at least the Chief went in, whilst a second diver tended him from the bulkhead door on the upper deck of the ship. The Chief swam straight down, then turned for'd into the centre passage. He was carrying a large floodlight to illuminate the area, but as the light was reflected from all the particles in the water it was still difficult to see, so he had to swim along waving his free arm in front of him, expecting to touch an invisible body; it certainly made the adrenalin flow. He was also wearing a communication set, linked to the surface, and Dave was able to talk to him as he went along. He was examining the cabins on the lower side of the ship, opening each door which was below him as he came to it, shining his light in, feeling around, saying, 'Nothing in that one,' then carrying on to the next. He had done all of the cabins and was getting near to the end of the passage, when they heard a scream on the communication set.

'What's happened, Chief?' said Dave.

'I have just touched an arm,' said the Chief, 'another body; I'm bringing it out,' and he brought the body to the surface.

They found no more bodies in the wreck. The ship was going to be salvaged and re-floated, and possibly they would find more bodies then, but some could have been swept out to sea with the fast running tide.

During his two years with the team, Dave took charge of probably one of the biggest bomb disposal operations since the end of World War 2. It happened during a week when his team were on their port diving week. He used to spend his leaves in Spain, and he was studying Spanish language at Highbury Technical College, Portsmouth during some evenings. On 2nd February 1968 he was at the school when someone told him that there was a telephone call for him. He answered it and found that it was the Duty Staff Officer, who told him that a bomb had been found in the River Thames, under Blackfriars Bridge, and what was he going to do about it? Dave told him that his boss was Bomb Disposal that week, and that at present he was in Lowestoft, but that he would call him so that he could get on to it.

'Forget that,' said the DSO. 'I've already spoken to your boss, and he has told me to contact you, the ball is in your court.'

'Okay,' said Dave, 'I will have my team on the road within one hour.'

The DSO said, 'Right, go to the Thames River Police HQ at Wapping.'

Dave got on the phone and an hour later they were on their way, blue lamp flashing, two-tone horn sounding. At Petersfield a police patrol car drew alongside them.

'What's the rush?' shouted the policeman in the front.

Dave told them.

'Follow me,' said the policeman, and they started the hairiest ride that any of them could remember, across red traffic lights, up the wrong way on dual carriageways, bumping across central reservations; it frightened the life out of Dave, and he thought he would be surprised if his hair had not turned grey.

At Thames River Police HQ, Wapping, Dave was briefed on the situation. A civilian diver who had been working on the suction end of a pipe for a refrigeration plant on the shore had stumbled across what he was fairly sure was a bomb. He had put a marker on it and reported it to the police. Because of the tides, it would not be possible to dive before 0300, so they spent the time preparing their diving equipment, talking to the Port of London Authority, and reconnoitring the area where the bomb had been discovered. There was a large crowd of reporters from the national daily newspapers besieging Wapping Police HQ.

When Dave made the initial dive, there were photograph bulbs flashing from every vantage point. The team used a River Police launch as the diving boat and the Gemini dinghy as the safety boat. The river was about 45 feet deep at that state of the tide. The current was very strong although it was supposed to be around slack water; in fact, it was never less than half a knot during the entire operation and most of the time it was over one and a half knots. The visibility was total zero and he had to identify the bomb by touch alone. By its shape he knew that it was a bomb, though it was two thirds buried in the river bed, at a 45 degree angle and the fins had long ago rusted away. He started to dig with his diver's knife and uncovered the slinging point – German! He felt the fuse pocket, and although he was unable to see any markings on it because of the zero visibility, he guessed that it was a 550 lb. German bomb.

There was only about an hour's diving time left, so the divers dug with their knives. There was a hard crust on the bottom but once through that it was easier going in the soft viscous mud. By 0400 it was mostly uncovered. The divers had been working in extremely difficult conditions, hanging on with one hand to avoid being swept away, and digging with the other hand. The current was so strong that breathing became difficult. Dave went down again, prior to suspending the diving. There was still no way of identifying the fuse: the bomb was still at the same angle as it had buried itself and Dave didn't want to change the angle in case the fuse re-started.

He took the team back to Wapping. He confirmed his identification of the bomb in the manuals that they carried; now he had to decide on how to deal with it. The Germans had fitted some ingenious fuses in their bombs, and one in particular, known as an anti-disturbance fuse, did not actually arm the bomb until after it had come to rest, so any subsequent movement of the bomb would cause it to explode. It had been impossible to identify the fuse, as even with underwater lights the visibility was still zero, and to have attempted to remove a twenty-five year old, unknown fuse in total darkness, now at a depth of 60 feet, in a fast flowing river, would have been an act of sheer folly. Dave also knew that the Germans had a habit of fitting a booby device, called a Zuss-40, under the fuse, which would activate the bomb if the fuse was withdrawn.

It was impossible to counter-mine the bomb *in situ*, because it was in the centre of a built up area and would cause considerable damage. Furthermore, it was only a few feet away from one of the buttresses of Blackfriars Bridge. Almost certainly, in its present position, an explosion would bring the bridge down. Dave thought of how unpopular he would be if he completed the task that a Luftwaffe pilot had failed to do.

For the same reason, he rejected the idea of slowly inching the bomb away from the bridge and counter-mining it in mid-river. The resulting shock waves would cause serious damage to buildings on either side.

There was only one alternative left: to raise the bomb, as gently as possible, from the river bed, keeping it at the same angle as it was at present, and to transport it to a place where it could be safely destroyed.

Having made his decision, Dave started to make the arrangements to carry it out. First he contacted the Port of London Authority and asked them to provide a lifting craft, which they willingly agreed to do. He had a conference with the London City police and they decided on safety restrictions to be imposed during the dangerous period while the bomb was being lifted and transported.

They agreed to close Blackfriars Bridge to all road and rail traffic during the lift, to stop all river traffic in the area and to evacuate the north bank of the river, in an area of 500 yards radius from the bomb. To actuate this when required, a police inspector was attached to the team, with radio contact to the Police Control Room.

They started diving again at 0945, just before high water. The first task was to fit lifting strops on the bomb. It had silted up again quite a bit, but it still lay at the same angle and the idea was to try and keep it at the same angle until it was finally disposed of. Dave went down for the last dive, to check the strops, to control the lift and to make sure that the bomb remained at the same angle. The Thames River Authority salvage vessel *Broadness* manoeuvred over the bomb and lowered its crane hook down to Dave who hooked it on to the strops.

By 1045 all was ready for the lift. All the agreed safety restrictions were imposed, and, at a signal from Dave, the lift began, the bomb broke free and Dave was satisfied that it remained at the same angle. At 1120 it broke surface. There was a moment of consternation when one of the strops slipped, but it was quickly secured and the lift continued. The bomb was lowered into a specially prepared bed of fenders and shock mats on board *Broadness*.

As the salvage vessel started down river at 8 knots, Dave thought it would be wise to impose further restrictions for safety reasons, and the police inspector, on his radio, closed each bridge and river tunnel to traffic, as the bomb passed. It was unfortunate that all of this happened during the peak lunch hour traffic but amazing to see the empty bridges with all the traffic building up at each end. Other river traffic passing was warned to proceed at dead slow speed.

During the journey down river, Dave closely examined the bomb fuse and found that it was an electric impact fuse; they would never know why it hadn't functioned.

At 1630 *Broadness* was one and a half miles off Southend Pier, and the depth was 60 feet. Dave decided that this would be an ideal position to countermine. The ship stopped and the bomb was lowered to the sea bed. The team moved into the Gemini dinghy, a diver went down and unhooked it, and the salvage vessel moved about one and a half miles away. Two 4-pound plastic explosive packs were secured to the bomb and linked to the dinghy by Cordtex explosive cord.

All shipping in the area had been warned that there would be a large underwater explosion in the area. Dave checked that there were no small boats in the vicinity and ignited a two minute fuse. The Gemini moved about 200 yards away.

There was the rumble of a full order explosion, and a white plume of water rose a hundred feet into the air. The shock was felt in Southend, but the bomb had been destroyed.

The *Broadness* dropped the team at Greenwich, where a big press conference had been arranged. The reporters fired questions at all of the team, and the final question put to Dave was, 'Didn't you feel any fear during the operation?' to which Dave replied, 'The most frightening part of the whole operation was the ride, with police escort, from Portsmouth to Wapping.'

They arrived back at their HQ in *Vernon* and found a big stack of congratulatory signals waiting for them, from MOD Navy, C in C Portsmouth, Thames River Authority, Captain HMS *Vernon* and other commands. Dave even had a signal from the Commodore, Ghana Navy. The telephone never stopped ringing as his friends and the Diving Officers from the other teams called him. He had to go to Southern TV in Southampton to be interviewed on Southern TV News. The whole team were invited to appear as guests at 'Sunday Night at the London Palladium', where they met Jimmy Tarbuck and Barbara Windsor. Finally they were all invited to a civic luncheon at the Mansion House in London, where the Lord Mayor, Sir Lionel Denny, presented them all with a signed copy of the book *The Living City*.

Many of Dave's former course mates called him and told him that they were having bets on what award he would get for his operation, one of the biggest since the war, and even his boss said, 'I think there should be some gongs going for this job.'

The Flag Officer, Portsmouth had inspected the team only two weeks before this operation. He had been very impressed with everything that he saw, and the work that the team were doing, and he said to the boss of the team, 'If you think that anyone in your team deserves special merit, you should bring it to my attention.' Dave was told later that after the Blackfriars Bomb, the Admiral's secretary rang up the boss and asked him if there should be any special mentions, but the boss told him that 'it was just a run of the mill job.' Having said that, it could not be reversed.

The team had certain tasks where they periodically had to carry out clearance of areas, they called them 'pot-boilers', and these they would carry out when they had a slack period of bomb disposal. The two most notable of these in their area were Beachy Head, on the south-east coast near Eastbourne and Denghy marshes on the Norfolk coast.

Usually they carried out these clearances approximately every six months and the Beachy Head one fell to Dave shortly after joining the team. Normally they would spend a week on this task, although they were on immediate call for any other task that came up.

They would drive to Birling Gap, near to Beachy Head, where there was good access to the beach, and place 'Danger – Unexploded Bomb' notices. These, and the Land-Rover which was marked 'Portsmouth Bomb and Mine Disposal Team', were enough to raise curiosity among the public, mostly holiday makers, so strict precautions had to be observed, to make sure that no one got hurt.

The beach below the cliffs was quite narrow and very rocky, and the team would line-out between the base of the cliffs and the sea, at low water, and carry out a search for explosive items. There were always quite a lot that had built up since the last search, mostly naval shells, 4.5-inch and bigger, washed up during the storms and lodged between the rocks, also smoke-floats and other miscellaneous items of ordnance. When they found something they would move it to one spot, until they had quite a large pile, and then they would place an explosive charge in the middle of it and the team would retreat to a convenient cave. Dave, using binoculars, would scan the beach in both directions, then, when he was sure all was clear, he would ignite a one-minute, slow burning fuse and join the others in the cave to await the ensuing bang.

The reason that they were so careful and meticulous about this operation was that his boss had told him of an incident that had happened in this very place a couple of years earlier. The team had been carrying out the usual search, and some curious youth, seeing the Land-Rover, had decided to follow them and see what they were up to. He shadowed them along the beach, keeping out of sight behind large rocks, of which there were many in that area. He noticed that they all seemed to keep going back to one spot, and going away again, then they all disappeared into a cave except one man, who bent over something, then he also walked into the cave. The youth couldn't contain his curiosity any longer; he jumped up and ran to the spot to have a look. The charge went off, and the team emerged from the cave to see a person rolling around on the ground. They ran to him, but he was already dead when they got there. A piece of shrapnel had gone straight through his heart but there was no other mark on him. They had to carry him a long way back to Birling Gap, where they called for the police and an ambulance.

Of course there was an Inquiry about the accident. The Officer-in-Charge was cleared, but he was criticized for not placing 'Danger' boards, and for not having a lookout on the top of the cliffs, who might have seen the youth. Since then, every precaution was taken to make sure that it couldn't happen again.

Most of the shells that they found were inert, solid shot shells, with no explosive in them. There were gathered up at the end of the week and taken to an MOD range, to avoid being called out again and again for the same object.

The other 'pot boiler' usually entailed a visit by the entire team; this was at Denghy Marshes off the Norfolk Coast. It was a bleak, sparsely populated part of the coast, and the area to be cleared was a World War 2 bombing range. It was also a treacherous part of the coast. To reach the actual bombing range, you had to negotiate about half a mile of salt marshes, a reed covered area with six-foot deep gullies of mud, which were full of water at high tide. Then you had a two mile walk out to the range, through soft mud in some places and firm sand in others. There were three big barges there, which had been the 'targets' for the bombing runs. They were sitting on the bottom, and covered with water at high tide. Besides being a practice range, during the war aircraft that had had to abort their mission for any reason used to jettison their load there before attempting to land. American Flying Fortresses were so heavily loaded that they used to use rocket devices attached to their wings to give them enough speed to get airborne. These were called JATO Units, Jet Assisted Take-Off Units, and the planes, once airborne, would jettison these over the range. Consequently, for about 500 yard radius around the barges, there were practice bombs, live bombs and JATO units, being covered and uncovered by subsequent tides. Fishing boats were forever getting their nets snagged on these obstructions, and this was the reason why this periodic clearance was carried out.

They always picked neap tides, the lowest low tides, when the sea retreated about three miles from the shore, so the team had to start walking out as the sea receded. They wore dry diving suits, carrying all their explosives, and were soon covered in mud from the gullies and soft mud patches. One of the divers said to Dave, 'Now I can see why we have to do all of those awful mud-runs.' By the time they got to the barges, the sea had disappeared in the distance, the sand was quite firm and many bombs and JATO units were visible. They started placing one-pound charges on each bomb and JATO, joining them all together with a 'ring-main' of instantaneous detonating cord. When they had a group joined together, the team returned to go behind or inside of the barges. Dave would place the one minute fuse, have a good look around to make sure that all was clear, ignite it and join the others at the barges. The area would erupt in sand and water, some full-order and others just the one pound charge. A lot of the JATOs were only partly expended and would burn fiercely. Then they would start doing the whole thing again, all of the time keeping a wary eye out to sea for signs of the returning tide.

They had to leave before the incoming tide reached the barges because it came in faster than a man could walk, and it would be up to their waist before they reached the marshes. This was the same area where, a few years earlier, two girls riding horses had completely disappeared without trace.

Dave returned to Denghy Marshes twice during his tour of duty with the team. On the second occasion, they actually had a helicopter attached to them. They set up a HQ at a farm near to the beach, and the team were flown out to the barges with all of their gear. It certainly beat the long trudge out there through the mud and gave them much more time on task to blow up more bombs. He found that it had another advantage. About halfway through the day, he saw the helicopter coming out from the shore; it hovered over the barges and started to lower something on the winch. He rushed across to the chopper and found that it had brought out a very large, hot kettle of tea. The pilot waved and headed back to the shore, and the team enjoyed an unexpected mug of hot tea: probably one of the most expensive mugs of tea ever made, thought Dave.

He also got one of the biggest frights of his life during that week. They had completed a ring-main, ready to blow up another lot of bombs. As usual, he had a good look around, lit the fuse and started to walk back to the barges. He was about halfway there, when he heard an engine and looking beyond the barges, he saw a light aircraft flying directly towards them, only a few feet above the sand. 'Oh Christ,' thought Dave, 'It's going to be here just about the same time that it explodes.' He watched the plane getting nearer, praying that it would pass over before the explosion, then, before it reached the barges, the beach erupted. He saw the wings of the plane jiggle, and it swerved to the right, climbing fast; it must have given the pilot the shock of his life when the earth blew up in front of him.

Another periodic inspection that the team used to carry out was the wreck of an American Liberty ship SS *Robert Montgomery*. This ship had been part of a convoy entering the Port of London during the war, whilst a German air-raid was in progress. She was just off Sheerness and, for some reason, she ran out of the main channel and ran aground. There was a dossier on this ship: she was carrying a cargo of high explosives, mostly aircraft bombs, which were fully armed, as the practice at that time had been to take them straight to an airbase and literally load them straight onto an aircraft, for dropping over Germany.

Photographs of the ship aground in 1944 showed that she looked like a ship at anchor, and she should have been unloaded at that time into barges.

There were rumours that if she exploded, it would be like an atomic bomb going off, and Sheerness would be devastated, but nothing was done. The greatest danger was that if another ship ran into her, the shock, with the now deteriorating explosives, could be enough to trigger off an explosion, so a coffer dam of shingle was built around her to prevent this from happening.

In the pack, photographs taken over the ensuing years showed the wreck gradually sinking into the bottom, so that less and less of the ship showed above the surface. Annual diving inspections revealed that her back had been broken with winter storms, and that bombs had spilled out of her onto the sea bed.

When Dave's team visited the wreck for an annual inspection, all that was visible were two rusting masts sticking out of the water. The gap in the ship's hull was much wider than the previous time, and bombs still lay on the bottom. Recommendations from these inspections were usually that the explosives should be raised and dumped or destroyed in deep water, but it would have been a very long and dangerous operation.

The team, over the years, had formed a very good relationship with the police in their area. Whenever they arrived at a town they would first call at the local police station, to leave their explosives for safe keeping, and there were occasions when, unable to find 'digs', they slept in the cells.

Once, driving into Herne Bay to deal with a mine washed up on the beach, they were not sure where the police station was, and Dave said to the driver, 'Ask that policeman directing traffic where it is.' The driver pulled up alongside the policeman and said, 'Which way is it to the nick, mate?' The copper, with a very pained expression on his face, said, 'Get this bloody Land-Rover off my foot!'

They would always call at police stations as they drove around the country, picking up items of ordnance that had been handed in, old hand grenades, mortar bombs, rounds of ammunition, and so on. Once the police gave Dave a beautiful Army officer's revolver that had been handed in by his widow; it must have been his pride and joy. Dave was reluctant to destroy it but that was the rules, and he blew it up with the other items on a demolition range.

The diving went on. A typical month's work in the log showed: a lost 4.5-inch cartridge in Portsmouth harbour; a lost exhaust cowling from submarine *Grampus*; a dome change on HMS *Cavendish* followed by another on HMS *Hardy*; fitting blanks on submarine *Aeneas*; a trip to

Lulworth Cove to inspect an underwater cable; diving on the wreck of a light aircraft found off Worthing, at first thought to be Amy Johnson's lost aircraft, later blown up by the team; a dome change on HMS *Lynx*; and a screw change on the RNR ship *Warsash* at Southampton.

There was also a search for a lost ladder in a deep area of Portsmouth harbour. They laid a jackstay on the bottom, and Dave and the Petty Officer diver carried out the search. It was pitch black and they swam along one side of the jackstay, Dave holding the jackstay in his right hand, and the PO diver's hand with his left. This way they covered an area of about eight feet each side of the jackstay. When they reached the end, at the sinker, they turned around and came back on the other side. In the absolute zero visibility it was pure luck that they found the ladder. After the dive, in the diving boat, Dave took the PO diver to one side and said, 'Don't you dare tell anyone in the team that we held hands down there.'

About that time a big emergency diving job came up. A very large American troopship, SS *General Buckner*, with 4,000 US soldiers on board, bound for Germany from the USA, managed to pick up a steel cable from a navigation buoy around her screws, at Spithead in the Solent, and was completely helpless, unable to move her screws.

It was about 5 p.m. Dave rounded up his team and they went out to Spithead for an initial inspection. The ship was 'anchored' by the buoy cables. It was a huge ship, with hundreds of heads looking down at them, Dave went on board to see the Captain; he had to make sure that the screws could not turn whilst divers were down, and he went back with the keys in his pocket that would prevent that from happening. All the authorities wanted to get that troopship out of there as quickly as possible, mainly because of the pollution in the Solent: imagine 4,000 toilets flushing incessantly.

Dave and the Chief went down on the screws first; they had to assess how big the problem was. As soon as he saw the screws, Dave's heart sank. There was chain cable around both of the screws and each link of the chain was about two inches thick and so heavy it would be difficult to lift a single link. So manhandling the cable off was out of the question; the weight of the cable which disappeared down to the sea bed would be enormous. When they came out of the water, Dave and the Chief said together, 'Acetylene cutting torch,' and the Gemini was sent back to bring out cutting gear and underwater lights.

It took thirty-six hours of continuous diving and cutting to free the ship, with everyone breathing down their necks every hour. The Yanks plied them with coffee and chicken and chips during the whole operation and when it was finished, Dave gave back the Captain his keys and told him that his screws were badly damaged; they would get him to Germany but he needed to dry-dock as soon as possible.

Before they got back into Portsmouth harbour the *General Buckner* was on her way out of the Solent.

CHAPTER 12

Minehunter

Dave had now spent two years with the Portsmouth Clearance Diving Team and his Appointer decided that he should go back to sea again. He was appointed as First Lieutenant to a minehunter, HMS *Kirkliston* in the Royal Dockyard at Rosyth in Scotland.

When he arrived at the ship he found that she was nearing the end of a major refit, being converted from a conventional minesweeper to a minehunter. She was still in dry dock and only had a skeleton crew; everyone lived in barracks ashore as the ship was in an unfit state to live in.

He was the senior officer in the crew at that time as the captain had not yet been appointed, and his main task was to oversee the work being undertaken, and to make sure that the ship would be ready for sea by the end of the refit.

He had two other officers, a sub-lieutenant and a midshipman and about thirty sailors. They had a Ship's Office, a mobile portacabin, on the dock side alongside the ship. They used to work really hard from dawn till dark, and gradually, the ship began to look like a warship.

This was the smallest ship that Dave had ever served on and unfortunately, being a tall person, he found that he had to walk around on board with a permanent stoop. Nevertheless he was forever bumping his head on the top of bulkhead doors and the pipework on the deck head, so much so that the top of his head always seemed to be bleeding and have scar tissue. He developed a very bad back which he thought was caused by the jarring shocks down his spine whenever he bumped his head.

It got so bad and was troubling him so much, that he had to go and see the Medical Officer in the barracks, who told him that he had a slipped disc, and that if it got any worse he would have to have treatment.

This came as a blow to Dave, who had put in so much work on the ship and didn't want to lose it. They had been told that on completion of the refit and work-up, *Kirkliston* would be sailing to Singapore to join a flotilla of minehunters based there.

So Dave lived with the pain of his slipped disc, visiting several civilian chiropractors ashore, hoping for a miracle cure but, in fact, it only cost him a lot of money and didn't seem to do much good.

Eventually the ship commissioned, the new Captain, officers and rest of the crew joined and they sailed to Portland and carried out the work-up. The date for the sailing to the Far East was set for the following Monday, but Dave was still suffering with his back and he was hoping that they would get to Singapore before he had to go for treatment. However on the Saturday morning, two days before sailing, he found that he was unable to get out of his bunk. A doctor was called, then an ambulance, and he found himself back in Haslar Naval Hospital. He tried to talk the doctor round, but he was adamant.

'You need ten days complete rest, flat on your back in hospital, then you will probably be fit enough to return to duty.'

Dave called his Appointing Officer and told him that he would be unable to sail with the ship on Monday. He went on '. . . but I don't want to lose this ship, I have done a lot of work to get it the way I want it, and I will be available to fly out and join it in about ten days time.'

'Don't worry, Dave,' his Appointer told him, 'she is your ship; I haven't got anyone to put in your place in any case. You just get fit and I'll fly you out.'

So Dave turned in, satisfied that his ship was safe.

Ten days later, after a complete recovery, Dave was back on the phone to his Appointer again, and to his horror he heard him say, 'I'm sorry, Dave, your Captain complained about not having a First Lieutenant so much that I had to fly out a relief, but don't worry, I am sending you to HMS *Hubberston*, a hunter in the same flotilla in Singapore.'

Dave cursed his Appointer, accusing him of reneging on a promise to keep his job open, but he knew it was no good, it was a *fait accompli.*

So he found himself back at Brize Norton, taking a RAF VC-10, a trooping flight to Hong Kong via Cyprus, Gan and Singapore. He liked serving in the Far East. When they landed at Gan, he noticed that all of the RAF personnel were wearing clothes, which they had to do when the trooping flights came in, as usually there were quite a few women on the flight.

At Changi airport he hitched a lift on a RN truck to the naval base, then from there, a boat took him down the Straits of Johore to Loyang, a Boom defence base where *Hubberston* was berthed for the night. They didn't expect him on board so early and were delighted to see him. The First Lieutenant that he was relieving had been on the same course qualifying for Clearance Diving Officer as him, so they knew each other well. The Captain was a Lieutenant-Commander 'Fly-boy': in other words, from the Fleet Air Arm. There were also two sub-lieutenants and a midshipman.

He was impressed by the cleanliness of the ship. He had been on Hunters in the UK and he knew how difficult it was to keep the wooden decks clean, especially with the UK weather, but here, where it was normally warm and sunny, all the woodwork was gleaming white, and the paintwork in good condition.

The coastal minesweepers, converted into minehunters, were the only wooden ships still in the Navy, made of wood so that they could operate close to the magnetic mines without activating them, as a steel hulled ship would. For the same reason, all of the metalwork on board was either aluminum or bronze.

She carried six divers: the First Lieutenant, the cox'n, a leading seaman diver and three AB divers. Dave knew most of the divers already. The mine-hunting sonar fitted to these ships was so good they could almost detect a beer can on the sea bed, and when carrying out a 'sweep', they could detect a ground mine lying on the sea bed about 500 yards ahead. The Control Room would call away the Gemini dinghy, manned by the divers, and while the ship stood about 300 yards away from the target, they would vector the dinghy over the contact by radio and the divers would lower a sonar reflector made of bronze to about three feet above the sea bed. It was called a Diabolo, and the sonar operator could see both the target and the Diabolo and would bring them together by giving directions to the cox'n of the dinghy by radio. The directions would go something like this: 'Go right, steady, steady, 30 yards to go . . .' then as the Diabolo and target came closer, he would say, '. . . 10 yards to go, hold that course, standby, standby, drop, drop, drop.' On the final 'drop', the dinghy would drop the Diabolo to the sea bed and remain anchored by it. A diver would go down and usually the mine would be within arm's length of the Diabolo. In exercises they would hook on a line, in order to recover the practice mine. In actual operations the Diabolo would be replaced by an explosive device which would be used to destroy the mine.

The officer that he was relieving spent a week turning over to him. It was hard work: loads of stores that had to be mustered, accounts that had to be audited, all the Service Certificates of the Ship's Company that they had to go through, then he left to return to the UK, and Dave was the First Lieutenant.

There were six mine hunters in the Flotilla, and a minelayer, HMS *Manxman*, which was their depot ship and accompanied them on all exercises and operation. They carried out lots of exercises with the Far Eastern Fleet. The diving around Malaya was magnificent, and they spent a lot of time in the Pulau Tioman area, an island that must be anyone's idea of a South Sea desert island: white sandy beaches, palm trees, high heavily wooded peaks. They often anchored here after an exercise and set up a barbecue on the beach. There was a village on the island, with grass huts, but they never used to see much of the villagers. The divers would take the Gemini and their diving sets to get some recreational diving in; the water was teeming with fish, all sizes and colours, and the underwater visibility was fantastic.

On one of these dives, Dave was sitting on the bottom, fascinated by the fish, which jumped every time that he breathed out, making a blurting sound with his set. He heard the safety boat, manned by the cox'n, come up above him, and felt a tug on his life-line, attached to a flat on the surface. He answered the 'Are you all right?' signal, and heard the boat roar away to check the other divers.

A black shadow passed over him. He looked up: it was an eight-foot shark, which passed over him from behind, about six feet from him, and disappeared at speed into the edge of visibility. Later on, after the dive, the cox'n said, 'What happened to you, sir? I came up and checked you on the life-line; next time I looked around you were sitting about twenty feet up the beach.' Dave didn't realise that he had moved so quickly.

There were some wonderful wrecks around the coast also. After a day of mine-hunting exercises, Dave used to persuade the Captain to search for a wreck with the mine-hunting sonar; there were many wrecks marked on the chart. They would hunt around the area until they found it, and then dive on it. There was one that they found that was surrounded by dummy anti-submarine mortar bombs, and they found out that the fleet used that wreck to represent a submarine near the bottom, and fire their anti-submarine weapons at it.

During one mine-hunting exercise, the sonar located a contact which the operator said seemed rather large to be a mine. They did a Gemini run on it, dropped the Diabolo, and Dave said that he would take the dive.

When he got down to the bottom he found that it was a bamboo cage, about the size of a large car, and it was choc-a-bloc with fish of all sizes, swimming around inside. The local fishermen used these traps to catch fish and this one had obviously lost its float to the surface; the fish could get in but not get out. Dave took out his diver's knife and hacked away at the rope binding until he had made a hole big enough for the fish to swim out.

As they swam out, he looked around. It was a flat sandy bottom, depth around 100 feet, and he thought, 'I am probably the first human being to have stood here in this spot.'

While he was in Singapore, Dave had the opportunity to dive on the most amazing wreck that he ever dived on. The Far Eastern Clearance Diving Team were based in the naval base, twelve divers that had the same responsibilities that he had had in the PCDT. The CD branch in the Navy is so small that almost everyone knows each other, and they usually served more than once with each other. Consequently divers from the ships would visit the team and vice versa. One lunch time the boss of the FECDT was in *Hubberston*'s wardroom for a drink and he said to Dave, 'We are going up to the *Prince of Wales* next week, would you like to come along?'

Dave knew what he meant. The Japanese had sunk the battleships HMS *Prince of Wales* and HMS *Repulse* off the east coast of Malaya during the war, and they had gone down with a heavy loss of life. When the British returned to Singapore after the war, the Clearance Diving Team had visited the wrecks once a year to raise the White Ensign over the quarterdeck. Nearly every CD that he knew would give his right arm to be able to dive on these ships and Dave quickly accepted the invitation. The FECDT had an MFV (motor fishing vessel) as a diving tender and they sailed in this the following week for the area of the wrecks.

It took a few hours to reach there. The wreck of the *Prince of Wales* was clearly marked. Eight divers prepared to go down, and Dave was one of them. The wreck was clearly seen on the echo sounding machine standing proud of the bottom; the depth to the bottom was 200 feet and to the highest point of the wreck 170 feet.

The sea was like a lake. The divers jumped in, and Dave put his head under the water and looked down. It was a fantastic sight. He could see the entire length of the battleship which was lying on her side. One of the 15-inch gun turrets for'd had come out of its mounting and was lying on the sea bed. They started down towards her. They had been briefed before the dive that they were not allowed to go down to the sea bed, which was 200 feet and beyond their diving limitations without prior approval from the MOD. They had been instructed to land on the hull, the ship's side, which was only around 170 feet. They were to go aft to the quarterdeck, where they would find a float secured to the ship by a wire pennant. It would be about 16 feet in length and they were to secure a new White Ensign to the wire. One of the divers had the ensign tucked into his wet suit. They found the float; the previous ensign had rotted away. They secured the new one and watched it fluttering in the current, above the quarterdeck.

One of the team had brought an underwater camera to take pictures of the ensign. Dave recalled seeing a previous photo in the RN *Diving Magazine*.

He looked down at the row of brass port holes under his feet. The remains of hundreds of British sailors were inside there. It was forbidden to enter the wreck, which had become the property of the British War Graves Commission. They started up towards the surface.

The west coast of Malaya was also very beautiful and good for diving. They went on an official visit to Bangkok after a big naval exercise at Lankawi and Phuket in Thailand. At the time these were little more than fishing villages, but have since turned into popular tourist resorts. During a run ashore in Bangkok, Dave got completely lost, but knew that if he could get back to the railway station, he could find his way back to the ship. He flagged down a taxi, but no one in Bangkok could speak English so by sign language he indicated to the driver that he wished to go to the railway station. He pumped his arms backwards and forwards, like a locomotive, at the same time making puffing noises, 'Ah,' said the driver; a look of understanding came on his face, and he indicated that Dave should get into the taxi. He ended up at a Thai kick-boxing stadium. They had been warned that the Thai people were so keen to be helpful that they would quite often get it wrong.

On one dive in the Mallaca Straits, they were diving near a lighthouse called the Five Fathom Bank lighthouse. This was a platform built in the sea with the lighthouse constructed on the platform. The diving around the platform was very boring, a pebble bottom with no plant life and very few fish, but as you swam out of the sun and into the shadow of the platform, things changed dramatically. It was teeming with fish and underwater plants grew in abundance; it almost seemed as if the fish were sheltering from the bright rays of the sun.

As the divers swam round to the other side of the lighthouse, they stopped in astonishment. There were three groupers, each the size of a cow, that took no notice of them and seemed to be just peacefully 'chewing the cud'. The divers swam quite close to them and the fish showed no fear whatsoever. Among Dave's many duties on the ship was as the Catering Officer, and he thought, one of the groupers would keep *Hubberston* supplied with fresh fish for a month. They did have a spear-gun with them, but no one had the heart to put a spear into such peaceful looking fish.

At the time that he was in the Far East, there was quite a lot of unrest and riots happening in Hong Kong. It was the days of Chairman Mao's *Little Red Book*, and communist terrorists were exploding bombs in the city.

Two of the minehunters were permanently based as guard ships in Hong Kong, and these were rotated in the flotilla. *Hubberston's* turn came round, and they left Singapore one morning for their tour of duty there. It was quite a journey for such small ships, especially during the typhoon season, and to avoid having to cross the China Sea, the route that they took was along the north coast of Borneo, stopping at Labuan to refuel, then across to the Philippine Islands, and following the western coast of these islands northwards until they reached the northerly point of the Philippines, then there was a relatively short passage of open sea across to Hong Kong.

It was particularly hazardous when there was a typhoon around, and they had permission to take shelter in the US naval base of Subic Bay, if necessary. For some reason there always seemed to be a typhoon in the vicinity whenever the minesweepers passed Subic Bay; maybe it had something to do with the lavish hospitality that the Americans offered them. It was a huge naval base, and also contained Clarke Field, a big US air base. It covered many square miles and the Americans had turned it into a 'little America'. They had shops, clubs, drive-in movies, sports stadiums, PXs, commissaries, and the Americans could live the same life as they did in the States, and buy anything that they could buy at home.

Dave talked to some US servicemen who had been out there for two years and had never been outside the gates of the base. This was a pity because the Philippine Islands was a beautiful country and it seemed criminal to travel that far and not see it. Dave got the impression that it was the town just outside the gates that put them off. Olongapo was a dirty city, full of bars and brothels. In fact, some Americans had been knifed whilst 'ashore' there, and this probably made a lot of people afraid to leave the base.

The British sailors, being what they are, all went ashore in Olongapo, with unfortunate results. The following morning the cox'n knocked on the door to Dave's cabin/office.

'Come in, Chief,' said Dave, 'what is the problem?'

'I'm afraid that we have had two diving watches stolen ashore, sir,' said the cox'n.

These were part of the permanent naval stores that Dave, as First Lieutenant, had on his charge. It included all of the diving equipment among which were four Rolex diving watches. They carried six divers, so it was the practice to issue them, against a signature, to the First Lieutenant, the cox'n, the Leading Diver and the senior AB diver. These watches had a nylon strap and the cox'n told Dave that the leading diver and the AB had both lost their watches in the same way. Two men had jumped them, one held the wrist while the other cut the strap with a knife, and it happened so quickly that they were gone before the divers realized what was happening.

Dave's heart sank. He saw hours of statements and paperwork before he could justify writing off two expensive diving watches. This paperwork would have to be include a report from the local police, so he told the cox'n to go down to the police station and report the theft.

An hour later the cox'n came back, white-faced. On the way to the police station he had had his watch stolen! Even although he was alert to the situation, they still took him by complete surprise and it happened so quickly. The robbers took off down a narrow street with the cox'n in hot pursuit, they went round a corner and as the cox'n turned it, he saw the nearest one duck as he ran. Too late, the Chief realized that there was a rope stretched across the road and he ran straight into it, and went sprawling. When he got up there was no sign of his assailants; they had now lost three watches.

Maybe the Yanks are right not to go ashore there, thought Dave. Three out of four watches lost in a single day.

In Hong Kong they became a patrol vessel, covering most of the many islands that make up Hong Kong. They patrolled the estuary of the Yellow River, keeping to their own side of the imaginary line that divided Red China from Hong Kong. On occasions they saw their opposite number, a Chinese gunboat doing exactly the same thing on their side of the line. Whilst they were there, there was a spate of bodies floating out of the Yellow River, most with their hands tied behind their backs. Although *Hubberston* never picked up any themselves, they saw a Hong Kong police launch pulling a body out of the water. They kept busy in other ways too. They

184

constructed many navigational beacons, to mark shallow rocks in the channels between the islands, the divers working with underwater, quick setting cement to fix them in the right position. They carried out a survey at Plover Cove, a bay that was being sealed off, the salt water being pumped out and re-filled with fresh water from the many streams that ran into it, in an attempt to alleviate the chronic water shortage in Hong Kong, and to make it less dependent on water from the mainland of China. One day, when *Hubberston* and the other hunter, *Sheriton*, were on exercises outside the harbour, they received a priority signal to return to harbour immediately, as a commercial air-liner had run off the runway and into the sea at Kai Tak Airport. They raced back in, expecting to start diving to rescue survivors, to find that the aircraft was just off the runway, the front part under water, but the tail section had broken off and all of the passengers had managed to file out through the hole in the back, and there were no casualties.

Kai Tak airport was a real hairy place to land. The runway had been built sticking out into the harbour, and on the approach run, aircraft actually flew through and lower than the surrounding skyscrapers. Dave had landed there once and, looking out of the aircraft window, he had been amazed to see people sitting on their balconies above him, as he flew past. The aircraft that had crashed had touched down too late and had run out of runway.

There was a big drug problem in Hong Kong, and one day the customs officers asked if his divers could help to search for a consignment of drugs that they believed had been dropped overboard from a merchant ship at anchor in the harbour. They went, of course, but Dave realised as soon as they started diving that it was a hopeless task. The water was filthy, no visibility, so you couldn't see anything; it was deep, over 70 feet, and the bottom was covered with debris of all kinds. They searched for an hour, but never found anything. The other thing about this dive that concerned Dave was that he had heard that Hong Kong harbour was the only recorded case where a shark had killed an RN diver. Normally sharks keep clear of humans, but on this occasion, the inquiry concluded that, with the zero visibility, the diver and the shark swam into each other and the shark turned on the diver. He died before they could get him to shore.

They did night patrols around the harbour, and once when coasting close-in to the waterfront, they came to an area where there was a large political meeting taking place. It must have been a communist meeting because as they passed close, they heard the ugly roar of the mob directed straight at them.

It wasn't all work of course. Hong Kong was a magical city. You could go ashore without a penny in your pocket and there was so much to see that you could have a good night's entertainment just walking around and seeing the 'sights'. However Dave felt that a lot of the 'mysterious Orient' atmosphere of the old days had gone.

They spent three months as guard ship then returned to Singapore, just in time to go on an official visit to Brunei with the rest of the flotilla. It was an amazing place. Much of the town was built on stilts over the water, but it also had a very modern city, dominated by the Sultan of Brunei's Palace, which had large domes which were painted with gold leaf and glinted brightly in the sun. The Sultan of Brunei was supposed to be the richest man in the world. His armed forces had all the latest equipment and there were quite a few Englishmen serving with his forces. They looked after the visiting RN ships very well. The flotilla had a hovercraft attached to them, to take Ship's Companies off to a sandy, desert island for swimming and to enjoy a barbecue. Dave went on an excursion by helicopter of the Brunei Air Force to a native long-house, miles into the jungle. As they flew over the Borneo jungle, he thought that they were covering a distance in about forty-five minutes that would take over a week to cover on foot.

The long-house was occupied by a tribe that not many years earlier had been cannibals and head-hunters. There were still shrunken heads in corners of the long-house. Different families lived in each section of the bamboo and grass building, and the sailors were treated to the local food, which included wild pig, and an alcoholic brew tasting like beer, which they had made themselves. One of the most interesting things that Dave saw was a Visitors Book that they all signed, and looking back to the days of 'confrontation', he saw entries where 'terrorist groups' had visited the long-house followed, a week later, by a Royal Marine patrol.

Everyone enjoyed the visit to Brunei and, when they returned to Singapore they found that they had to prepare for a visit to Japan. The British government had been approached by the Japanese, who were interested in buying the RN mine-hunting system that we were using, so *Manxman* and four Hunters were being sent to demonstrate it. It was a long journey for small ships like mine-hunters, but they would have their depot ship and a RFA tanker to accompany them.

All went well except that it was extremely rough during the first part of the trip. They intended to refuel from the tanker around the northern part of the Philippines, but found that the weather was too bad for fuelling at sea as planned. The situation was becoming serious as the Hunters were getting low on fuel, so they closed the shore and finally managed to find a sheltered bay where the tanker anchored and they were able to refuel.

They entered the Inland Sea of Japan, berthed at the Japanese naval academy, and carried out their demonstration runs from there, spending the week there. After that they called at Tokyo for a week of rest and relaxation before starting the return trip to Singapore.

CHAPTER 13

The Portsmouth Team

When the ship berthed back in Singapore, Dave found a letter waiting for him from his appointer. He had now spent over two years with the Far Eastern Fleet in *Hubberston* and his Appointer asked him if he would like to return as Officer in Charge of the Portsmouth diving and bomb disposal team. He was delighted and readily agreed. The team was now called the Portsmouth and Medway Clearance Diving Team, and he would be on the staff of Flag Officer Portsmouth and Flag Officer Medway. The MOD had also adopted the American name of EOD, Explosive Ordnance Disposal, instead of Bomb and Mine Disposal.

When he arrived at his office in HMS *Vernon*, he found that the set-up was very much the same as when he left. They were all different ratings in the team but he knew most of them in any case.

He started off his new job by going through all of the reports on proceedings to the Flag Officer and he discovered that unexploded ordnance was still appearing at the same rate of about one incident a day, and at least one mine a month.

The reports of large operations were forwarded immediately after the operation, but the small incidents, such as a shell or a hand-grenade, were tabulated and forwarded in a monthly report. This recorded the time, date and place, description of the item, and how disposed of. They did get called out for false alarms; for instance, quite often a calor gas cylinder would be reported as a depth charge, but their feelings about these were that they would rather be called out for a false alarm than have someone hurt by something that wasn't reported.

The officer that he had relieved on the team was retiring from the service, and he had actually been his Course Officer when he had qualified. Dave had to smile at his humour. One of the monthly reports read: Item – reported ground mine; Place – Isle of Wight, off Ryde Pier; Item actually found – Toilet cistern; Method of disposal – flushed in deep water.

His first job with the team was quite a big diving operation. An RAF Hunter jet fighter aircraft had crashed into the sea off Wells-next-the-Sea, Norfolk. As this was the third Hunter that had crashed in recent months, the RAF wanted to recover the aircraft in order to find the cause of these accidents and they had asked the Navy to carry out the recovery. As Wells-next-the-Sea was in Dave's area of operations, he was told to undertake this task and he moved most of his team up there, where they checked into lodgings. An MOD Salvage Boom Defence Vessel arrived the next morning and the team went on board. Good bearings of the exact spot where the plane had plunged into the sea had been obtained and it didn't take too long, using the echo sounder, to find the wreckage on the bottom.

It wasn't very deep, only about 30 feet, and the weather was good, so they started diving immediately. They had been told that the pilot had not been able to bail out, so that they could expect to find human remains. In fact, all that they found of the pilot were small pieces of human flesh which they picked up and put into plastic bags; the largest piece found was a shoulder and upper arm. The crabs had already been busy. All of the body recovered was put into buckets of water on board and taken ashore each evening to be handed over to the coroner. When you consider that in the Hunter aircraft, the engine was directly behind the pilot, it's easy to see why very little of the body was found.

The plane itself had also disintegrated into very small pieces, the largest being the engine, the tail section, and the wheels. They worked there for a week. The foredeck of the salvage vessel was covered with parts of the aircraft, and her derrick had been very useful for lifting the heavy items such as the engine out of the water, and by the end of the week, they reckoned that they had recovered most of the aircraft.

On the last day of diving an Air Commodore from RAF Odiam had come on board to watch the operation. At the end of the day, he thanked the divers and he offered Dave a lift back to Odiam in his light aircraft. So Dave had a comfortable ride from a local RAF station to Odiam, then on by RAF car to Portsmouth, while the rest of the team drove the Land-Rover and 30-cwt. truck back with the gear.

The following week they were called out late at night. The coastguard reported that a fishing vessel had picked up a German mine in her nets and had it on board. She had reported it to the coastguard and started to enter Folkstone harbour, but the Harbour Master had refused to let them enter and had ordered them to move one mile off-shore, anchor their boat, abandon ship and return to Folkstone in their dinghy, which they did.

When Dave and the team arrived there, about midnight, the skipper and one of his crew went out with them in the Gemini dinghy to his fishing boat where they found a perfectly preserved German GD ground mine, still in his nets on the upper deck.

They cut the mine free from the net, doing as little damage as possible to the net, then they rigged a strop which they rove around the mine, and, using the fishing boat's davit, they lifted it, swung it outboard, and lowered it to the sea bed.

Dave and the divers then transferred to the Gemini, with their diving gear and explosives, and told the skipper that he could now return with his boat to harbour, and to inform the coastguard that the mine would be exploded at 0400. The fishing boat left, and a diver went down and attached a 4-pound demolition pack to the mine. He returned to the Gemini with the Cordtex which was attached to the demolition pack. They put on a two minute fuse, secured a float to this and waited until two minutes to four. At that time they started the outboard motor, ignited the fuse and sped away from the area. Dave had an awful memory of once when he had ignited the fuse and then found that the outboard wouldn't start. There had ben a mad scramble of divers pulling their knives out to cut the fuse before it reached the Cordtex. He had made a silent vow on that occasion always to start the engine before igniting the fuse.

The GD went off with a full order; it was always a satisfying feeling to feel the thump and see the plume of water rise into the air.

About 3 o'clock one morning Dave had a call from the Duty Commander in MOD, who said, 'If I told you that there was a certain tanker coming into a certain harbour and there was the threat of limpet mines being used against her, how long would it take you to get your team moving?' Dave told him that they could be on the road within an hour, and the Commander said, 'Right, no further action for the present.'

Needless to say, Dave found it difficult to go back to sleep; his mind was working overtime. Should he alert his team now? Or could it turn out to be a false alarm? He had heard through the diving grapevine about these 'cloak and dagger' jobs, as they were commonly called; they were usually carried out by the Fleet Clearance Diving Team, which had a world wide commitment; then he remembered that at the present moment they were deployed on the west coast of Scotland, diving on a missile testing range.

In any case, the decision was taken out of his hands. Within half an hour the Commander was back on the phone.

'Right, get your team together and go to the main police station in Liverpool; there you will meet Lieutenant-Commander X, who will brief you on the situation. Your lads are to wear plain clothes but take their uniforms.'

Dave called his Chief Diver, and told him to muster the team, get into *Vernon* and to start loading the gear. He called the main gate at *Vernon* and told them to wake the members of his team that lived on board, and to tell them to get across to the Diving Section. Next he called his Petty Officer Diver, who was in Hunstanton with three of the team, on an EOD job. He of course had kept Dave informed of where he would be at any given time. He told the PO to get his group and drive to Liverpool police station and meet him there, and thinking he would throw in an air of mystery, said, 'You will easily recognize me; I will be wearing a red rose in my lapel, and have a rolled-up copy of *The Times* under my arm.'

In three quarters of an hour they were all on the move, most of them catching up with lost sleep on the way to Liverpool.

When they arrived there, Dave sent them off to find some lodgings, and then to return to the police station. Dave went in and saw an Inspector, who took him to a room where Lieutenant-Commander X was drinking coffee and reading a newspaper. He introduced them. The young Lieutenant-Commander was in plain clothes, of course, and Dave guessed that he was in Naval Intelligence, if only because he looked like a young James Bond.

He said, 'Come on, Dave, let's go for a drive,' and he took Dave out to his car, which to his great disappointment was not an Astin Martin.

They drove down to Liverpool docks, which were pretty quiet at that time of the morning, and walked along the jetty, Dave thought so that they couldn't be overheard, and he was told the story.

The Liverpool Docks Authority had received a letter from someone claiming to be an Arabic Freedom Group, informing them that an Israeli tanker would be arriving in the port in two days' time, for a week's stay, and during that time, they intended to sabotage the ship unless she was refused entry. On normal occasions a threat like this would probably be ignored as being from some crank, but on this occasion, as the Port Authorities themselves had not been informed of her arrival, they had to take it seriously.

So Dave was told that he had to put himself at the disposal of the Captain of the tanker. He was to visit the ship daily with two or three of his men in plain clothes; there would be full security on board by the crew, and if the Captain had any suspicions whatsoever, they were to carry out a full bottom search of the ship's hull immediately. And in any case, they were to carry out a bottom search one hour before she sailed.

Later on in the day, the rest of Dave's team joined them from Hunstanton, and they all settle down to wait.

The tanker arrived the next morning. Dave and the other officer went on board to meet the Captain, and it was agreed that he would come on board every morning, and would be ready to come out to the ship, at any time, at the Captain's request.

During that week, Dave and his team struck up a rapport with the Israelis, spending a lot of their time in the crew's recreation bar. One of Dave's team looked very Jewish and the team for a long time had teased him about it, rubbing their noses and calling him 'my boy'. He took it all in good part, and, although he wasn't Jewish he played along with the gag. The tanker crew also noticed that he looked very Jewish, and one of Dave's team, devilishly, told them that he was a Jew. From then on, Simon had no peace. All of the tanker's crew begged him to come back to Israel with them; they promised that they could guarantee him a good job training the Israeli Forces in diving, and that they could arrange for his family to join him in Israel. Simon played along with the prank and never disillusioned them that he was not Jewish. It was a big joke in the team. When he told them that he was in the Royal Navy for twelve years, they just said, 'Desert! come back on the ship with us.'

There were no incidents during the week. The security on and around the ship was very, very strict. On Friday she was due to sail at 1100 and Dave brought his team down at 0900 to carry out a full ship's bottom search. They were all in uniform and the operation was watched with great interest by the tanker's crew.

They carried out a 'necklace' search, starting at the bow and working their way along the whole length of the hull. The divers were all clipped onto the main necklace line about six feet apart, and there wasn't any part that didn't get searched: under the bilge keel, inside inlets and outlets, and at the stern, all of the rudder and screws area.

At 1030 Dave was able to report to the Captain that his ship was clear; they had a last beer together and promptly at 1100, she let go her lines and headed out into the Mersey.

Right up to the end the crew were beckoning for Simon to come aboard, and they were terribly disappointed that he didn't. The team packed up their equipment and headed back to Portsmouth.

One evening the team and their families were having a social evening in the *Vernon* Club, when Dave received a phone call from a Petty Officer CD1, who was in the Portland diving team. He told Dave that a dredger had come into Portland with a 4.5-inch shell jammed in the chain of buckets, which was preventing the dredge chain from operating. This was a common occurrence in that area. Dredgers brought up shingle for building purposes; there were several RN gunnery practice ranges around there, and they often brought up shells, mostly inert, solid shot shells without explosive in them. Dave told this to the CD1, who was newly qualified and on his first job. He told him to inform the dredger Captain that they would be down to Portland first thing the following morning, to cut the shell free from the dredging gear.

The CD1 went back to the Dredger captain and told him this. The Captain had dredged up many of these shells; he was convinced that this was a solid shot shell, and he wanted to get back to the dredging ground: time meant money. He also managed to convince the CD1 that it was solid shot, and he said, 'We have acetylene cutting gear on board, can't you do it tonight so that we can get back to sea?' The CD1 agreed, and he started to cut the shell out. It wasn't inert, and it exploded; he took the shrapnel burst in his chest. They moved quickly to get him to hospital, but he died in the hospital; this was the first EOD casualty that Dave was aware of.

There was quite another big diving operation came up shortly after that. The Flag Officer's Duty Staff Officer called him up and told him that a civilian SCUBA diver had found a wreck off St Helier, Jersey in the Channel Islands, that he had seen several large bombs around the wreck, and he told Dave to take his team and investigate.

When he said Channel Islands, Dave thought quickly. Much as he would like to dive in Jersey, he knew that the Channel Islands came under Flag Officer, Plymouth, and the EOD responsibility was under the Plymouth Clearance Diving Team. He had been told to go and could just take his team and go, but there was great rivalry between the teams, even jealousy, and he knew that he would be accused of 'poaching' by the Plymouth team if he went. So he explained to the Duty Staff Officer that Channel Islands were under the jurisdiction of the Plymouth team, and to his relief, he said, 'I know that, but the Plymouth team are on a task in North Wales, you are the next nearest.' So happily they went to Weymouth, got priority on the ferry, and arrived at St Helier. He was met by the Senior Police Officer, the Mayor of St Helier and the civilian diver who had been diving on the wreck.

The story was that a German transport ship, the SS *Arnold Maask* had sunk on 22nd May 1943, during the German occupation of the Channel Islands. She had been carrying a cargo of high explosives and it wasn't clear whether she had been sunk by the RAF or had struck a reef. She was only about one mile off St Helier and lying in 50 feet of water.

It was the peak of the summer tourist season and St Helier was bursting at the seams with holidaymakers. The Lord Mayor didn't want to alarm the tourists so Dave agreed to keep things low key. The civilian diver offered to take them out on his boat, and Dave gratefully accepted the offer, especially as it was a spacious motor cruiser with compressed air charging facilities, and they headed out, towing the Gemini, to the Grune aux Dardes Reef.

The civilian knew dozens of wrecks around Jersey, it was his hobby, and the Channel Islands are littered with wrecks, many from the war, but also from much earlier.

Dave and the PO took the first dive. The visibility was perfect, but the wreck had been almost flattened to the sea bed with winter gales, and there were large steel plates sticking up all over the place the largest pieces being the shafts, engines and boilers. It was a bit puzzling also because they found two sets of screws of different sizes. Later they were to find that a large sea-going tug had sunk in almost the same spot years after, and the wreck that they were diving on was, in fact, two wrecks mixed together.

When they started looking under the steel plates, they began to find bombs, 100-pound aircraft bombs, probably destined for airfields in Jersey, to be dropped on Britain. The wrecks were in a kelp forest about eight feet high, which didn't help the search.

They stayed in Jersey for three days, during which time they had sighted at least sixty bombs, and it was obvious that there were many more under the debris. Each time they came ashore the press was waiting and Dave played it down as much as he could, telling them that they had found some explosives, which would be blown up at a later date. The worrying thing about the disposal was that the town of St Helier was built on a stratum of rock which ran out to sea, and the wreck was lying on the same rock stratum. If the explosives were blown up *in situ* there could be a whiplash situation along the stratum which could cause considerable damage in the town.

On the afternoon that they finished their survey, the civilian driver took

194

them to another wreck that he knew; it was at about 60 feet, and it was a German cargo ship, sitting on the bottom upright. She had gun sponsons with the guns still in place, looking in remarkably good condition. Under the sponson, in a locker, were dozens of rifles and German helmets; it was a very interesting wreck.

The team enjoyed Jersey, especially the night life. Some of the team sent 'wish you were here' postcards, mischievously, to the Plymouth team in Wales.

On arrival back in *Vernon*, Dave had to make out his report to the Flag Officer. He reported that it was a serious situation, so much deteriorating explosive lying only one mile from St Helier. It was obvious that it could not be destroyed *in situ*, because of the amount of explosive, and the whiplash effect which could ensue.

His recommendations were that a naval EOD team should undertake the task of raising the bombs, using mine-lifting air bags, and transporting them into deeper water, further out to sea, where they could be safely counter-mined.

He also suggested that, as the Portsmouth team had carried out the survey, they would be the best team to carry out the operation. He wrote this knowing full well that the boss of the Plymouth team would never agree to it, and would fight it tooth and nail.

Eventually, the Plymouth team did carry out this operation, as Dave had recommended, and after it was finished, the Officer in Charge was awarded the MBE, and his Chief Diver the BEM.

There seemed to be a higher than average period of sea mines after that. The first one was a British buoyant mine off Flamborough Head, Yorkshire. Two sub-aqua divers had found it, and from their description, they knew that it was a British mine. They searched for two days, in deep gullies with long streamers of seaweed, but they never found it.

Even before they left Flamborough Head, they had a message from the Duty Staff Officer, telling them to proceed to Shoreham harbour, where a Brighton fishing vessel, the *Mary Jane*, had picked up a mine in her nets.

They used their blue light to get to Shoreham as quickly as possible. This time the fishing boat skipper had carried out all of the correct procedures. As soon as he realized that he had a mine, he lowered his nets and the mine to the sea bed, buoyed them, and took a fix of the position on his Decca navigation set, informed the Coastguard by radio, and returned to harbour.

The skipper agreed to Dave chartering his boat for a day. Dave gave him a signed note to this effect, which meant that he could make a claim on the MOD for a day of lost fishing. It was very foggy as they left harbour, towing the Gemini, heading for the position on the Decca Navigator. The skipper had made a good job of fixing the position, as the Dan buoy loomed up through the mist, exactly where he said it would be.

The depth was 44 feet. Two of them went down; visibility was quite good, and the mine was identified as a German buoyant GY mine: 7 horns, 660 pounds of high explosive. The case had rusted through, almost half of the side had gone, the explosive was exposed and crystallising, very dangerous. They saw that a lobster had made its home in there and decided to have it. Then they were quite startled to find that a conger eel had also taken up residence there, so, keeping a wary eye on the conger, which can be very aggressive, they started to cut the Skipper's nets free, so that he could recover and repair them.

By 1610 they were ready to counter-mine, and they moved into the Gemini and told the skipper to stand off. They placed their charge into the mine case, avoiding lunges from the conger; the lobster they already had. When they were ready, they fixed the two minute fuse, ignited it, and headed across to the fishing boat.

There was a juddering roar, a surging geyser of dirty, grey water, then a large patch of scummy water with bursting bubbles and quite a lot of dead and stunned fish, some quite big. They waited while the fishing boat collected the fish; at least they would have some 'catch' to show for their day's work.

When they arrived back in harbour, they found that no one had heard the mine explode; the sound had been completely deadened by the fog.

Two days later, they had much the same scenario at Clacton. A Burnham-on-Crouch fishing vessel, *Girl Betty*, had trawled it up in its nets five miles off Clacton, lowered it to the sea bed and marked it. It could have been the same one that had been trawled up a month earlier; both of them had a lobster in the end. On the earlier occasion the fishermen had rapidly got rid of it, dropping it without a marker. They carried out the same routine, chartering the fishing boat. This time the mine turned out to be a German ground mine, type GD, in 70 feet of water, 1600 pounds of explosive. Again it went with a Full Order and a 300 feet plume of water.

Travelling around in the Land-Rover was always hilarious, with the constant banter that went on, the witty jokes and remarks, the ogling of the girls that they saw. On their way back from Clacton, everyone was cursing Smithy who was passing wind continuously, 'dropping his guts' as the divers crudely put it. He was doing it so frequently, they were all freezing cold, driving along with all of the windows open to get rid of the smell. In the end Dave had had enough.

'Stop the Land-Rover,' he said.

The driver pulled up.

'Smith, out of the van,' said Dave. 'But sir I can't . . .' said Smithy.

'Out!' said Dave, and Smithy, still protesting got out of the car.

'Drive on,' said Dave, and they left him there, somewhere north of London, dressed in his No. 8 working rig, to find his own way back to Portsmouth.

Two weeks later, it was back to Clacton, same type of mine, same Full Order. After this one, Dave recommended to Flag Officer, Portsmouth that a minehunter should be sent to the Clacton area to carry out a search, as it was obvious that the Germans had laid a considerable number of mines there.

Occasionally the team would get a signal from Flag Officer, Portsmouth, telling them to carry out an underwater sabotage attack against one of the ships working-up at Portland. The signal would read, 'Exercise Awkward, the PMCDT will carry out an underwater sabotage attack against HMS *Devonshire* between 2359 and 0500 tonight at Portland.' At the same time HMS *Devonshire* would receive a signal saying, 'Exercise Awkward, Intelligence has revealed that underwater saboteurs are operating in your area. Probability that *Devonshire* will be attacked between 2359 and 0500.'

Operation Awkward was the code word for defence of ships against underwater attack. It had three States of Readiness, State 1 being almost equivalent to Action Stations. *Devonshire* would assume State 3 on receipt of the signal, that is 'Underwater attack is possible.' In this State, the duty watch would patrol the deck as armed sentries, underwater lighting would be rigged around the ship, so that frogmen could be seen by the sentries, boats would patrol in the area around the ship, a radar watch would be started because in a calm sea, the heads of the divers coming to the surface could be picked up, and bottom lines would be rigged on the ship, in case a ship's bottom search had to be carried out.

The team would arrive at a remote part of Portland harbour and prepare their equipment for the attack. They brought two Gemini dinghys, and Dave would be the diving supervisor in one of them, with four divers and a stand-by diver. The Chief Diver would be the same in the other dinghy, again with four divers and a stand-by diver.

On these exercises, Dave always tried to cause as much confusion on the ship being attacked as possible. They had a number of ruses to do this. He would send in a couple of divers on the surface, using a snorkel and a mask, to try and attach a dummy limpet mine just below the water line. If the ship being attacked was alongside the jetty, sometimes a snorkel swimmer could edge his way along the jetty wall without being detected, and place his limpet.

Sometimes they would lay off the target ship, in the dark, avoiding the boat patrols, and they would place round plastic floats about the size of a man's head in the water, with a diving mask on, to drift down towards the ship. Then they would hear the sentries' whistles blowing, and the Tannoy on the ship reporting that a diver had been sighted on the port bow. Sometimes the plastic floats were put in the water with 8-inch nails sticking out of them, looking like small contact mines to drift down towards the ship; these usually caused quite a lot of chaos.

Of course the target ship knew by now that she was under attack, and would assume 'Awkward State 2'; this meant more sentries and the patrol boats would start dropping weighted thunder-flashes at random intervals, a large firework that went off underwater, in an attempt to deter the divers. In actual operational conditions, these would be one pound explosive charges, which could knock a diver out if it was close enough.

The ship's divers on board would start getting their gear ready to carry out a bottom search.

Sometimes one of the Geminis would just tear alongside the ship at speed, to start all the sentries' whistles blowing, and firing a few volleys of blank ammunition, to cause more confusion.

Another ruse that Dave tried, which sometimes worked, was to have one of his team, dressed in uniform, to arrive in a taxi at the ship's gangway, and go on board carrying a kit-bag and a hammock. He would have 'forged' Draft Orders, drafting him to the ship, and he would tell the cox'n that his train had just arrived at Weymouth. If the attack was already under way everyone on board was under pressure, and sometimes the cox'n would just send him off to one of the messes, and tell him to come back nd see him in the morning. Once there, the draftee would conceal a 'bomb' that he had in his kit bag.

As the night went on, Dave and his Chief would launch a diver carrying a limpet mine, to attack the ship. Some got caught, others got through, but they were all told that they had to surface and take a compass bearing at least once during their attack run. This was mainly to give the sentries an idea of what a diver's head looked like on the surface: it wasn't very big, and it didn't stay there for long. It also gave the radar operators the same opportunity.

This part of the exercise was always the most nervewracking for Dave, the overall supervisor. When you have eight divers, swimming on their own in the water, particularly on a pitch black night, windswept and pouring with rain, it can be very stressful.

The rules of the 'game' were, when each diver had finished his attack, he would surface, swim to the accommodation ladder rigged for this express purpose, climb on board, report to one of the 'referees', and give him his name. There were several referees on board on the staff of Flag Officer Sea Training, and their job was to assess how the ship had performed during the Awkward Exercise. The referee receiving the diver's name would call Dave on the hand-held radio and tell him, 'Diver Smith reported on board.' Dave couldn't relax until all eight names had been reported.

The ship was allowed to interrogate the divers; they wanted to know where the limpet had been placed and how long before they exploded. Normally they would take the 'prisoner' into a compartment below the water-line to interrogate him, the theory being that someone who is sitting on top of his own bomb is going to be quick to tell them where it is.

In the heat of the moment, both sides used to get carried away at times. Dave had heard of one ship that carried Royal Marines who carried out the interrogation, and one referee wandered into the compartment to find that the marines had rigged a dynamo to the prisoner's testicles, and were about to give him electric shocks to make him tell where the limpets were. He quickly discouraged them from doing this.

Dave himself remembered one occasion, when the Gemini had been creeping along the dockyard wall, preparing to launch a diver, when an alert shore patrol sentry had jumped from a height of about ten feet into the dinghy; they heaved him into the sea.

Once the 'attack' was completed, the team would get their gear together and head back to Portsmouth leaving the ship to carry out its necklace search for limpets.

About a week later, in the middle of the night – most of these things seemed to happen in the middle of the night – Dave received a telephone call from a major in the Royal Engineers Army Bomb Disposal Team, saying that he had been called out to a German bomb in Walthamstow Reservoir, and, as it was unexploded ordnance found in a reservoir, and as it was a sea mine, it was the Navy's responsibility, so he had called Dave. Dave was quite surprised, as the Army were not averse to poaching the Navy's responsibilities, but he thanked the major and told him that they would be there in about an hour. He called the team out, informed the Duty Staff Officer of what he was doing, and in just over an hour they arrived at the West Warwick reservoir in Walthamstow.

The mine was completely exposed, resting in about a foot of mud and water. Dave and his Petty Officer made a preliminary inspection of the mine, which they found to be a German ground mine, Type GC, the main charge of which is 1,500 pounds of Hexamite explosive.

The outer case appeared to be in remarkably good condition, being made out of a non-ferrous metal. Closer inspection of the bomb fuse showed it to be somewhat mutilated. The screws of the detonator plate looked in good condition and Dave decided that that would probably be the best entry point.

Discussing the plan with the police, Dave found that the reservoir was being drained for cleaning when the mine became exposed. They had already carried out an evacuation of nine factories and private houses within a 1,000 yards radius. They had also spoken to an old man who could remember a stick of land-mines being dropped during the Blitz, which had straddled the reservoir. He said that there were three explosions. Dave knew that these landmines were normally dropped in sticks of four, and guessed that the fourth one had fallen in the reservoir. Dropped by parachute, when it had fallen into the reservoir, it would have sunk and pressure would have caused it to act as a sea mine, arm itself, and sit on the bottom waiting for a ship to pass overhead.

It was obvious to Dave that counter-mining *in situ* was out of the question, as it was in such a built-up area, so it would have to be rendered safe. The way that the bomb fuse was mutilated meant that he would not be able to gag or immunise the fuse, so it would have to be 'steamed-out'. He called the major in the Royal Engineers and asked him for two steam generators. The major told him that they would be there within an hour.

Dave and the PO went back to the mine to start the render-safe procedure. These mines were fitted with an outstandingly dangerous combination of actuating and anti-removal devices, and it had to be assumed that any or all of the following devices could be fitted: a magnetic and/or acoustic system;

an arming clock 'booby-trapped' with an anti-removal device; a 6- to 8-day timing circuit; and a light-sensitive mechanism.

When these mines were first used, in the early years of the war, they were dropped in river estuaries and approaches to ports, and they sank so many ships that, within a week, the movement of British ships was paralyzed. They were the first of Germany's secret weapons. The Navy were desperate to get one of these mines to find out how to deal with them, which they finally did, thanks to the efforts of a few brave men. The Germans dropped one on Portsdown Hill, deliberately it was thought, in an attempt to beat the British effort to discover their secrets. This one worked; whilst they were stripping the mine very carefully, they uncovered a light sensitive meter, which actuated the mine, killing the men who were working on it. Some of these mines even had a brain; before dropping them they could set a number of times that a ship could pass over them before they were actuated. So if they set 30, it meant minesweepers and merchant ships could pass over it while the mine counted them, then, when you thought that the area was clear, the thirtieth ship would pass over it and the mine would explode.

So Dave and Roy, his PO, treated the mine with a great deal of respect. Using phosphor-bronze tools, which wouldn't give a magnetic signature, and keeping as quiet as possible, they removed the screws from the detonator plates. Inside it was in immaculate condition; it was painted green, the German writing on the plates was still clearly readable, and all the wires had tallies attached to them, with German writing on. One by one Dave cut all these wires and isolated them. He tried to remove the detonator, but it was stubborn and resisted his efforts. The leads being cut, Dave decided, as it was now comparatively safe, to leave it rather than exert any undue pressure on it.

It was now ready for 'steaming-out'. This method meant directing live steam onto the explosive, which caused it to liquify and run out of the casing where it would cool off and become solid again.

Whilst waiting for the steam generators, he had the team building a sand-bag area around the mine for the liquid explosive to run into and then reset.

The steam generators arrived; and they started them up. They took the steam hoses out to the mine, and probes were attached to the hoses and placed through the holes in the mine casing which they had made, and these were directed at the explosive.

By 1800 all was ready to commence steaming-out. The police were informed and they started to control the Liverpool Street to Cambridge railway line. The steam was switched on and Dave watched from the reservoir bank. It was necessary to carry out this part of the operation from a remote position because of the extreme change of temperature on the explosive; however he noticed with satisfaction that the liquid was running out from the mine. The other reason to keep well clear of the mine during the steaming-out was that the smoke from the boiling explosive was very toxic and, if it came in contact with the skin, could cause severe dermatitis.

The steaming-out took six hours, stopping every hour to reposition the probes, and around midnight, Dave declared the mine clear of explosive.

The next two hours were spent filling sand-bags with the reset explosive and laying them along the reservoir bank ready for burning. At daylight it was ignited and burned fiercely for fifteen minutes. Dave removed the arming clock, a beautiful piece of brass mechanism which they found was still in working condition, and which they later presented to the Joint Services EOD School. He then put a small piece of plastic explosive on the detonator and the bomb fuse and blew them both. The mine case was now safe and free from any explosive and the police said that it would be removed in a couple of days.

A few months after this operation, Dave was called into the office of the Chief of Staff, and informed that his name was being put forward for an award for the Walthamstow mine. Then shortly afterwards, he received a letter from Buckingham Palace, in which it said that the Queen had been most graciously pleased to appoint him a Member in the Most Excellent Order of the British Empire for Gallantry and, after that, he was proud to go to an Investiture at Buckingham Palace to receive the insignia of the Order from Her Majesty the Queen.

On the big day, Dave was permitted to take a guest to the Investiture at Buckingham Palace, and he had invited his mother.

She was overwhelmed, she had not been out of Durham very many times, and now she was visiting the residence of the Queen. It was, without a doubt, the biggest day of her life: mine too thought Dave.

Inside the Palace gates it was very crowded, all civilian gentlemen wearing morning coats and top hats, ladies in hats and new dresses. Dave was in uniform and there were quite a few uniformed personnel.

Ushers led them up a magnificent staircase, lined with soldiers in silver breast-plates, plumed helmets and drawn swords, to the Throne Room at the top. Here the recipients were separated from the guests and the guests were seated in the Throne Room facing the two thrones, one for the Queen and the other for the Duke of Edinburgh.

The recipients were taken into an annex from where they would be called into the Throne Room, in order of the seniority of the award. One of the aides de camp briefed the recipients on the procedure: no one was to wear head gear, so there would be no saluting. As each person's name was called, they would march straight out, until they were directly in front of the Queen, who would be on their left. They would halt, turn left, take four paces forward, halt, bow the head, and the Queen would hang the medal on their left breast. If she spoke to you, you answered Yes or No Your Majesty; if she spoke to you further, you would address her as 'Mam'; when she stepped back, you bowed again, took four paces back, turned right and marched off. In Dave's case it would be a double act, as his Petty Officer, who had been at his side during the whole of the Walthamstow Mine episode, had been awarded the British Empire Medal, and they would receive their awards together.

The Queen did speak to them; she asked Dave if the bomb had been very dangerous. Dave replied, 'Yes, your Majesty, but we have been well trained.'

After the ceremony, his mother told him that, after watching the first recipients receiving the Knighthoods, she thought that he would be 'Sir David' when he came out.

Dave had reserved a table for lunch at the restaurant on the top of the GPO tower. The waiters soon found that it was a celebration of some sort, and when they found out what it was, they sent a bottle of wine to their table.

Whilst they were carrying out one of their routine sweeps of the beach below Beachy Head, they were staying at Eastbourne. It was a foggy night and they heard on the BBC news that two ships had collided out in the Channel, and one of them, the SS *Texaco Caribbean* had sunk. Unfortunately she had sunk with her bows on the bottom and her stern only a few feet below the surface.

This part of the English Channel is one of the busiest shipping lanes in the world and it wasn't many minutes before a German freighter, the SS *Brandenburg* came along, before any warning to shipping had been issued, and she ran into the submerged stern of the *Texaco Caribbean*. It was still quite foggy, and the freighter probably tore a large section of her bottom out, as she sank within minutes with substantial loss of life.

The next morning, the Duty Staff Officer contacted Dave and asked if his team could go out to the wreck site and give any assistance they could.

They drove along the coast to the nearest point to the wreck; it wasn't far off shore and they could see vessels in the area. They launched the Gemini and it didn't take long to get out to the area. There was already a civilian salvage vessel on site, from a Southampton commercial salvage company, and in their diving team were two ex-RN divers, one of whom Dave knew quite well. They were engaged in searching the wrecks for bodies and had already recovered two.

Dave offered their assistance, which was accepted, but, although they dived all that day, no more bodies were found. At the end of the day, they made their way back to the shore and the Land-Rover to continue their clean-up of Beachy Head.

Dave would never forget one of the most striking memories that he had of diving. As they were swimming across the *Brandenburg*, they saw that one of the hatches was open. They swam across to the open hatch, and looked down into the hold. It was full of gleaming Mercedes Benz saloon cars.

Their next big EOD job was at Haile Sands near Cleethorpes. Some school children on a school outing had been digging in the sand at low water, and came to a Perspex dome. Looking through it, they could see instruments, and they realized that it was an aircraft. The police were called, and they called the RAF Bomb Disposal Team, as explosives found on crashed aircraft are their responsibility. There then followed a bit of a farce. The RAF EOD team discovered that it was a war-time Beaufighter; and they managed to dig down to one of the wings and found that it had cannons and belts of ammunition still fitted. The Beaufighter could also carry bombs but they were unable to get down to the bomb racks to see if any bombs were on this aircraft, because as fast as they could dig, the hole filled up again with sand and water. This was one of the parts of the east coast where the coastline is made up of dangerous, shifting sands; the tide recedes a great distance, and in places turns to quicksand as the tide returns.

The RAF had an Aircraft Preservation Society and a museum where they kept veteran aircraft and they decided, as this aircraft appeared to be complete, they would recover it and move it to the museum. However, it proved to be more difficult than they expected. The sand refused to give up the aircraft, and the attempt ended with three of their recovery vehicles getting bogged down and having to be abandoned, to be covered by the next tide. They asked the Army to assist but an Army tracked vehicle also got stuck and also covered by the tide. In the end, having rescued all their vehicles, they decided to abandon their plans for the aircraft, and blow it up. Dave and his team got the job.

They arrived at the site and at low water, they started digging to try to get under the aircraft. They found the same problem as had the Army and the RAF; the hole filled in as quick as they could dig. However, they did manage to see under the wings, and to confirm that it didn't carry any bombs. After that they dug as quickly as they could and managed to make a hole under the fuselage. In this hole they placed a 5-pound demolition charge with Cordtex explosive cord attached. They secured a detonator and a two minute fuse to the Cordtex, by which time the hole had almost filled again and the charge was buried. Dave told his team to prepare another 5-pound charge and have it ready to place after this one had exploded. They then ignited the fuse and retreated about 200 yards, to shelter behind the Land-Rover.

When it exploded, it threw sand and pieces of aircraft high in the air, and before the debris had fallen, they rushed back with the second charge. Much more of the aircraft was exposed in the resulting crater, which was rapidly filling in again, so they quickly placed the second charge where it would have the most effect, and retreated once again behind the Land-Rover.

They did this seven times, and there was very little of the aircraft left; even the wheels were blown into the air. After the last explosion, they gathered up all the aircraft debris and threw it into the final crater, which was quite deep, and they watched as the hole filled in and buried everything.

A month later, another civilian diver reported that he had seen explosives on the wreck of a German U-boat, three miles south of Selsey Bill, that he had been diving on. They arranged to meet the diver at Selsey, and he offered the use of his diving boat, which Dave accepted as it was a long trip out to the wreck, and it would be a lot more comfortable. They towed the Gemini, and on the way out, the Scuba diver told them that the submarine had a torpedo protruding half out of one of its for'd torpedo tubes; the warhead had rusted through and the explosive was visible.

He had a marker on the wreck, and said that he would go down with Dave and show him where the explosive was. It was about 60 feet and Dave was surprised to find that the submarine was almost intact. The Scuba diver headed aft, Dave followed him, and found that he was being taken on a guided tour of the submarine, with the civilian diver pointing out all the brass fittings and the precious metal parts. It was obvious that he was more interested in salvaging the metal, which he could sell, than the explosive. Finally they came to the torpedo tubes. Dave checked them; they were all empty, except one which had this torpedo protruding. As the diver had said, the warhead had rusted through and it was still about half full of explosive. They surfaced. Dave briefed the PO diver on the situation, and he went down with a four-pound explosive pack to put into the warhead. When he returned, they attached a two minute fuse, ignited it, and moved off about 300 yards. It resulted in quite a big explosion, and Dave was satisfied that the warhead had been destroyed.

They returned to Selsey, with the Scuba diver, who was eager to get back to the wreck to see what metal parts had broken loose in the explosion.

Dave had now been about two years with the PMCDT and knew that he would be coming up for a rotation soon.

Their next call-out was at 0400 one morning, and was to Herne Bay, Kent. A fishing boat, the *Harvester 2*, had lifted an object, 7 feet long, 26 inches in diameter and about 1,200 pounds in weight, in her nets. It was obviously a German ground mine and she had lowered it to the bottom and marked it.

They arrived at Herne Bay about 0700 and were met by the chairman of the local council and the skipper of the fishing boat, who told them the position of the mine. It was about two miles off shore and marked with a big yellow float.

They launched the Gemini from the beach and set out. The marker buoy was very easily sighted, and they dived on the mine. The police in the meantime were touring Herne Bay, telling people to keep their windows open because of the blast.

The mine was a German magnetic ground mine, type GC, and they placed countermining charges, followed by the usual procedure and blew it. It went with a full order and they were surprised to see dozens of big cod fish, stunned and flopping around on the surface; some were as big as 3 feet. They spent about half an hour cruising around among the fish, hauling them into the Gemini, or jumping into the sea to recover them, until the Gemini was almost gunwales under with the fish. The team's wives were going to be happy with their freezers full of fresh cod.

When they got back to the beach, they found the council chairman anxiously waiting for them. He told them that they had heard the explosion, seen the plume of water rise into the air, then had a long wait for them to return. They told him about the fish and he was all smiles when they presented him with a big cod. He took them to a local pub and bought them lunch.

His appointing officer called Dave when he got back to the office and informed him that his next job was to be a two years exchange of duty with a lieutenant in the US Navy. This sounded very exciting, but it wasn't to happen for about another nine months; in the meantime, he would be relieved from his present job in about a month's time. He would then take up an appointment as second in command at the Deep Trials Unit at Alverstoke; he liked the idea of this job also.

His relief arrived a month later and, after a week of turnover, he caught the Gosport ferry across Portsmouth harbour to the Deep Trials Unit. That's how close it was; in fact, he would still remain living in the Wardroom at HMS *Vernon*, and travel daily to the DTU.

The Officer in Charge was a Lieutenant-Commander, a veteran Navy Diving Officer; what he didn't know about diving wasn't worth knowing. He showed Dave around the Unit. It was all very high tech, and mainly consisted of a very large compression chamber, fitted with adjacent chambers where men could be locked in or locked out, to the main chamber. There were also smaller locks where food, medicine, etc. could be locked into the main chamber.

The main chamber itself had a very large pool in the centre, where divers could practise work in the water at different depths, meaning, of course, different pressures. This chamber was regularly tested to 2,000 feet, which to Dave, who had only dived to 200 feet, seemed amazing.

At the time that he joined the DTU, they were engaged in proving decompression tables from different depths, currently 1,000 feet. Volunteers from the Diving Branch were used to carry out these trials. Most divers love diving, but the other incentive was the diving pay. In deep diving, they are paid by 'minutes under pressure', and as one of these trial dives could last anything from seven to fourteen days, even longer if someone has a 'bend', the pay for one of these dives could be quite substantial.

The tables had been calculated by Diving Medical Officers and had to allow for the depth of dive, the amount of time spent at that depth, the 'stops' on the way up from that depth, and the amount of time required at each 'stop'. For a table to be accepted, they had to achieve ten 'bend free' dives at that depth.

It was called saturation diving. They had discovered that when diving under pressure, the inert gas being breathed, either nitrogen or helium, turned into a liquid that entered the blood stream and flowed around the body. For this reason, divers coming back to the surface had to stop at predetermined depths to allow this gas to return to the lungs and to be breathed out as normal. If a diver came up too quickly or without 'stops', the gas would turn to bubbles in his blood stream and travel around his system. Bubbles passing joints in the body caused pain, which the divers called a 'bend'; in severe cases these could cause paralysis. Or if a bubble went into the heart or the brain it could cause death.

The decompression stops were calculated for the maximum depth, and the time spent at that depth. However, they found that if a diver remained under pressure, there came a point where his blood stream was completely saturated by the inert gas, and when that point was reached, it would take the same amount of time and 'stops' to return to the surface: hence the name 'saturation diving'. These were the tables that they were proving when Dave joined the Unit.

By using saturation diving, it meant that a team of, say, twelve divers could enter a decompression chamber on an RN diving vessel, and be compressed to a depth equivalent to the sea bed where they would be working. Attached to this chamber would be a submersible decompression chamber, into which three divers could enter, close the hatch, and the SDC could then be unlocked from the main chamber and lowered to the sea bed. The divers then could leave the SDC, wearing breathing sets, and carry out the work that they were engaged in. When all three divers had spent one or two hours in the water, they would all return to the SDC, close the hatch, be hoisted back to the ship, and locked back onto the main chamber; they could then enter the main chamber for food and sleep, whilst another shift of divers could return to the sea bed. Bear in mind, they are all still at the same pressure as the sea bed. This routine could be carried on for weeks, or until the underwater task was completed. At this time they would all return to the main chamber and be brought back to surface pressure, using the tables that they were now proving. It might take fourteen days to get back to surface pressure, during which time the ship could be back in harbour.

Of course, they would breathe oxy/helium mixture gas during the dive, because of the narcotic effect of nitrogen in normal air, nitrogen narcosis. Helium didn't have that affect, but it did effect the vocal chords and made everyone sound like chipmunks, so helium scramblers were used for communication between the 'pot' and outside, which turned their voices normal again.

This method of Saturation Diving was used successfully in the recovery of gold bullion from the wreck of the cruiser HMS *Edinburgh*, sunk by a German U-boat off North Cape during the war. This cruiser was carrying the gold to Russia and was lying in about 800 feet of water. A RN deep diving vessel spent several weeks salvaging the gold from the wreck, and recovered all of it. When she arrived back in port, the diving team were still carrying out their decompression stops.

Two days after Dave joined the Unit, they started one of the trial dives. Six divers entered the 'pot' and settled down in the main chamber; the doors were clamped shut, and the boss said over the internal Tannoy, 'Everyone well in the pot?' They all held their thumbs up, and the senior diver replied, 'All well in the pot.' The boss said, 'Leaving surface,' and he opened the main valve and oxy/helium gas hissed into the chamber, and the depth gauge pointer moved away from zero. As this was Dave's first dive as Deputy Supervisor in the DTU, his duty was to keep a log of the proceedings, noting the time of every incident, and monitoring the oxygen percentage of the gas in the chamber, and, of course, learning the correct procedure, so that he would also be able to supervise deep dives.

There were several glass ports in the chamber, where a close eye could be kept on all of the divers at all times. During the initial stages of the dive, the divers could be seen clearing their ears, to equalise the pressure on both sides of their ear-drums. If one held his arm up, they would immediately stop increasing the pressure, until such time as he gave the OK sign. Sometimes they might even have to ascend a few feet so that the diver could clear his ears, but it was out of the question to continue going down until the ear was clear; that would result in a burst eardrum and aborting the dive.

It took about an hour to reach 1,000 feet. The air stopped hissing, and the Supervisor said 'Reached bottom, 1,000 feet, all well?' and again he would get the reply, 'All well in the pot.'

They didn't do any 'wet' diving that day, just prepared for a seven-day stay at that depth. They all had bunks in the chamber, and regular hot meals were locked into them; they were under surveillance the whole of the time. In the evening, a TV was pushed up against one of the glass ports, and the sound was piped in over the interval Tannoy, so that they could watch TV. During every dive there was a Diving Medical Officer in immediate attendance; he had a cabin in the Unit, and he monitored the health of the divers, giving advice as necessary, locking in medicine if required, and in serious cases, such as a bad bend, having himself locked in to attend the patient. There were occasions where the decompression main chamber was being brought back to the surface under saturation diving tables, and the doctor in another annex chamber was being brought back to the surface under a different set of tables.

Whilst a dive trial was in progress, Dave and his boss were watchkeeping, 4 hours on and 4 hours off, with the rest of the surface crew, including the doctor. In the present stages, each dive was approximately of three weeks duration, a week on the bottom and two weeks to surface. On the way up, if any of the divers developed symptoms of decompression sickness, the 'bends', this usually showed itself as pains in the joints, the elbows, knees and shoulders. If they were moving up to the next 'stop' when it occurred, the Duty Supervisor would stop the ascent and begin to pressurise the chamber again, in other words, take them deeper. If they were already at a 'stop', he would also increase the pressure. This had the effect of relieving the pain in the diver with the 'bend', and when the pain had gone, the Supervisor would stop at that depth. The Medical Officer would then start to calculate a new set of tables to get back to the surface. If a 'bend' recurred as they started to move up, they had to go through the whole procedure again; it had the effect of increasing the total period of the dive by several days.

On the second day of the dive, the divers would take turns at dressing in a wet suit and breathing apparatus, and going into the pool to work. To stimulate work, there was a harness rigged in the pool; they put their shoulders against this harness and swam against it. The amount of effort they were putting into it was measured on a scale.

Although the pool was only 10 to 12 feet deep, because of the pressure in the 'pot', it was the equivalent to a diver leaving a submersible decompression chamber at 1,000 feet in the sea, and carrying out work on the sea bed.

Dave, watching them through the glass port, used to compare it with space travel. Although the men were only a few feet away from him in the chamber, it would take at least two weeks before they could step out onto 'the surface' again; at least astronauts could return to earth quicker than that.

So he spent most of his days at the DTU. Between the trial dives they had to prepare the chambers for the next dive, carrying out routine maintenance, replenishing gas supplies, carrying out pressure tests, etc.

Also between dives, he would take his turn as Duty Diving Officer in HMS *Vernon*. Every day, during non-working hours, a duty diving team was detailed to carry out any emergency diving that might be required in Portsmouth harbour. These were tasks like a foul screw on an RN Ship, possibly a ship berthing that had got one of its berthing hawsers around its screws, and the duty diving team would be called out to clear it.

Another job that came up regularly, especially at weekends in the summer, was treating civilian recreational Scuba divers who had developed a 'bend'. The Duty Diving Officer would get a telephone call informing him that a civilian diver was on his way by helicopter to *Vernon*, with a suspected bend, developed whilst diving on a wreck at Brighton, or wherever.

The Duty Diving Team were called out to prepare the decompression chamber, at the Diving School, and a medical team with an ambulance would be waiting at the heliport to transfer the patient to the chamber. Speed was essential in getting a 'bend' case to the nearest decompression chamber, but if a helicopter was used for this purpose, it had to fly very low, because flying decreased the pressure and aggravated the symptoms.

Usually a companion would accompany the patient, and he would give a history of the dive: how deep? how long under pressure? any previous diving during the past twenty-four hours? The patient would be put into the 'pot' after an examination by a Medical Officer, and one of the duty diving team would also enter the 'pot' to act as stand-by diver. They would then be put under pressure as dictated by the therapeutic decompression tables, always at hand near the decompression chamber. The treatment usually lasted a few hours and after that time the diver could leave the pot, although he was advised to remain within an hour's travel of a pot, in case of a recurrence.

Dave could remember times when patients would literally be queuing up to use the pot, and they would have to commandeer the chamber at the Submarine school, and even the one at Portland.

The time passed very quickly at DTU. It was a very busy period, and he had very little time off. There were few incidents, the most serious being a CPO diver who developed 'bend' symptoms during one of the trial dives. He was treated in the usual manner, but every time they got close to the surface, the bend would reoccur, and they had to increase the pressure again. Of course the other five divers were also in the chamber and were going up and down with him. They spent a long time in the chamber during that dive; at one stage they allowed his wife to come in to see him and speak to him on the Tannoy, as she was getting a bit anxious. The situation was finally resolved when they allowed pressure to decrease by just cracking the valve and letting the gas slowly bleed slowly out of the chamber. They reached surface pressure without the bend recurring. The Chief was taken to the Naval Hospital at Haslar for a check-up, and was pronounced fit for normal diving to 180 feet, but unfit for deep diving. Although Dave was still an 'in-date' diver, that is medically fit, and with the necessary time spent under water, he was rather glad that he was over the age limit to take part in saturation diving.

He still had four months left before he had to take up his appointment in the USA, and he was given the job as Technical Adviser to a film company that was making an instructional film for the Ministry of Defence about Operation Awkward, defence of ships against underwater attack.

He had to spend quite a lot of time in the film company's offices in Soho, London; he was given the script to read, which he had to translate from English into Navalese, navy language, which can be quite different. Then he sat in at the interviews of actors for the casting of the characters in the film. Dave asked why they didn't use the naval personnel, of which there would be many at the locations and who already spoke Navalese. The producer said that they had tried that before and they found that sailors tended to 'ham it up' when they acted, whereas actors came out more realistic. Dave saw his point.

The story involved an RFA and a frigate, and the MOD was responsible for providing the locations for shooting the scenes. The RFA was easy enough, and they did a lot of shooting on one in dry-dock in Plymouth and another at Pulau Tioman, Malaya.

Frigates were more difficult as they were so busy they were literally run off their feet. They must have used five different frigates, although in the film it was always the same ship. They had to have good underwater visibility for the underwater scenes, so locations were at Gibraltar, Singapore, Hong Kong or anywhere that the MOD could find a frigate with a day to spare.

So Dave and the film crew, in three months, flew all over the world to get the 'shooting' in. A frigate had to berth at Nassau, in the Bahamas, for four days repair work on her sonar dome, and the film crew had to fly there to get in underwater shots. They did use naval personnel as 'extras', and one of the actors, who was playing the part of a Petty Officer who had to go down into the mess-deck and detail the sailors off for upper-deck sentry duty, was so realistic and 'acid', that even the real sailors were frightened of him and used to disappear from the mess-deck whenever he came down.

Dave had to leave his job before it was fully completed, but he did see the finished film later on and was very impressed by it.

CHAPTER 14

US Navy

Dave flew to Washington, DC to take up his new appointment and was met at the airport by the officer that he was relieving there. He had a big American car, a Ford Fairlane shooting-brake, which he had bought from the officer that he had relieved two years earlier, so Dave said that he would buy it from him when he left. They drove into Washington, then into Maryland and followed the Potomac River south to a very small town, twenty-seven miles south of Washington. It was called Indian Head, and it was here that the US Navy Base was situated, and where he would spend the next two years. It was in this base that the US Navy EOD School and the EOD Facility was and where he would be working.

The base covered quite a large area and was on the banks of the Potomac. The river must have been about two miles wide at that point and on the other side was the US Marine Base of Quantico in Virginia.

He was taken to the house where the officer that he was relieving lived, a wooden bungalow with a big White Ensign flying from a flag-pole. There was a big sign declaring it to be the 'British Exchange Officer's Quarters', and the other officer, Jim, told Dave that he could move in there, in one week's time, when he departed for the UK, in the meantime he would be living in the Bachelor Officers' Quarters.

The rest of that day was taken up with being introduced to everyone that he would be working with, then down to the 'Diving Locker' to meet the EOD Diving Team and to see their set-up. He was told that he would spend his first two weeks there, becoming familiar with US diving equipment and learning how to use it. He was taken to the clothing store, where he was issued with full US Navy khaki uniform, which was the uniform that he would wear whilst in the States, though with it he wore his RN cap and his medal ribbons. He was issued with two gold bars, to be worn in the collar, to denote his rank as Lieutenant.

He had to get used to being called 'Lootenant', instead of 'Leftenant', and he heard the divers describing him as 'the Limey Lootenant'. He met his Commanding Officer, a Commander, a big Texan called 'Red' Moody, who said, 'Well, what do you want to do in the States, Dave?' He told him that this was his first time in the States, and he would like to see as much of it as he could. The Commander said, 'OK, that's my job, I'll make sure that you see as much as we can fit in.' From that time on Red Moody attached him to lots of different Projects, taking him all over the US.

By that time it was mid-day and Jim took him to the O-Club, the Officers Club, where he met many more officers, and where the Budweiser flowed freely. One officer said, 'You like Mexican chow, Dave?', he said that he really had never tasted it, and the officer said, 'Come on, half a dozen of us are going to the Long-Horn Bar for lunch, including you.' So they all made their way to the Long-Horn Bar, which was just outside the main gate to the base. It was owned by an ex-Navy Bosun's Mate, and was obviously a popular watering hole. Dave found that he loved Mexican chow, and was hooked on it there and then, especially as this was washed down with Margaritas, tequila! That ended the first day; he spent the rest of that day in his cabin, in bed, in the BOQ.

The next day Jim picked him up and took him down to his new office. The EOD Facility was about fifteen miles further south of the School; it was a Research and Development Centre for EOD, and a lot of civilians worked there. The whole area was densely wooded with pine trees and not very many houses. Indian Head itself was a one-horse town with a filling station and a drug store. Jim and he went over all the books he needed to know, and he met a lot more people; some of their EOD development were way ahead of anything that he had seen in the UK, especially with fibre-optics. On the other hand, America didn't have hundreds of mines and unexploded bombs lying around as in the UK, so we were probably ahead in that department.

Jim left at the end of the week and Dave moved into the British Exchange Officer's Quarters, and took over his new car. He started his conversion course to US breathing sets. There was a huge diving tank, almost the size of a football pitch and about 30 feet deep, where he started using the US Mk 6 set. They used helium as the inert gas, which seemed very wasteful as helium gas is so expensive. The RN couldn't afford to waste it the way that the US Navy did. At home in the DTU at Alverstoke, all the gas used in the deep dives was reclaimed, cleaned and used again on the next dive. The other thing that Dave found it difficult to get used to was not wearing a nose-clip. RN divers use it because it is much easier to clear your ears, and you learn to breathe in and out through your mouth. Still, he soon adapted to its absence and by the end of his course he could use all of their equipment.

He found that he liked the American way of life: the big cars, with petrol, or as he soon began to call it 'gas', at a few cents a gallon, so that it didn't really matter if you drove a big car, and with the roads almost deserted of traffic once you were away from the cities, it was a pleasure to drive. Their interstate motorways amazed him; to drive along an eight-lane highway, stretching as far as you could see, without another vehicle in sight was really something. He used to enjoy the long drive every morning from the base to his office, a long straight road through a pinewood forest, keeping an eye open for deer on the road, which were very common.

The CO made good his promise and soon he was given his first project. It was to design a tool that could find unexploded bombs that had buried themselves in the ground, at different depths and at different angles.

They had already done the initial work on this project. They had found a factory in Massachusetts that had developed a machine for detecting pipes buried under the ice. They had designed it for the oil industry in Alaska, for tracking oil pipes, and the Navy Department wanted to investigate if a similar machine could detect buried bombs. This had been fully discussed with the directors at the factory, and they were in the process of developing a machine that they said would detect buried bombs.

Dave, as Project Officer, had to visit the factory every month to check on the progress of the project and eventually to arrange trials, and if they were successful, to arrange acceptance trials for the Navy EOD facility.

For his first visit, the Administration Department 'cut' his orders. He was to fly from Washington to Boston, where he would pick up a rental car and drive to Springfield, a town close to the factory. He was booked into a hotel for three days, during which time he would have meetings with the Company Project Officer.

A Navy car drove him to the airport in Washington, and he flew Delta Airline to Boston. He had a wonderful view of the Statue of Liberty as he passed over New York. In Boston he picked up his rental car, and he had quite a long drive inland to reach Springfield. The traffic in Boston was horrendous, but once out of the city, it was a pleasant drive. He checked into his hotel, and went out for a meal and a drink in a bar. He got talking to the bar owner, who turned out to be yet another ex US Navy bosun's mate, and when he found out that Dave was in the British Navy, insisted that the drinks were on the house and told Dave to come back there every time that he was in Springfield.

In the factory the next day he found that they had reached the prototype stage of the UXB Detector. It looked like a large lawn mower and, although the electronics were not yet completed, it would work on the same principle as a radar set firing a radio pulse straight down into the earth and receiving echoes back from solid objects that it struck. These would be displayed on a cathode ray tube, and a print-out much like a depth recorder would give a picture showing the depth below the surface and the posture of the object. The theory looked good, but it hadn't reached the practical stage yet. They also showed him their 'pipes under the ice' machine, which worked on similar lines.

He returned to Washington and reported to the committee who would eventually have to assess the possibility of acceptance.

He kept up his practice dives from the diving locker, usually diving in the Potomac River, all of which had to go into his Personal Diving Log, to remain qualified for RN diving pay. He did get attached to a project which was testing a towed underwater sled, at Panama City in Florida. There was a US Diving complex at Panama City and they stayed there, whilst they went out diving each day. The sled was towed by a powerful boat. It carried four divers in Scuba gear, lying on the sled with their heads protected by a Perspex windscreen to prevent them from being swept off. It could be controlled so that it could skim along a few feet above the sea bed and weave from side to side. It had been designed for searching for ground mines; when a practice mine was sighted, one of the divers dropped off the sled and placed a marker buoy on the mine. Panama City also had an underwater habitat called SeaLab about half a mile out to sea in the Gulf of Mexico. It was a US experimental program, running along the same lines as the Space Program. Dave swam around SeaLab with the other divers but they weren't allowed to go into it. The night life in Panama City was a bit wild, maybe because it was a Navy town; it had dirt streets and was very primitive.

The weather in Indian Head took some getting used to. It saw the extremes in temperature. In summer it was almost unbearably hot, made worse by the very high humidity that made the perspiration stream out of you. Fortunately every building and vehicle was air-conditioned.

In the winter it went to the other extreme, with heavy snowfalls that quickly closed the roads until the snow ploughs got going, and the temperatures were several degrees below freezing, with huge icicles everywhere. You had to carry and wear snow chains; if you got bogged down in the snow, and you didn't have snow chains, the police would give you a ticket.

The day arrived, after several visits to Springfield, when the bomb detector arrived at Indian Head, and Red Moody told Dave it would be tested in the Mojave Desert in California where they had an EOD team based. He was told to go on ahead, to a US Marine Base at 29 Palms in the desert, where he would be allocated about an acre of desert. He was told to mark it out, and bury ten 1,000 pound bombs, at different spots, at different depths and at different angles. He was to take accurate measurements and draw up a plan so that only he would know the exact places where the bombs were buried. The EOD team at 29 Palms would assist him to do this.

This time Administration cut his orders to fly to Los Angeles, pick up a rental car and drive out into the desert to 29 Palms. He was due to arrive in LA at 2 p.m. local time, and he thought, at least the roads won't be too bad, as he had been warned of the traffic chaos that reigned in LA. Unfortunately his plane was delayed for three hours in Chicago, and he arrived in LA in the middle of the peak traffic hour. He found himself driving along this twelve-lane freeway, bumper to bumper traffic, perusing all these strange signs to places he had never heard of. He knew he had to head for San Bernadino or Riverside, but you have to be in the correct lane to exit. It was no good getting into the right hand lane and thinking, 'I'll just stay in this lane until my exit comes up' because a sign would suddenly say, 'Right lane must turn right'. Added to that, there was the problem that some exits went off to the left.

More by luck than judgment he found himself on the right road, and the landscape changed to desert, just like the movies, with the occasional coffee stop, where the guy behind the counter would say, 'What'll it be, Bud?'

He arrived at 29 Palms Marine Base. They were expecting him and checked him in to his cabin. In the mess he felt the curious glances, as he did everywhere he went. Many of the American officers had never heard of the Exchange Scheme, and the glances were saying, 'What's this limey officer doing here in half American uniform?' They were always very friendly though, never with any animosity; he thought that a lot of then engaged him in conversation just to listen to his English accent.

He met the EOD team the next day and they took him to an area of sand

and scrub which had been allocated for the trial. With tape measures they accurately measured out a square piece of ground, marking it off with tape. Ten inert 1,000-pound bombs were already stacked up near the area. Dave selected ten positions in the square, and with a mechanical digger, they dug ten holes at varying depths from 3 feet to 15 feet, and lowered a bomb into each hole, resting them at different angles. When this was done, Dave made an accurate plan of the test area, indicating where each bomb was located, the depth that it was at, and the angle of the bomb. There was only one plan and Dave kept it in his briefcase. They then filled in the holes and spread the surface sand around to make it look natural again.

It was almost Christmas and the EOD diving team invited Dave to join them at a nearby restaurant, where they were having a party with their wives and girl-friends. They had a very good evening, as it was a typical divers party, but unfortunately it ended in violence, and Dave saw the violent nature of some Americans. One man accused another of insulting his wife and a row started. Everyone was trying to calm them down, but finally, one invited the other to settle it outside. They both headed for the door, with everyone still trying to get them to shake hands. As the first one went through the door, he spun round with an open penknife in his hand which he stuck into the other man's thigh, then he turned and ran off into the desert. It all happened so fast that he was gone before anyone realised what had happened.

Two of the team went after him to try to bring him back. The one who was stabbed was bleeding badly but it turned out to be a superficial wound, and he was bandaged up and seemed OK. The police were not called; servicemen try not to get police involvement in internal squabbles, unless it is absolutely necessary.

The next morning they told Dave that they hadn't been able to find the sailor, and he had gone on the run, deserted, and he still hadn't returned by the time that Dave returned to Washington.

A couple of days later the bomb detector arrived, with three officials from the factory in Massachusetts. Dave took them to the roped-off area and told them that there were ten UXBs buried on the site; he gave them half a dozen photocopies of the area, blank, but marked off into 5-yard squares, and he told them that at the end of the day, he wanted their final copy returned to him, with the position of the bombs indicated on the plan, with their depth and attitude if possible.

They started running their 'lawn-mower' up and down the area, stopping occasionally to investigate an 'echo'. Dave spent an hour with them, mainly to learn about the controls on the machine, and to decipher the 'read-out', then left them to it.

At the end of the day he returned and they gave him their final plan. He thanked them for their work and they left to return to Springfield. After making arrangements for the bomb locator to be returned to Indian Head, he went back to his cabin to compare their results with his master copy. The results were reasonable although not brilliant. Three of the bombs were spot on for location and depth, another two had the location within two yards, although the depths were incorrect, another one was within five yards but the depth was wrong, two were way out, and two had not been located. The angle and attitude of the bombs was only correct in one case. He wrote up his report, together with the plans and read-outs, for his CO, and the following day he returned to Indian Head.

Each year the EOD fraternity hold a 5-Nation Conference, between the USA, UK, Canada, Australia and New Zealand. The object is to discuss development in EOD techniques, and to exchange ideas between each other, each country taking a turn at hosting the Conference.

On Dave's first year in the States, it was Australia's turn to host the Conference. Dave had only ever attended one of these meetings, and that was when it was being held in *Vernon*. Nor had he ever got to Australia in all of the years that he had been in the Navy, so he was pleasantly surprised when Red Moody asked him if he would be a US delegate for that year's Conference in Sydney, Australia. He was also very flattered as there was always fierce competition to be a delegate at these Conferences. He was asked to read a paper on the bomb locator, so he guessed that was why they had invited him.

There were six officers in their group, including Red Moody, and they flew via Los Angeles and Hawaii to Sydney. The conference was held in HMAS *Watson*, a shore establishment in Sydney. It was a very interesting conference. The Australians were good hosts, inviting them to their homes, taking them out on outings to the Blue Ridge Mountains and on a diving expedition. At a cocktail party, an Australian officer came up to Dave and said, 'You must have led a chequered career.'

Dave said, 'What do you mean?' and the man said, 'Well, you are wearing British war medal ribbons, and now you are serving in the US Navy.'

Dave explained that he was still in the RN, and he thought that the Exchange Officer Scheme must be one of the best secrets going. He couldn't help being amused at the thought that after thirty years in the RN, it had been up to the US Navy to get him to Australia.

They landed at San Francisco on the way back. Red Moody took them back to Washington via San Antonio, Texas, where he lived, to partake in 'the best Mexican chow in the States'. Dave thought that he was probably right.

He got his second project on arriving back. About that time, the Cunard Liner SS *Queen Elizabeth II* had a bomb alert in mid-Atlantic, and a team of Royal Marine EOD personnel were parachuted into the sea alongside the ship to deal with the incident. The US War Department decided that they had to have this capability, to place an EOD team with all of their tools, explosives and equipment into inaccessible places such as deserts, jungles or mid-ocean. They called the Project EOD Parachute Insertion and Dave was made the Project Officer.

He spent a lot of time in the US Navy Yard in Virginia, building the package. The container was made of fibreglass and contained everything that would be required on an EOD operation, packed securely in foam rubber against shock. The container was very much like the roof rack containers fitted to most cars. On top of the container, and securely fastened to it, was the heavy duty parachute pack, while under the container was an uninflated rubber dinghy. The whole package sat on a flat small wheeled trolley, which allowed it to be launched from the ramp of a transport aircraft.

In practice, this package would be launched off the ramp, and at the same time two EOD divers jumped and opened their parachutes. The main parachute of the package was opened by a line attached to the aircraft. Once the parachute opened, the dinghy fell clear and remained attached to the container by a 6-foot wire pendant, whilst the dinghy automatically inflated. When the dinghy hit the sea, the container would settle into the dinghy, and the two divers who had jumped would climb into the dinghy, open up the container, and rig the outboard engine. Once this had been done, the rest of the team jumped and joined them by parachute.

When Dave took the package back to Indian Head, Red Moody said, 'Right, you will now have to test it. The only parachute trained EOD team that we have is in Hawaii; you will have to take your package out to Pearl Harbor for trials.' 'Oh no, not Hawaii,' thought Dave.

There was a lot of talk about sending Dave to Fort Bragg, to put him through a parachute jumping course, but, much to his relief, they decided that his age was against this, so Dave and another US Navy lieutenant left for Pearl Harbor, the package going by US Airforce.

Unknown to Dave, the other lieutenant had phoned ahead to a friend of his, based at Pearl Harbor, so when he stepped off the plane, he was surprised to receive a traditional Hawaiian welcome. This officer's wife stepped up, placed a lei around his neck, kissed him and said 'Aloha.' He spent a pleasant two weeks in Hawaii. The jumps went perfectly; they used a twin rotor helicopter with a loading ramp, and they took the package up at least twice a day.

Dave went up with them for every jump and watched the whole operation from the chopper launching the package and the divers into the harbour. Every exercise was successful. Dave felt that he would like to jump with them, and was encouraged to do so by the diving team, but they all knew that they would be breaking regulations if he did, so they forgot that idea.

He saw a good bit of the island, driving inland to see miles and miles of pineapple fields, and the gap in the mountains where the Japanese planes had come through on the infamous day that they bombed Pearl Harbor. He saw the Arizona Memorial marking the place where the battleship had sank on that day.

It rained for about an hour every day; you could almost set your watch by it. You had glorious sunshine, then the rain started, and an hour later the sun was out again, and within minutes everything was dry once more. He even managed a couple of days on the well known Waikiki beach.

He returned to Indian Head and everyone agreed it had been a successful trial.

Shortly after that he was sent out to the Mojave Desert again, attached to a team that was testing shaped charges on bombs. They were trying to achieve a partial explosion, rather than a full order which would destroy everything in the vicinity.

Administration said to him, 'We sent you to Los Angeles last time; this time we will send you to Las Vegas. You can spend a day there then drive to China Lake, in the desert where the trials are taking place.' This suited Dave; he had always wanted to see Las Vegas.

On arriving there, he found that there were 'one armed bandits' everywhere, in the airport, in the toilets, almost everywhere you looked. He had been booked into the Holiday Inn, and, after taking his luggage there, he quickly went out to explore. The casinos were fantastic, the size of football pitches, with crap tables, Black Jack, roulette, and hundreds of slot machines. There were women with buckets full of quarters working, sometimes ten machines at a time, just moving from one machine to another, putting in quarters and pulling the handle. Girls were walking around with trays of drinks, all of which were free. All that they wanted you to do was gamble; they made so much profit, they could afford to give free drinks.

The casinos never closed, open twenty-four hours a day. There were no windows and no clocks, so that you didn't know whether it was light or dark outside. Lots of people come up from Los Angeles; they work all of the week, then at weekends they came to Las Vegas to gamble.

Walking from one casino to another, the streets were always full, and the place was a mass of flashing neon lights. A man came up to Dave and said, 'Excuse me sir, I wonder if you could give me a few minutes of your time?' Dave was immediately wary and alert; he had been told that Las Vegas was full of con men. The man went on, 'I work for one of the Wedding Chapels, and I need a witness for a marriage, would you mind helping?'

There are dozens of Wedding Chapels on the 'Strip' and you can get married on the spur of the moment. Dave was still suspicious and said, 'I'm sorry, but I am not an American.'

The man said, 'That's all right, sir, any nationality can be a witness.'

Dave thought, 'What the hell! it will be a different experience,' and he went with the man to a white wooden chapel, where inside he could hear a church organ.

They went in; it was very nice, laid out like a chapel, lots of flowers, and in front of the altar was a minister, and two kids, a girl and a boy, dressed in jeans and tops, who didn't look any older than sixteen. As soon as they stepped in, the organ broke into the Wedding March, the man indicated that Dave should sit in one of the pews, and the marriage ceremony went ahead. When the minister pronounced them man and wife, Dave was beckoned forward. He congratulated them, kissed the bride, and watched while they signed the register, and then he signed as a witness.

The man who had 'recruited' him led him back to the door, said, 'Thank you very much sir,' and shook him by the hand. Dave went outside. He looked down at his hand; there was a 10-dollar bill in it.

He enjoyed his time in Las Vegas, thinking that it was a city that everyone should see at least once. When you drive out of LV, it suddenly stops being a city and you are out in the desert. Dave wasn't a gambler, but the atmosphere is contagious, so he did try his hand at some of the 'slots'. He changed some dollar bills into silver dollar coins. You never saw a one dollar coin anywhere else in America, but Las Vegas was swimming in them. He came away from there with a pocket full of silver dollars.

Next morning he drove to the Navy base at China Lake. He met the team that were engaged in the Shaped Charge Trials and spent a week with them. They used to go up into the desert, where they had a locked bunker of shells and bombs which they were using on the trials, and they were having a large percentage of success at opening the shells with only a partial explosion. The temperature in the desert was way over 100 degrees Fahrenheit, and you had to drink a lot to replace the perspiration. China Lake, in fact, was a lake but at the time that Dave was there it was just dry salt flats. Nearby was the infamous Death Valley, where many of the pioneers opening the West, with their waggon trains, lost their lives trying to cross the Mojave Desert.

Near to where they were working there was a wooden tool shed, where they kept their shovels and picks. They also kept their water in there, where it kept reasonably cool in the shade. Dave went into the shed to bring a bottle of water for everyone to drink, and while he was in there, he heard a curious sound, and turning round he saw a rattlesnake coiled up in a corner. It was shaking its rattle and was poised, obviously ready to strike. Dave jumped backwards as it lunged to strike and it missed.

He ran back and told the others, who went back and dispatched the snake with shovels; they gave the rattle to Dave.

Dave's two year tour in America was coming to an end, and when he got back to Indian Head he found that his relief would be joining in about six weeks. He was also approaching his fiftieth birthday and compulsory retirement. He regretted this because he loved the Navy life; he was still an active diver and an expert in EOD, but rules were rules and he would be retiring.

Red Moody told him to take two weeks leave, so he set out in his car and drove to Texas, a part of the country that he had always wanted to see. He went to San Antonio, which he had liked the look of on his earlier fleeting visit. There is a lot of Spanish spoken there and as he spoke quite a bit of Spanish himself he found it very useful. He visited the Alamo, a Mission Station that is an important part of American history, and he found the River Walk, which winds its way through the city, very beautiful.

From San Antonio he drove south towards the Mexican border and a part of Texas called the Big Bend. This is the newest National Park, covering several hundred square miles. The Big Bend is formed by the Rio Grande making a big bend and enclosing what is now the National Park. It is very remote, about 250 miles from the nearest town, and is made up of desert, scrub, prairie and mountains. He had heard about it from Texans, but very few other Americans had ever heard of it. It was a place to 'get away from it all'; there was one small town called Terlingua with one motel and a trailer park. Tourist attractions were river rafting on the Rio Grande, which went through a very deep canyon in that area, and pony trekking.

It was possible to wade across the Rio Grande in places, to Mexico on the other side, but there was nothing there. The people who lived there were strange, a lot of hippy types and artists. Dave thought that most of them were 'drop outs', and many were running away from something: a failed business, a failed marriage or the law. He went into a shop that sold different kinds of rock and Indian arrow heads. It was run by an old couple who spoke German and whose English was not very good. When they found out that he was British, they began to act rather strangely, and Dave had the feeling that they were escaping from a Nazi past.

Two old sisters ran the river rafting business, and they also advertised tours to an old quicksilver mine in the desert. It was miles away from anywhere and they had bought it, with several acres of land, just by paying off the unpaid back taxes. It sounded interesting so Dave booked on the tour. He found out that so few people visited this place that there hadn't been a tour out there for over a year.

They set out early in the morning; there were two other people, Dutch, and their guide was a cowboy called Gordon, dressed in jeans, cowboy shirt and hat, who spoke in a deep Texan drawl. He sounded and looked like everyone's idea of a cowboy. They drove in a jeep over flat prairie land, there were no roads, with the sun just coming up over the rim of the mountains behind them.

As they drove, he told them the history of the quicksilver mine. It had been discovered just before 1900, by some cowboys building a camp fire. They had collected some big rocks to contain the fire in a circle, and when the fire was lit, they noticed this silver liquid being exuded from the heated rocks. They discovered that this was quicksilver, mercury, and the mine was formed.

They drove for about a couple of hours over this flat terrain, then ahead, among some low hills, they could see some buildings. When they arrived there, they found that it was a small village in ruins. There was a large cave dug into the side of one of the hills, with narrow rail tracks going in and a couple of broken buggies; this was the mine.

Gordon warned them to watch where they stepped and where they put their hands, as there were quite a few snakes and scorpions around, and gingerly, with lamps, they went into the cave. The workings went in a long way, and there were old tools and machinery, and old oil lamps everywhere. At the face of the mine he pointed out the veins of quicksilver, which were reflected in the light from the lamps.

When they emerged they looked at the broken, rusting machinery still in place, where the ore had been lifted above the mine and put into a long revolving screen, which got rid of all of the dust and small pieces, and at the end, a furnace where the ore had been heated, and the spouts where the quicksilver had run out and been collected. Apart from the rust, a lot of machinery looked as though it would still work. The mine had produced quicksilver until the 1920s when the price fell so much that it was no longer a viable proposition, and it had closed and been abandoned.

They sat on some benches and ate sandwiches and beer that Gordon had brought in an ice box, and it was pleasant sitting in the sun talking. Gordon pointed out some vultures circling around them, turkey buzzards he called them, waiting for the remains of their lunch.

They wandered around the village which had been built for the mine workers, small one roomed terraced houses, a school house for the children, a saloon and a General Store, which, Gordon said, sold everything.

The workers, of course, came from the other side of the Rio Grande, illegal immigrants from Mexico. They nicknamed them 'wet backs' because they had swam across the river. Gordon told them an interesting story about the mine-workers and the General Store. The workers were not allowed to go anywhere else except the village because they were illegals; they were paid in Company Scrip Money, which they could only use at the General Store. They were probably charged outrageous prices, and the Company mail man had orders to vet all of the workers' incoming mail, to make sure that no Sears Roebuck mail order catalogues got into the village, which would give the 'wet backs' the real price of articles that were sold in the Store.

They spent the whole of the day exploring the village and the mine, finding lots of interesting artefacts, and, as the sun sank towards the horizon, Gordon made a camp-fire and produced four beautiful steaks and salad from the ice-box, and started to barbecue them. It got dark very quickly and they had a very pleasant evening, eating their steaks by fire-light, washing it down with coffee laced with Kahula.

The journey back didn't seem to take half so long, bouncing over the prairie in pitch darkness. Dave didn't know whether Gordon drove by compass or by following a star, but there were no other indications to give him directions. He wondered if it would be another year before another tour visited the village.

CHAPTER 15

The Final Years

Dave enjoyed his two weeks leave, and eventually, his relief arrived, and he returned to the UK, HMS *Vernon* and retirement. There was a Mess Dinner in the Wardroom, where he was 'dined out' with two other leavers. He was presented with a crystal diver in a standard suit by the Diving Branch, another one in a Scuba set by the EOD team, and a silver rum barrel by the Wardroom.

He had already decided to live in Spain when he retired; he had a villa there, and any job in the UK would be an anticlimax after the Navy.

However Fortune smiled on him. He hadn't been out of the Navy for many months, when he received a letter from the Superintendent of Diving asking if he would be prepared to return to the service for another four years.

About the time that Dave left the service the North Sea oil industry was getting under way, and these companies were offering RN divers a much higher salary than they could ever hope to achieve in the Navy. Obviously many divers left the service, causing an acute shortage in the Diving Branch, and Dave was being offered a post in the Diving School in Vernon, to turn out new divers.

He accepted it gratefully and was soon back at work. He passed the diving Medical Examination, re-qualified as an 'in date' diver, and joined the staff in the School. His main duties in the school were as Divisional Officer for about two hundred junior rates; in charge of the Permanent Diving Stores worth about £500,000; instructional duties in various diving subjects; in charge of diving displays at Portsmouth Navy Days and some large schools, which were really recruiting drives; lecturing in RN Diving and EOD, some of these lectures being to Civilian Associations; Diving Inspection Officer to all RNR establishments and ships throughout the country. Every so often during the year he had to take command of the RN diving tender *Ixworth*, either taking it to, or bringing it back from, Oban in

Scotland or Falmouth in Cornwall.

When the diving classes were at Horsea Island, or diving at Spithead, Falmouth or Oban, he was able to accompany the classes for which he was the Course Officer, and so was able to get some diving in himself to remain an 'in date' diver.

He loved the trips on the *Ixworth*. It was used for the deep diving training up to 180 feet. Diving regulations stated that for dives deeper than 140 feet, a decompression chamber had to be in the immediate vicinity of the dive site, so *Ixworth*'s 'main armament' was an 8-man decompression chamber. Her other purpose was to carry all the diving equipment for deep diving to the dive site; this equipment would be used by several classes during the term. There were cooking facilities on board, but it wasn't used as accommodation; all the classes and instructors lived in 'digs' ashore during the two weeks or so that they were carrying out their deep dives.

There was a permanent crew on board the *Ixworth*: a Chief Petty Officer in charge, a Leading Seaman carrying out the duties of 'buffer', a stoker for the engine-room, and two able seaman for helmsman's duties, manning the berthing lines, anchor, and upper deck maintenance etc.

During the summer term, deep diving was carried out off Falmouth, but during the winter months, the long Atlantic rollers made diving difficult, and, at times, impossible at Falmouth, so during the winter months, the deep diving venue was shifted to Oban in Scotland. It seemed ridiculous to move up to Scotland in the winter, where the weather was usually worse, but experience had shown that it was always possible to find sheltered water and the depth required, in the lee of the numerous islands off Oban.

So at the beginning and end of each term, Dave would board the *Ixworth* and take command, mainly for the navigation during the passage. He and the Chief would take alternate watches, plotting the course on the chart, using Decca Navigator, radar fixing, and visual compass bearings. *Ixworth* was about the size of a fishing trawler and at times, in severe weather, they took quite a hammering. The passage to and from Falmouth was relatively short, but travelling up to Oban could take up to two to three days, and it always seemed to be very rough in the Irish Sea. They were given permission to put into Douglas in the Isle of Man, whenever it was really rough.

So he saw quite a bit of Douglas IOM during the next four years. Travelling from Portsmouth to Oban, everyone was usually ready for a break by the time that they reached the Isle of Man and Dave got to know the Harbour Master quite well. They would stay in 'digs' overnight in

Douglas when they stopped there, in fact, in the same boarding houses that used to be HMS *Valkyrie* and an Italian POW camp God knows how many years ago, and where they had looked for a German pocket battleship off Ramsey.

On at least two occasions, when all of his crew were seasick, and when they were all looking forward to a few hours with a steady deck under their feet, they were refused entry into Douglas, because of the heavy swell at the harbour mouth which made it too dangerous to negotiate an entrance, and they had to press on to their destination.

North of the IOM, after passing the Mull of Kintyre, the weather was usually better as they were in more sheltered waters, in the lee of the Western Isles of Scotland. They passed through some quite narrow channels, and some of the scenery was breath-taking. It was quite usual to see herds of red deer through the binoculars. In these narrow channels, when the tide was running, there were rip tides and whirlpools, and the water was treacherous; you had to keep a close eye on the steering, because, for no obvious reason, the ship would suddenly veer from one side to the other. This could be quite alarming as there were places where rocks could be seen just breaking the surface.

Dave liked Oban. It was quite a small town, and very Scottish; the people were friendly, and had got used to the diving classes spending the winter in the town. Everyone spoke with a strong Scottish brogue.

After he had delivered *Ixworth* to Oban or Falmouth, he would usually spend a couple of days with the diving classes, and get a few dives in himself, then return by train to *Vernon*. At the end of the term, he would reverse this routine, bringing the ship back to Portsmouth.

On one of these return journeys from Oban, it had been a very rough passage; in fact, it was one of the occasions when they had been refused entry to Douglas.

Dave always kept the Middle Watch, midnight to 0400, and he had turned in early. It was easier to lie in your bunk than try to stand on your feet. He had fallen asleep, when he was woken by a loud bang and a shuddering of the ship, as it rolled heavily. He jumped out of his bunk, expecting the Chief to call him to the bridge at any moment, but the ship came upright, and everything seemed to be OK, so he thought, 'We must have been hit by a freak wave,' and he turned back in again.

He was called at fifteen minutes to midnight, and went onto the bridge to relieve the Chief.

They were rounding Land's End, and Wolf Rock Lighthouse was flashing on the starboard bow. 'All's well, sir,' said the Chief, 'but we must have a fierce tide running against us; we have only covered about four miles in the last hour.' The Chief finished his report and disappeared. Dave took a Decca fix, plotted it on the chart, and settled down in the Captain's Chair.

Half an hour later he said, 'Watch your steering, helmsman, that's the third time that you have been way off course.'

The sailor on the wheel said, 'It's very difficult to steer, sir, she's going from one side to the other.'

Dave took another fix; they had barely covered two miles. He took over the wheel and said to the helmsman, 'Put your life-jacket on, go up onto the fo'c'sle and check the anchors.' The helmsman came back, white faced, he said, 'The starboard anchor has gone sir, the starboard cable is running out through the hawse pipe.'

Dave stopped the engine and told him to call the leading hand and the other seaman.

He remembered the bang and the shuddering, that was when the anchor had gone; a heavy sea must have broken the slip holding the anchor inboard. When he had his party on the bridge, he sent them onto the fo'c'sle to start heaving in the anchor with the electric capstan. As they were doing this, he wondered if the anchor would still be on the end of the cable when it came up; the Navy tended to frown upon ships that lose their anchor.

The leading hand called up from the fo'c'sle, 'Anchor is clear of the water, sir, some old lines are fouling it.'

Dave rang 'Half Ahead', brought the ship around on course, handed the wheel back to the helmsman and went for'd to have a look.

The anchor had been burnished silver with its drag along the bottom. There were a couple of rusty, old wires hanging over its flukes, and they spent another half an hour clearing this, then they hauled it home, and secured it with another slip and a wire stop through the anchor shackle.

Dave returned to the bridge, resumed normal speed, and, after the next fix, found that they were now doing their normal 10 knots. No wonder they hadn't been covering much ground and the steering had been erratic. He thought, thank goodness it had happened here in open water and not just before they entered the Solent: he would have been popular if he had dragged up all of the telephone and power cables between the mainland and the Isle of Wight.

He still had his home in Spain and went there for all of his leave periods.

231

He always took a late leave, and was the Duty Diving Officer in Vernon during the leave periods. The North Sea oil rigs gradually built up their complements of divers, and stopped pinching them from the RN, who also began to build up their requirement of divers.

During one of the leave periods, towards the end of Dave's time in the Navy, Argentina invaded the Falkland Islands. The Captain of *Vernon*, who lived on the base, and Dave started to recall essential personnel. In the Diving Branch they formed twelve-men teams who were flown out, with all their equipment, as they were formed, to join the Task Force on its way to the Falklands.

We eventually had several of these teams out there, and they did an outstanding job, covering themselves in glory.

In the opening stages of the war, Argentine aircraft were dropping bombs on our ships from an altitude that was too low for the bomb to arm itself before it hit. Consequently some of our ships found themselves with an unexploded bomb which had passed through several decks before coming to rest.

There were stories of divers diving into flooded magazines to render safe UXBs underwater, and on one occasion, where they had a UXB in a compartment below the water line, they cut square holes in the decks above the bomb, which they hoisted up, keeping it at the same angle, then, once above the water line, they cut a hole in the ship's side, and lowered the bomb into an inflatable dinghy which they had filled with cornflakes, commandeered from the Ship's Stores. The cornflakes were to give the bomb a nice 'nest' to rest in and keep it at the same angle. The divers then took it and dumped it in deep water, while the holes in the ship were welded up again.

Dave and the Captain were discussing this in the mess one evening, and Dave said, 'Look, sir, I'm surprised that they don't send me out there with one of these teams. I'm an "in date" diver, I've had a lot of experience of EOD, and I speak Spanish; I thought I would be ideal.'

The Captain sighed and said, 'I know, Dave, I would like to be out there too, but the truth is we are too bloody old.'

As everyone knows, the Falklands were eventually liberated, and the diving teams returned, with many well earned decorations.

Dave's extended time in the Service came to an end. He had enjoyed his Navy; he had joined in 1943 and finally left in 1983. This time he left without feeling that he was being discarded at the peak of his profession.

As the Captain had said, diving is a young man's game, and he was getting past it.

So he left *Vernon*, to return to his home in Spain, and, whether it was subconsciously planned or not, he arrived at the main gate just as the 'Still' was sounded on the Tannoy. It was sunset. He turned to face the Ensign staff, stood to attention, and watched the White Ensign being lowered. As the Last Post was sounded on the bugle, he was filled with a flood of emotion; how many times had he watched this ceremony?

He turned and walked away; he didn't look back.